Y0-BTC-499

Regulation of Purine Biosynthesis

Regulation of Purine Biosynthesis

J. FRANK HENDERSON
The University of Alberta
Cancer Research Unit
McEachern Laboratory
Edmonton 7, Alberta, Canada

ACS Monograph **170**

AMERICAN CHEMICAL SOCIETY

WASHINGTON, D. C. 1972

ACMOAG 170 1-303 (1972)

Library of Congress Catalog Card 72-88561

ISBN 8412-0153-6

PRINTED IN THE UNITED STATES OF AMERICA

GENERAL INTRODUCTION

American Chemical Society's Series of Chemical Monographs

By arrangement with the interallied Conference of Pure and Applied Chemistry, which met in London and Brussels in July 1919, the American Chemical Society undertook the production and publication of Scientific and Technologic Monographs on chemical subjects. At the same time it was agreed that the National Research Council, in cooperation with the American Chemical Society and the American Physical Society, should undertake the production and publication of Critical Tables of Chemical and Physical Constants. The American Chemical Society and the National Research Council mutually agreed to care for these two fields of chemical progress.

The Council of the American Chemical Society, acting through its Committee on National Policy, appointed editors and associates (the present list of whom appears at the close of this sketch) to select authors of competent authority in their respective fields and to consider critically the manuscripts submitted. Since 1944 the Scientific and Technologic Monographs have been combined in the Series. The first Monograph appeared in 1921, and up to 1972, 168 treatises have enriched the Series.

These Monographs are intended to serve two principal purposes: first to make available to chemists a thorough treatment of a selected area in form usable by persons working in more or less unrelated fields to the end that they may correlate their own work with a larger area of physical science; secondly, to stimulate further research in the specific field treated. To implement this purpose the authors of Monographs give extended references to the literature.

Contents

Preface

PURINES AND THEIR DERIVATIVES participate in almost every area of intermediary metabolism as substrates, cofactors, and regulatory molecules; they also comprise part of the structure of nucleic acids and are required in various ways to express genetic information. At the physiological level, they are directly involved in vasodilatation, platelet aggregation, and in the action of many hormones, and they help provide the energy required for muscle contraction and nerve transmission. In some organisms purines are involved structurally in scales, shells, and reflecting surfaces such as the *Tapitum lucidum*. The mode of excretion of endproducts of purine metabolism is an important discriminant in studies of comparative biochemistry. In recent years purines have been manufactured for use as flavoring agents for food, and purine derivatives and analogs are pharmacologically useful as immunosuppressants, inhibitors of viral and tumor growth, and as diuretics and central nervous system stimulants. Gout is a fairly common human abnormality of purine metabolism, and several rare, inherited deficiencies of enzymes of purine metabolism have recently been discovered; at least one such case is associated with severe central nervous system pathology. Obviously, an understanding of the biosynthesis and metabolism of purines is of broad biochemical, biological, industrial, and medical interest.

The study of purine metabolism, as well as of other areas of biochemistry, has gone through several phases of development. First the naturally occurring purines and their derivatives were characterized; this began in 1776, reached one high point in 1929 with the discovery of adenosine triphosphate, and reached another in 1954 when guanine ribonucleotides were found in cell extracts. Next, the reactions involved in the biosynthesis and metabolism of purines were identified, and the enzymes involved were characterized; much of this work was accomplished between 1887 and 1959. Finally, the main preoccupation at present is the quantification and regulation of purine metabolism and its integration into the whole of cell physiology; this phase began around 1955–57. (These three phases overlap extensively, and work in the first two areas continues to the present; studies relevant to control can be traced back to the nineteenth century. Nevertheless, these distinctions have some conceptual utility.)

The present volume is concerned with regulation and is restricted to the regulation only of one aspect of purine metabolism—that of the biosynthesis of the purine ring by the so-called "pathway of purine biosynthesis *de novo*." This process is of interest not only because it is the first and essential step in purine metabolism in nature but also because it is not required by all types of cells and has different functions in those cells in which it does occur. This pathway is also used for the industrial production of certain purines, and aberrant rates of purine synthesis are responsible for some human diseases. Finally, this pathway is the target for a variety of drugs. Although there are numerous reviews of the reactions and enzymes involved in purine biosynthesis, its regulation has not previously been examined in detail.

During 15 years of explicit study our understanding of the regulation of purine biosynthesis has progressed to the point where many important elements in regulation have been identified. Although the operation of these factors in intact cells and tissues is not always clear, we now at least know what questions to ask in this regard. In addition, recent discoveries in certain areas of this field suggest that exciting and new developments are on the horizon. Finally, for various reasons there is a tendency to concentrate attention on only certain regulatory factors without giving due weight to others; this lack of balance is partly the result of emphasis on selected portions of a large, scattered, and difficult literature and tends to lead to unnecessary and sometimes unwarranted simplifications and generalizations.

It therefore seems appropriate to make this effort to prepare a thorough review of the present state of knowledge regarding the regulation of purine metabolism. In doing so I have defined the term "regulation" broadly to include all factors which actually or potentially affect the rate of purine biosynthesis or constituent parts of the pathway. I have attempted to consider as many different regulatory mechanisms and factors as possible and to make a thorough survey of the literature; inevitably this involves some degree of subjective selectivity and of sheer oversight. The discussion is not limited to an evaluation of the present state of the field but also includes factors whose potential regulatory significance is suggested but not yet thoroughly investigated. In addition, every attempt has been made to evaluate critically our knowledge of regulatory mechanisms, to integrate information when possible, and to show the complexity of the over-all regulation of purine biosynthesis. Finally, a prime consideration has been the operation and regulation of this pathway in intact cells, tissues, and organisms, and an effort has been made to evaluate studies of cell extracts and individual enzymes in the light of the physiology of the whole organism.

The task of preparing this volume has been made lighter by many helping hands. In particular I wish to express my sincere appreciation to Anita A.

Letter for manifold assistance throughout the preparation of the manuscript and to Daena Letourneau for so accurately and cheerfully typing the manuscript and many drafts. L. B. Brox provided many helpful and critical comments, particularly regarding Chapter 5. Finally, I thank my students, colleagues, and especially my wife for their patience and support.

Alberta, Canada
March 1972

J. FRANK HENDERSON

Nomenclature

THE 1964 RECOMMENDATIONS of the International Union of Biochemistry are generally followed for the names of enzymes. The "recommended trivial names" are used in the text, and Enzyme Commission numbers are in general given at the first use of an enzyme name. The commonly accepted names of those enzymes not yet listed systematically by the Enzyme Commission have been used.

The intermediates of the pathway of purine biosynthesis *de novo,* which are mentioned frequently in this book, present some difficulties regarding nomenclature. Traditionally they have been described as "ribonucleotides" of various cyclic and acyclic bases. This involves a rather broad interpretation of the term "ribonucleotide," and the Enzyme Commission has preferred to use the formula "phosphoribosyl-base." In addition, some investigators use nomenclature that is completely different from either of these systems. In this book the Enzyme Commission names of these intermediates are used exclusively, but the position numbers of substituents are omitted. The traditional nomenclature and that used here are compared below.

Traditional	*Enzyme Commission*
Phosphoribosylamine (PRA)	Phosphoribosylamine
Glycineamide ribonucleotide (GAR)	Phosphoribosyl-glycineamide
Formylglycineamide ribonucleotide (FGAR)	Phosphoribosyl-formylglycineamide
Formylglycineamidine ribonucleotide (FGAM)	Phosphoribosyl-formylglycineamidine
Aminoimidazole ribonucleotide (AIR)	Phosphoribosyl-aminoimidazole
Aminoimidazolecarboxylate ribonucleotide (CAIR)	Phosphoribosyl-aminoimidazole carboxylate
Aminoimidazole-*N*-succinocarboxamide ribonucleotide (SAICAR)	Phosphoribosyl-aminoimidazole succinocarboxamide
Aminoimidazolecarboxamide ribonucleotide (AICAR)	Phosphoribosyl-aminoimidazole carboxamide
Formamidoimidazolecarboxamide ribonucleotide (FAICAR)	Phosphoribosyl-formamido-imidazole carboxamide

Many investigators, including the author, would disagree with one or another decision of the Enzyme Commission regarding nomenclature in this area. On the whole, however, their recommendations appear sound, consistent, and useful, and therefore they are used here without amendment.

Abbreviations have been kept to an absolute minimum. Traditional abbreviations for the intermediates of the pathway of purine biosynthesis are based on the nomenclature system not used here, and the Enzyme Commission names do not lend themselves to useful abbreviations. These names are consequently not abbreviated at all.

P_i and PP_i are used for orthophosphate and pyrophosphate, respectively; -P is used for the phosphoryl group in printed compound names and -Ⓟ for the phosphoryl group in structural formulas. When used, other abbreviations are those used without definition by the *Journal of Biological Chemistry.*

The structure and nomenclature of folate and its component parts, as well as the abbreviation which will be used for the structure of H_4-folate, are given below:

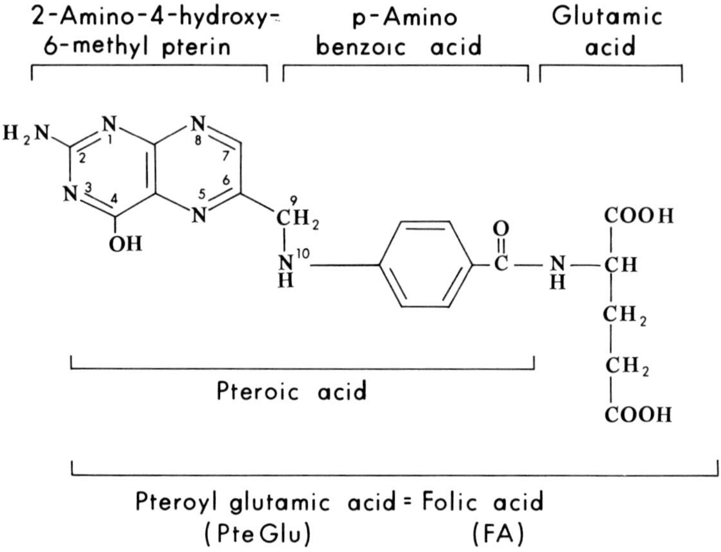

2-Amino-4-hydroxy-6-methyl pterin | p-Amino benzoic acid | Glutamic acid

Pteroic acid

Pteroyl glutamic acid = Folic acid
(PteGlu) (FA)

H_4 - Folate
(abbreviated form)

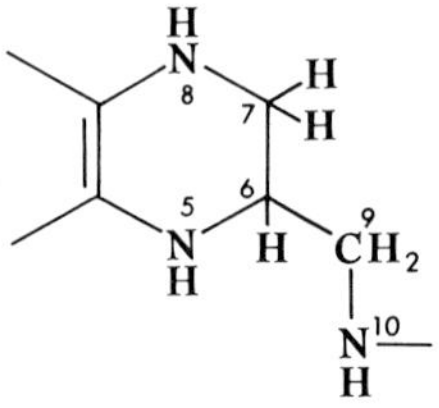

Names of microorganisms and designations of microbial mutants are those of the original authors, and no attempt has been made to change these to suit current nomenclature practices. Various units have been used to express enzyme activity and specific activity, and it is not always possible to convert these to one common set of units. Because these values are used here only to compare data within a single published paper, the numbers are given without units.

Chapter

1

Purines in Nature—An Overview

NATURE CONTAINS a variety of purines and an even more diverse array of their glycosidic derivatives. The vast number of enzymatic reactions involving purines and the wide scope of their metabolic functions may well be imagined, and these will be sketched out in summary form in this chapter. Unfortunately, there are no really comprehensive discussions of purine distribution, metabolism, and function which are completely up to date. The most recent reviews are the chapters by Hartman (*1*) and by Kit (*2*) in Greenberg's "Metabolic Pathways," and a major portion of a textbook "Nucleotide Metabolism" written by the present author and A. R. P. Paterson (*3*). These sources should be consulted for greater depth and for references to the original work on which this chapter is based.

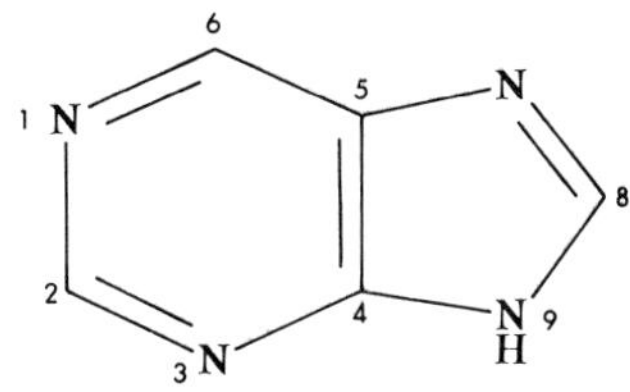

Purine

Occurrence of Purines in Nature

Purines are found inside cells predominantly in the form of nucleotides, or 9-(5′-phosphopentosyl) derivatives in which D-ribofuranose and 2-deoxy-D-ribofuranose are the most common sugars.

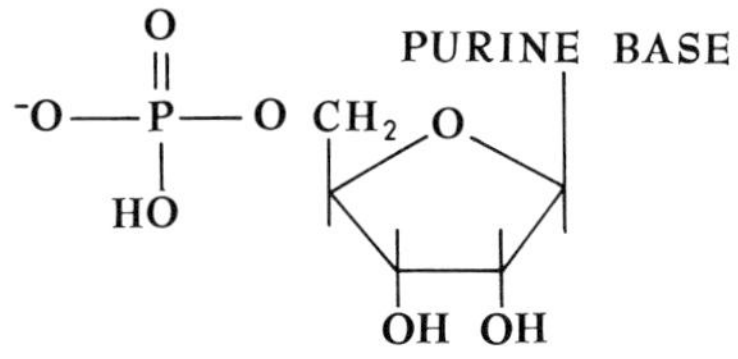

Purine ribonucleotide

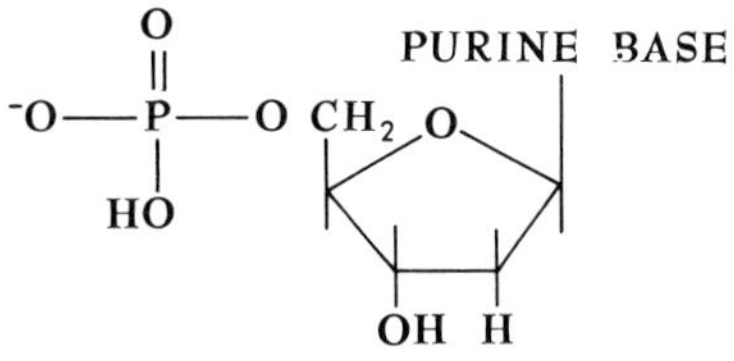

Purine deoxyribonucleotide

(The custom of drawing purine nucleotides, nucleosides, and related compounds in the syn conformation will be followed here although there is ample reason to believe that they really are in the anti conformation in aqueous solution.) Nucleotides may be variously substituted, particularly as di- and triphosphates and as phosphomonoesters; these low molecular weight compounds are operationally called acid-soluble nucleotides as they are soluble in the dilute solutions of perchloric and trichloroacetic acids commonly used to kill and extract cells.

A larger quantity of purine nucleotides exists as polymers or polynucleotides, in which pyrimidine nucleotides also participate. Ribonucleic acid is composed of purine and pyrimidine ribonucleotides whereas deoxyribonucleic acid is composed of purine and pyrimidine deoxyribonucleotides. Each type of nucleic acid is, of course, tremendously heterogeneous with respect both to gross composition and nucleotide sequence. Nucleic acids containing more than about 10 nucleotides are insoluble in cold dilute perchloric and trichloroacetic acids. In many animal and bacterial cells nucleic acid or acid-insoluble nucleotides may comprise 80–90% of the total nucleotide content.

Outside of cells purines exist predominantly as nucleosides (9-pentosyl derivatives) and purine bases themselves. Purine nucleosides derived from the breakdown or catabolism of the nucleic acids, as well as those derived from the most common mononucleotides by dephosphorylation, are also of two types: ribonucleosides and deoxyribonucleosides.

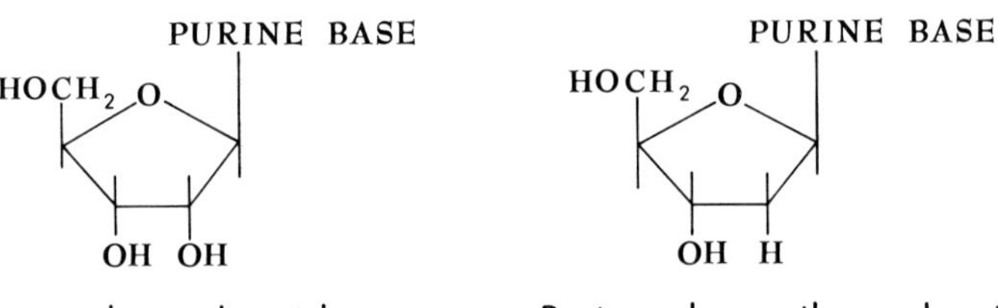

Purine ribonucleoside

Purine deoxyribonucleoside

Adenine and guanine are the most common purine bases in both kinds of nucleic acids and in the lower molecular weight nucleotides.

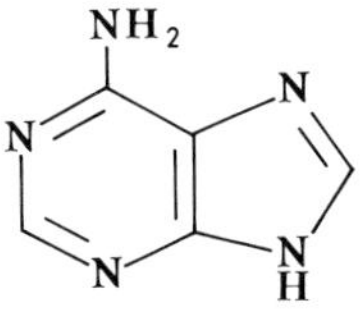

Adenine

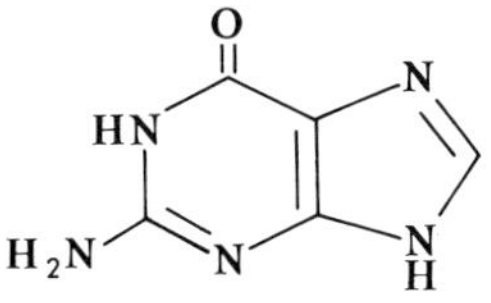

Guanine

Three other common purines may also be noted.

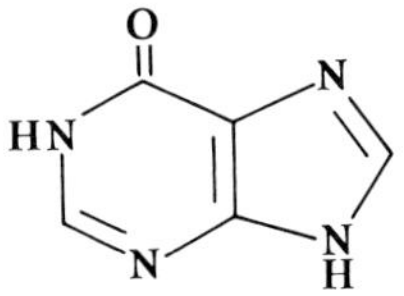

Hypoxanthine

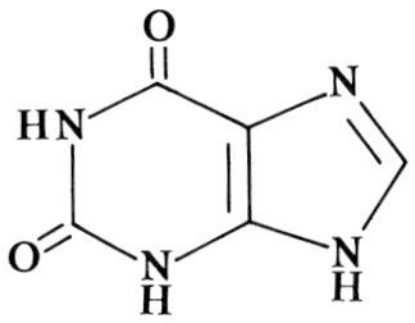

Xanthine

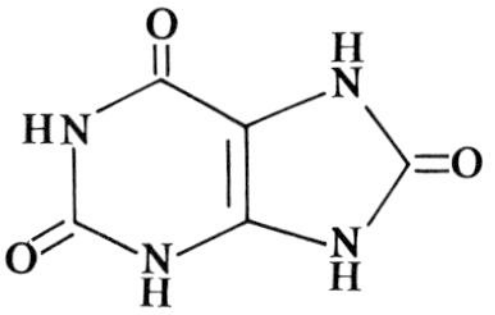

Uric acid

Hypoxanthine and xanthine occur in ribonucleotides and ribonucleosides, and as free bases they are metabolic intermediates in the formation of uric acid. Uric acid is the endproduct of purine metabolism in man and the endproduct of all nitrogen metabolism in many organisms. Uric acid occurs predominantly as the free purine base.

The quantitatively and functionally most important acid-soluble purine nucleotide in cells is adenosine triphosphate, which must be considered together with the closely related adenosine mono- and diphosphates.

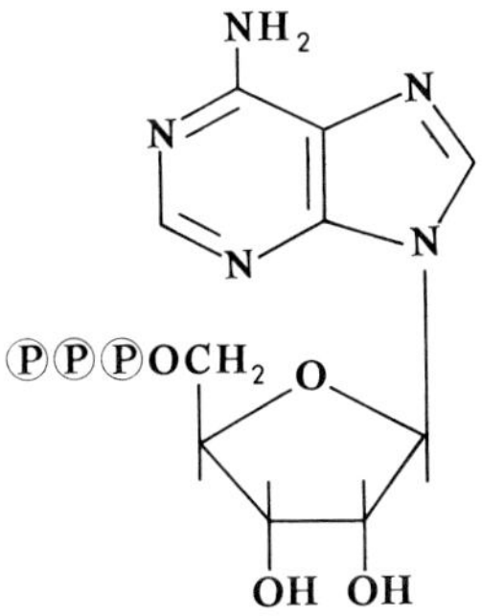

Adenosine triphosphate

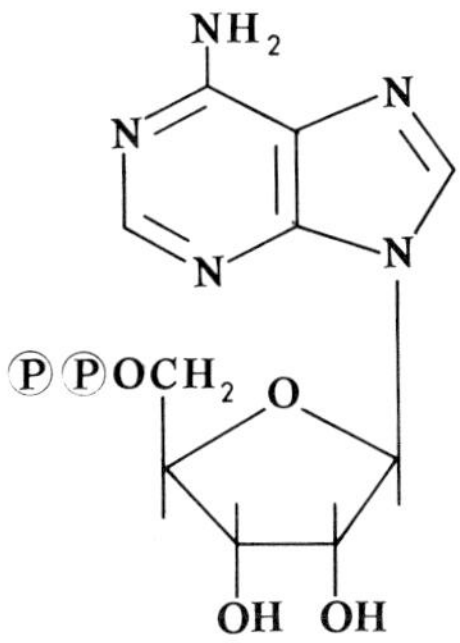

Adenosine diphosphate

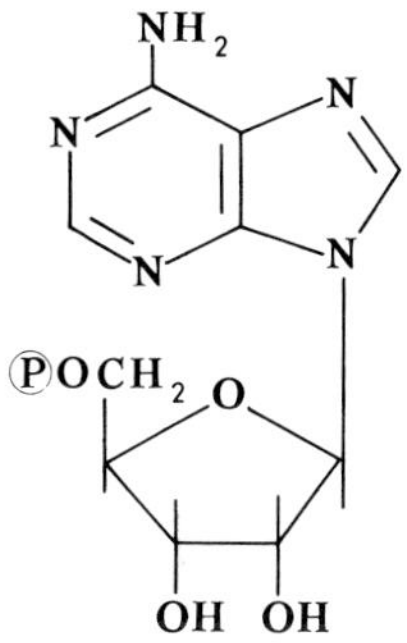

Adenosine monophosphate (Adenylate)

Next in quantitative importance is the family of guanine ribonucleotides, of which the triphosphate is again predominant.

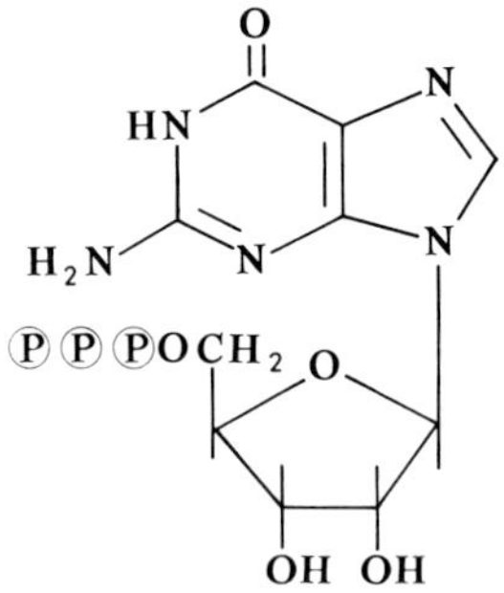

Guanosine triphosphate

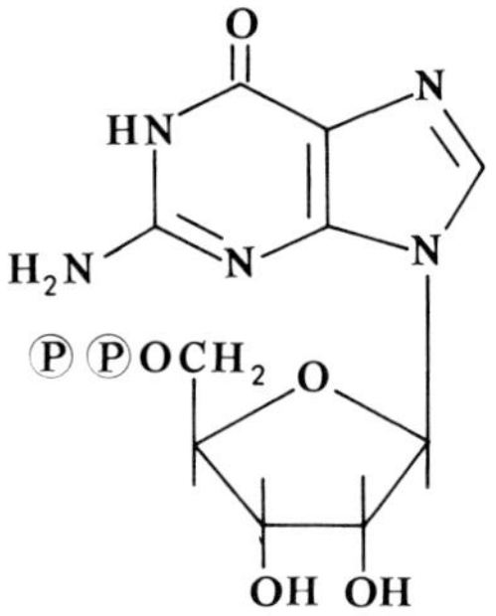

Guanosine diphosphate

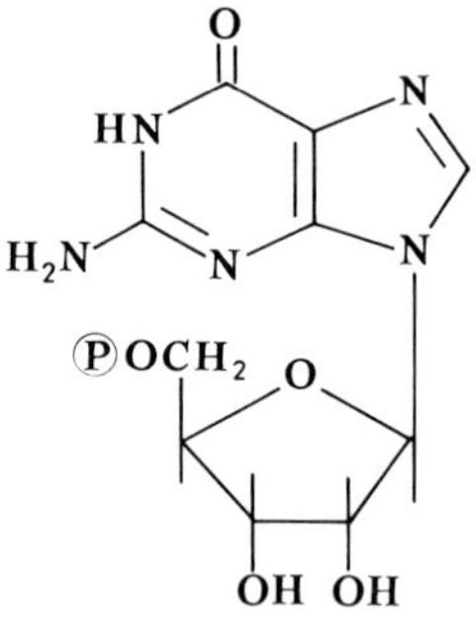

Guanosine monophosphate
(Guanylate)

Three other purine ribonucleotides occur in cells only in very small amounts, but, as described later, they are important intermediates in purine metabolism.

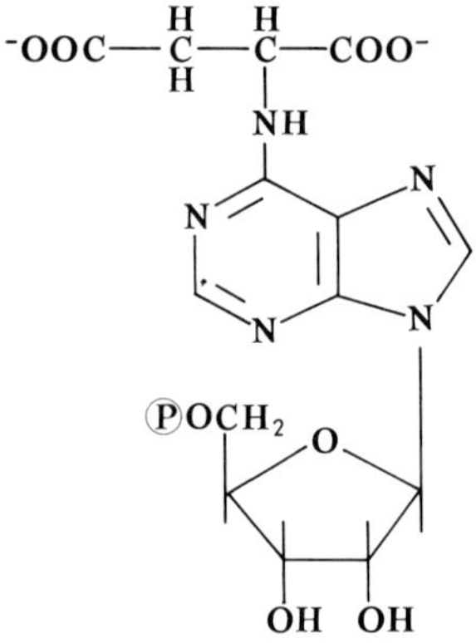

Adenylosuccinate

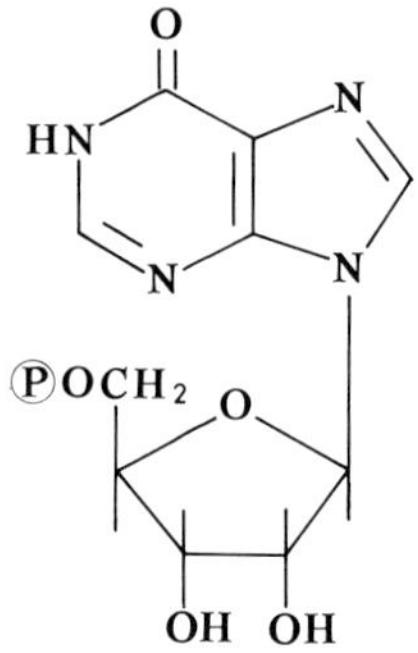

Inosinate

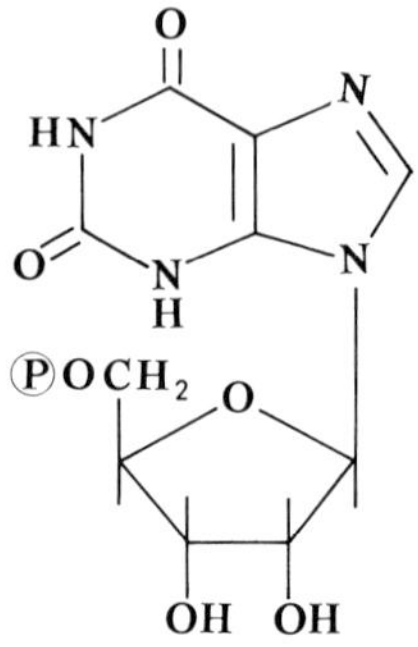

Xanthylate

These nine purine ribonucleotides may be thought of as being at the hub of purine metabolism, from which many other compounds are formed. Among these derivatives are the deoxyribonucleotides deoxyadenosine triphosphate and deoxyguanosine triphosphate, which with pyrimidine derivatives are substrates for deoxyribonucleic acid synthesis.

By pyrophosphorolytic reaction of purine ribonucleoside triphosphates with a variety of phosphorylated compounds, a series of so-called group-transfer coenzymes of the type purine ribonucleoside diphospho-X may be formed. Their functions are discussed below. Among the types of compounds which are thus linked with purine ribonucleotides are: sugars and sugar derivatives, sulfate, pyridine ribonucleotides, isoalloxazine and corrinoid derivatives, and amino acids.

Purine ribo- and (to a lesser degree) deoxyribonucleotides incorporated in polynucleotides may be methylated to form nucleotide derivatives of 6-dimethylaminopurine, 2-dimethylamino-6-oxypurine, 1- and 3-methyladenine and -guanine. Other uncommon purine derivatives found in nucleic acids include 6-(2-methyl-3-butenyl)adenine, 6-(aminoacyl)adenines, and related compounds. Methylated purines which do not occur in nucleic acids include the common beverage ingredients, caffeine, theophylline, and theobromine.

A number of unusual purines, purine nucleosides, and structural analogs of these are produced by fungi and to some extent by other plants as well. Many have growth-inhibitory properties and hence may be called antibiotics; these are described in detail by Suhadolnik (*4*).

Functions of Purines

The exact function in the cell of origin of such purine derivatives as the nucleoside antibiotics, caffeine, and other plant products which appear to be endproducts of metabolism is not known. Predominantly extracellular purines in animals, such as uric acid, are endproducts of metabolism which are destined to be excreted. The common rapidly growing bacteria do not secrete purines.

The functions of intracellular purines, which are carried out almost exclusively in the form of ribonucleotide derivatives, are of three main types: intermediates in energy metabolism, components of group-transfer coenzymes, and structural components. In addition there are a number of roles that may be termed regulatory or physiological functions.

The fact that purine nucleotides are components of ribo- and deoxyribonucleic acids has already been alluded to. This type of structural role is, of course, of tremendous biological importance, and this field is so vast that it cannot be discussed here in depth. Purine bases or ribonucleotides also furnish part of the amino acid histidine and parts of the vitamins riboflavin and folate; the relationship of purine metabolism to the synthesis of another vitamin, thiamine, is described in detail in Chapter 7.

Group-transfer coenzymes, in which purine ribonucleoside diphosphates (or in some cases, monophosphates) act as carriers of groups which will be enzymatically transferred to some acceptor, have already been introduced. These groups include sugars, sulfate, alkyl groups, acyl groups, hydride and hydrogen ions, and electrons. This type of purine ribonucleotide coenzyme is almost ubiquitous in cellular metabolism.

The free energy derived from biological oxidations is largely converted into chemical energy in the form of adenosine triphosphate, which is generally considered to be the most important mobile carrier of metabolically available energy in cells. Cleavage of the pyrophosphate bond linkages in adenosine triphosphate (or related nucleoside triphosphates) generates free energy which is made available, directly or indirectly, to drive energetically unfavorable reactions.

So-called physiological functions of purines include mediation of hormone effects by 3′,5′-cyclic-adenylate and possibly 3′,5′-cyclic-guanylate, regulation of cell division and growth in plants by 6-(4-hydroxy-3-methyl-*trans*-2-butenylamino)purine and related compounds, the vasodilatory action of adenosine, the possible role of adenosine triphosphate as a neurotransmitter substance, and the aggregation of platelets induced by adenosine diphosphate.

Finally, adenine nucleotides, as indicators of the state of energy metabolism of cells, often help to regulate the rates of energy-producing or energy-utilizing enzymes and metabolic pathways. In many cases such control is believed to be mediated through the binding of adenine nucleotides to distinct and relatively specific sites on the enzymes in question.

Metabolism of Purines

As mentioned, nine purine ribonucleotides form a hub about which most other aspects of purine metabolism are focused. Figure 1-1 shows that purine ribonucleotides are interconverted by a system of six enzymes arranged in two cycles; inosinate is the common intermediate. Adenosine monophosphate (adenylate) and guanosine monophosphate (guanylate) link the two cycles of purine ribonucleotide interconversion with the respective di- and triphosphates which are more directly involved in nucleotide functions.

The cycles of purine ribonucleotide interconversion involve both deamination and introduction of amino groups. Adenylate is hydrolytically deaminated to inosinate whereas the deamination of guanylate to form inosinate is reductive. The amination of inosinate to form adenylate is a two-step process, involving the amino acid aspartate. Aspartate reacts with inosinate to form adenylosuccinate, which is then cleaved to adenylate. In contrast, the forma-

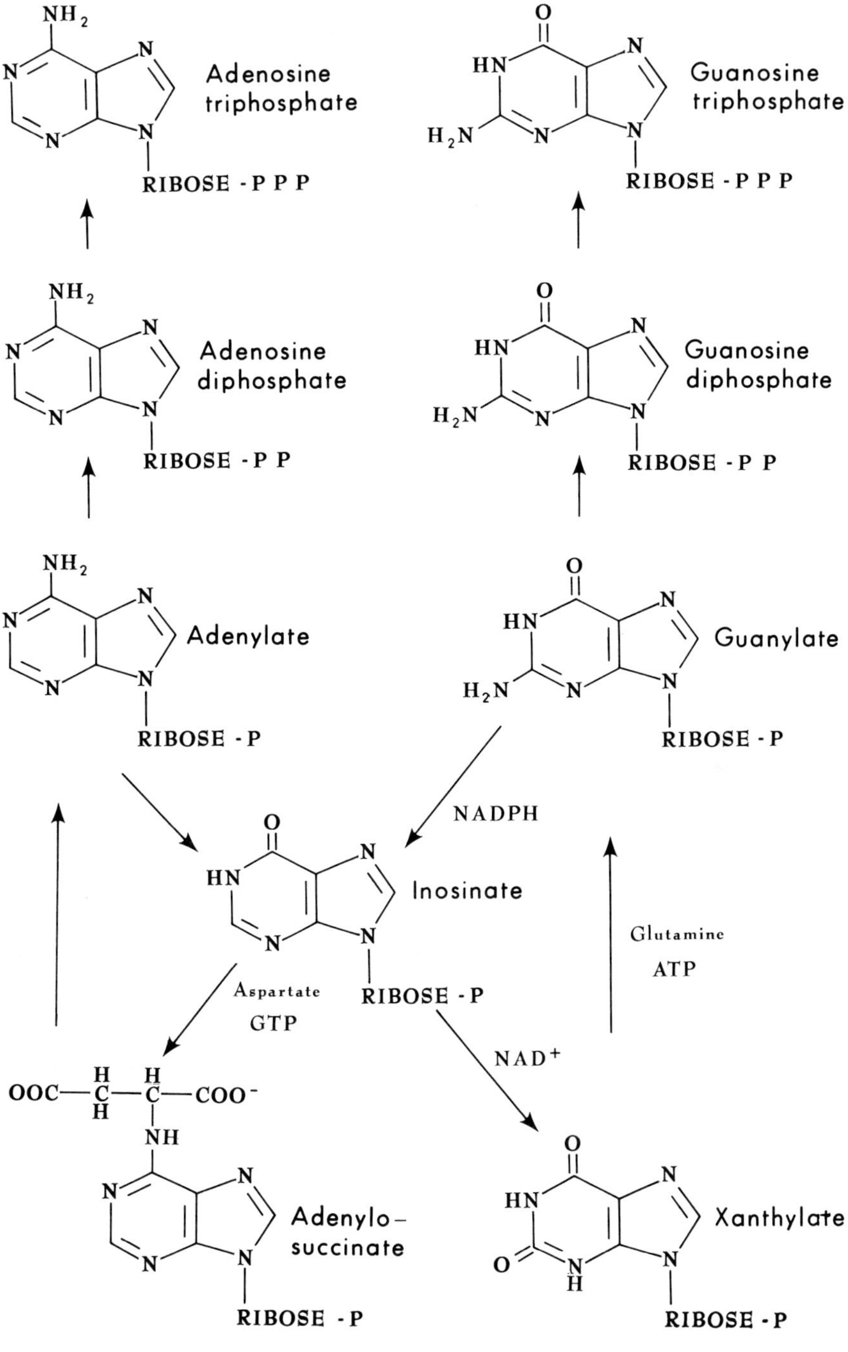

Figure 1-1. Reactions of purine ribonucleotide interconversion

tion of guanylate from inosinate first involves oxidation to xanthylate, and this intermediate then reacts with the amide group of the amino acid glutamine. It must be emphasized that the relative rates of the six enzyme reactions involved in these cycles vary greatly in different cells, and in some organisms not all of these reactions are present.

It is the purine ribonucleoside di- and triphosphates that are primarily involved in the various functions described above.

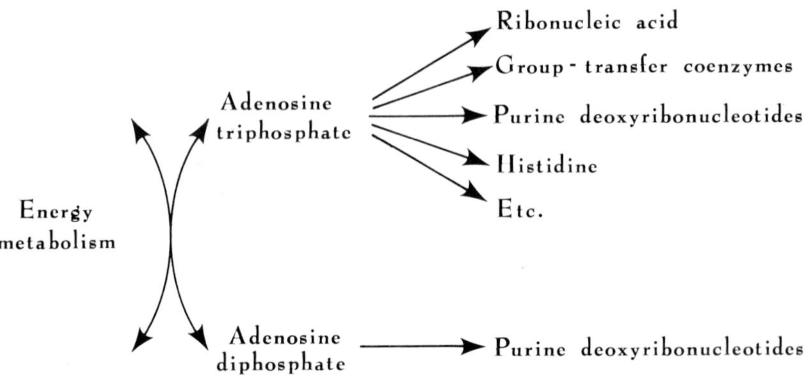

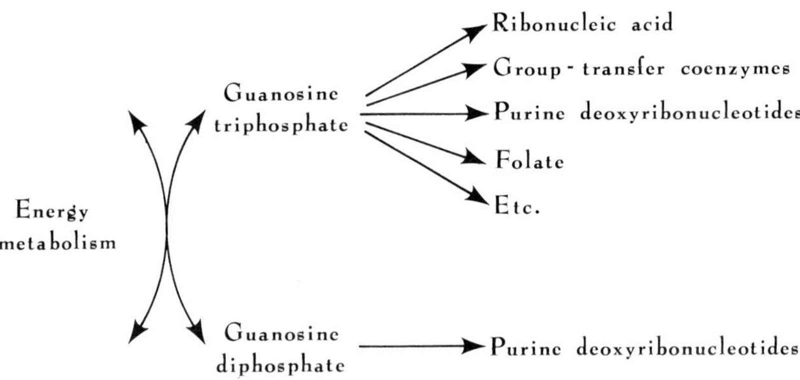

Purine ribonucleotides are catabolized *via* dephosphorylation, deamination, glycosidic bond cleavage, and oxidation. Deamination and oxidation reactions may take place at various levels as shown by the following scheme.

Deamination:

Nucleotides:	Adenylate	→	Inosinate
	Guanylate	→	Inosinate
Nucleosides:	Adenosine	→	Inosine
	Guanosine	→	Xanthosine (rare)
Bases:	Adenine	→	Hypoxanthine
	Guanine	→	Xanthine

Oxidation:

Nucleotides:	Inosinate	→	Xanthylate
Nucleosides:	(No reactions known)		
Bases:	Hypoxanthine	→	Xanthine
	Xanthine	→	Uric acid

All of the purine ribonucleoside monophosphates which are involved in the cycles of purine ribonucleotide interconversion may be dephosphorylated although so far as is known dephosphorylation of adenylosuccinate is not extensive in most cells. The ribonucleosides so formed may be phosphorolytically cleaved to the free purine bases plus ribose 1-phosphate although in some systems they may be hydrolytically cleaved instead. As indicated above, some nucleosides may be deaminated as well. It must again be emphasized that the rates of these reactions may be quite unequal in a particular cell type, and some may be entirely absent.

Uric acid is the endproduct of purine metabolism in man and the higher primates and is excreted in the urine. Other animals may convert it to allantoin, allantoate, urea, or carbon dioxide plus ammonia, any one of which may be the predominant endproduct in a particular species. As discussed in more detail below, in some organisms uric acid (or urea derived from uric acid) is the endproduct not only of purine metabolism but also of the metabolism of all amino acid nitrogen.

Purine ribonucleotides may be synthesized from purine bases, from purine ribonucleosides, or from non-purine-containing precursors. Adenine, hypoxanthine, guanine, and xanthine may be converted to ribonucleoside monophosphates in reactions which use phosphoribosyl pyrophosphate as the ribose-phosphate donor. For example:

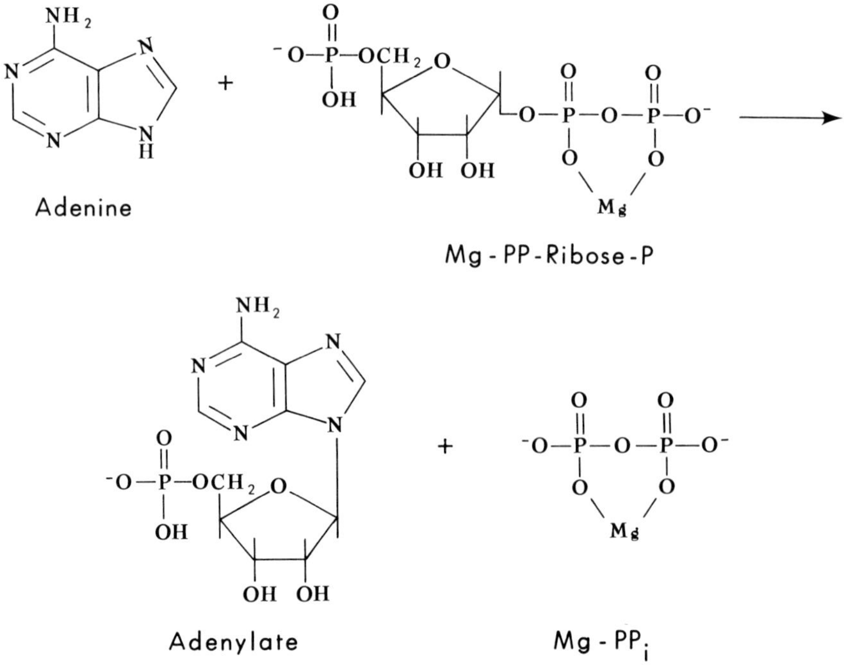

Adenine + Mg - PP - Ribose - P ⟶

Adenylate + Mg - PP_i

Several different enzymes are involved, and there are marked variations in the relative rates of these reactions among cells. Studies of these enzymes have been reviewed recently (*5, 6, 7*).

Purine ribonucleosides, especially adenosine, may simply be phosphorylated by purine ribonucleoside kinases, with adenosine triphosphate as source of the phosphate. The physiological significance of these reactions is not yet clear.

Both of these processes, of course, presuppose the prior synthesis either of purine bases or of purine ribonucleosides. These may be either synthesized from other purine derivatives within a given cell and reutilized or supplied to the cell from outside itself. In the latter case they may have originally been formed by other cells of the same multicellular organism or have been supplied in the diet. In any case there must exist in nature a mode of purine synthesis which uses non-purine components. This process is called purine biosynthesis *de novo*.

Purine Biosynthesis de novo

The pathway of purine biosynthesis *de novo*, especially the several mechanisms by which the rate of this pathway is regulated, is the subject of this book. The 10 reactions of purine biosynthesis, with their eight substrates and associated cofactors, are described in detail in the next chapter. In those cells which are not supplied exogenously with purines this pathway is obviously essential for life. It is most often present even in those cells which do have an exogenous purine supply, thus providing two or more alternative routes by which the biologically essential purine nucleotides can be made. Only a few organisms lack one or more of the enzymes of purine biosynthesis, and these consequently must seek nutritionally favorable environments.

The functions of purine biosynthesis *de novo* in all cells which possess the requisite enzymes (in conjunction with possible alternative pathways) are to furnish the acid-soluble purine ribonucleotide coenzymes of energy metabolism and the group-transfer coenzymes, as well as the purine ribo- and deoxyribonucleotide substrates required for nucleic acid synthesis and other structural functions. In some organisms this pathway has an additional function—that of converting the nitrogen produced during protein and amino acid catabolism to uric acid.

Purine biosynthesis *de novo* is sufficiently important to many animal cells that toxicity and growth inhibition result from the administration of drugs that inhibit it. Such drugs are used, at least experimentally, in cancer chemotherapy, for immunosuppression, and for the treatment of some parasitic infections. Perhaps because of the importance of the pathway, as indicated by its pharmacological sensitivity, inherited defects resulting in the total or partial deficiency of this process have not been reported. Its lack in mature mammalian erythrocytes is not harmful because these cells can obtain purines from other sources.

Inherited or environmentally induced increases in the rate of purine biosynthesis can, however, have pathological consequences in man. The usual result of such overproduction is that uric acid accumulates and eventually may precipitate in sites where it can do harm; gout is the result.

Mechanisms of Regulation of Purine Biosynthesis

The complexity of the pathway of purine biosynthesis *de novo*, with its 10 enzymes and eight substrates and its different rates and different functions in different cells, at least potentially allows a variety of regulatory sites, factors, and mechanisms to be important.

The regulation of the activity of each of the constituent enzymes of this pathway may be considered first. Properties of the enzymes of interest in this regard are their equilibrium constants, Michaelis constants, maximum velocities, product inhibition constants, optimum pH and ionic strengths, and requirement for specific ionic environments, if any. The available information (which is sparse) on these subjects is given in Chapter 3. Unfortunately, at the present stage of our understanding of this subject, the little information which is available (except possibly for the Michaelis constants) cannot be readily applied to the operation of this pathway in intact cells.

Other factors which might bear on the regulation of individual enzymes of purine biosynthesis are the possible presence of isozymes, the possible activation of inactive enzyme precursors, the possible irreversible inactivation of any of the enzymes, and the possible role of association and dissociation of enzyme subunits. The fact that at least three of the enzymes under consideration consist of subunits is discussed in Chapter 3, and the evidence that this feature of the first enzyme of the pathway might have regulatory significance is discussed in Chapter 5. Little is known about the other possibilities mentioned above.

There is ample evidence that in one system or another the concentrations of each of the substrates and cofactors required for purine biosynthesis are important regulatory factors and may limit or stimulate the rate of this pathway. Since this is the case, further questions must be asked regarding the competition of the enzymes of purine biosynthesis with other reactions which require the same substrates and cofactors. These are discussed at some length in Chapter 4.

Finally, the activities of individual enzymes may be inhibited or stimulated by endproducts of the pathway or by other metabolites. This appears to be relevant to the control of the first enzyme of the purine biosynthetic pathway, and the mechanisms of inhibition and possible physiological significance of this phenomenon are studied in Chapter 5.

The total amounts of each of the enzymes of purine biosynthesis are obviously also of interest with respect to regulation. Unfortunately, little is known about the control of enzyme amounts for this pathway, but the information which is presently available is summarized in Chapter 6.

Regulation of the amounts and activities of individual enzymes of the purine biosynthetic pathway is obviously of great interest, but it is the pathway as a whole that has physiological significance and the regulation of which is of primary concern here. The pathway cannot operate more rapidly than the rate of its slowest reaction, and hence concern regarding control tends to focus about the so-called pacemaker or rate-limiting step. It is often assumed that the first enzyme of this pathway is rate limiting, and the evidence on this point is evaluated in Chapters 4, 5, and 10. The possibility must also be considered that the identity of the rate-limiting step may vary with experimental conditions or from one cell or organism to another.

So far as is known, all the enzymes of purine biosynthesis are in solution in the cell, and problems of regulation arising from membrane binding and intracellular localization have not been considered. These enzymes may, however, have some organization, and aggregates of several of them may exist.

Finally, it must be kept in mind that the pathway of purine biosynthesis *de novo* has quite different functions in different organisms, and hence the types of regulatory mechanisms operative may differ.

Certain specialized aspects of the control of purine biosynthesis have been reviewed by Henderson (*8*), Stadtman (*9*), Blakley and Vitols (*10*), and Momose (*11*).

References

1. Hartman, S. C., "Metabolic Pathways," Greenberg, D. M., Ed., 3rd ed., Vol. 4, p. 1, Academic, New York, 1970.
2. Kit, S., "Metabolic Pathways," Greenberg, D. M., Ed., 3rd ed., Vol. 4, p. 70, Academic, New York, 1970.
3. Henderson, J. F., Paterson, A. R. P., "Nucleotide Metabolism," Academic, New York, in press.
4. Suhadolnik, R. J., "Nucleoside Antibiotics," Wiley-Interscience, New York, 1970.
5. Murray, A. W., Elliott, D. C., Atkinson, M. R., *Progr. Nucl. Acid Res. Mol. Biol.* (1970) **10,** 87.
6. Murray, A. W., *Annu. Rev. Biochem.* (1971) **40,** 811.
7. Raivio, K. O., Seegmiller, J. E., *Curr. Top. Enzyme Regulation* (1970) **2,** 201.
8. Henderson, J. F., *Progr. Exp. Tumor Res.* (1965) **6,** 84.
9. Stadtman, E. R., *Advan. Enzymol. Relat. Areas Mol. Biol.* (1966) **28,** 41.
10. Blakley, R. L., Vitols, E., *Annu. Rev. Biochem.* (1968) **37,** 201.
11. Momose, H., *Protein Nucl. Acid Enzyme (Tokyo)* (1968) **13,** 781.

Chapter

2 The Pathway of Purine Synthesis *de novo*

THE EARLY HISTORY of the study of purine biosynthesis *de novo* is not generally known today although some of this pioneering work bears directly on the question of the regulation of this pathway. A brief description of these early studies is presented here.

Early Evidence for the Existence of the Pathway

Uric Acid Synthesis in Uricotelic Animals. Uric acid was the first purine to be recognized in nature; it was discovered in 1776 both by Scheele (*1*) and by Bergmann (*2*). These workers had found uric acid in human urine and human bladder stones, and it was soon afterwards recognized as a major nitrogenous constituent of the excreta of birds and reptiles. By the middle of the nineteenth century it was accepted that whereas urea was the major endproduct of nitrogen metabolism in mammals, uric acid occupied this position in birds and reptiles.

The first direct evidence for the biosynthesis of uric acid from non-purine precursors in birds was reported in 1886 by Minkowski (*3*). Of the total nitrogen found in the urine of normal geese, 60–70% was in uric acid, 9–18% was in ammonia, and 3–4% was in urea. Following total hepatectomy both the total excretion of nitrogen and the percent of the nitrogen found as uric acid were decreased. Whereas normal geese fed a diet of oats excreted 1.5–2.0 grams of uric acid per 12 hours, hepatectomized birds excreted only 0.1 to 0.15 gram in the same period, and this comprised only 3–6% of the urinary nitrogen. Ammonia contained 50–60% of the urinary nitrogen in hepatectomized geese whereas urea contained 3–4%, the same relative proportion as in the controls. The administration of ammonium salts or of the amino acids leucine or glycine resulted in an increased excretion of ammonia in hepatectomized geese although urea was not metabolized under these conditions. Following criticism of the drastic surgical procedure involved in these experiments, Minkowski (*4*) repeated these studies after ligating blood vessels supplying the liver, with similar results. These results were confirmed and extended by Lang (*5*). Kowalewski and Salaskin (*6*) furnished further evidence that uric acid can be synthesized from ammonia in the liver. They perfused goose livers with blood to which ammonium lactate had been added and observed that the blood uric acid concentration rose 121–151% after 25 passages whereas increases of only 39–47% were noted in the controls.

Sperm and Egg Development. A second type of evidence which led to the recognition of purine biosynthesis from non-purine precursors came from studies of sperm formation and embryonic development in eggs. Shortly after his discovery of nucleic acids Miescher (*7*) began extensive studies of sperm synthesis in migrating Rhine salmon. During migration the testicle weight of these fish rose from between 15 and 20 grams to between 300 and 400 grams; almost all of this weight increase was sperm, which was found by analysis to be 49% nucleic acid. Miescher recognized that the salmon did not eat during migration and that sperm were formed at the expense of the nucleic-acid-poor musculature, which underwent a marked loss in weight.

Silkworm (*Bombyx mori*) eggs were analyzed by Tichomiroff (*8*) soon after they were laid and also when the larval forms were developed after an incubation period of 13 days. Although his identification of individual purines cannot now be credited because of the analytical procedures used, the total nucleic acid purine content clearly increased from about 0.02 to about 0.2 gram per 100 grams of eggs. Uric acid, which must also have been present, was not determined.

More extensive studies followed, using hen and duck eggs. Kossel (*9*) failed to detect purines in the yolk of freshly laid hen's eggs whereas the embryo after 15 days of development yielded 0.28% guanine and 0.66% hypoxanthine plus adenine. Mendel and Leavenworth (*10*) used more accurate methods and reported that the purine nitrogen (from guanine, adenine, and hypoxanthine) per hen egg increased 10-fold during two weeks of incubation. Uric acid again was not measured, but these studies clearly demonstrated the synthesis of nucleic acid purines during embryonic development.

Growth of Mammals on Low-Purine Diets. A third form of demonstration of the synthesis *de novo* of nucleic acid purines was based on the growth of mammals on purine-free or at least low-purine diets. As early as 1891 Socin (*11*) succeeded in maintaining the health and growth of mice for up to 99 days using a diet of egg yolk, starch, cellulose, and water during studies of iron utilization. Later, McCollum (*12*) also used low-purine diets in his study of the utilization of inorganic phosphate for nucleic acid synthesis in growing rats. Finally, Osborne and Mendel (*13*) and Abderhalden (*14*), in extensive and elaborate growth experiments using purified foodstuffs, clearly demonstrated that purines are unessential articles of the diet. This conclusion has been confirmed repeatedly by subsequent investigation.

Before the latter studies, Burian and Schur (*15*) demonstrated the synthesis of purines in growing mammals by direct measurement. The purine contents of whole suckling rabbits and puppies were analyzed at birth and after growth for several weeks on milk diets. In one experiment with rabbits, for example, a body weight gain of 167 grams in 18 days was accompanied by an increase of purine nitrogen (not including that in excreta) of 104 mg. Although the milk on which these animals were fed did contain some purines, this source could not have accounted for all of the observed increase in the purine content of the tissues.

Urinary Excretion of Endproducts of Purine Metabolism on Low-Purine Diets. Purine synthesis *de novo* in adult, non-growing mammals was more difficult to demonstrate, and studies of this problem remained controversial and disputed for many years. Studies with most laboratory animals were difficult because they excrete allantoin instead of uric acid. Although this compound was discovered by Prout in 1818, it was not generally considered to be an endproduct of purine metabolism until the early part of the twentieth century (*16*, p. 165). Benedict (*17*) first observed, however, that the Dalmatian coach hound excretes a considerable amount of uric acid in addition to allantoin. He maintained one such dog on a low-purine diet for nearly a year, during which period it excreted more than 100 grams of uric acid. Less than 10% of this could have come from the preformed purines of the tissues of the animal, and this study thus first demonstrated that the ability to synthesize purines is not limited to growing mammals but is characteristic of adults as well. Kapeller-Adler *et al.* (*18*) later demonstrated continued allantoin synthesis and excretion in non-Dalmatian dogs fed a low-purine diet for 5 days, and similar observations have been made many times since then.

Rockwood (*19*) in 1904–05 was among the first to demonstrate continued uric acid excretion in men fed low-purine diets for up to 18 days. However, the classical example of this type of evidence for purine biosynthesis *de novo* is the study of Kollmann (*20*) with a 26-year-old woman fed a low-purine diet for 50 days. During this period she ingested 0.3 gram of purines, gained 3.9 kg in body weight, and excreted (not including menstrual periods) 18.37 grams of purines. It is apparent that purine synthesis was occurring.

Conclusions. In the light of present knowledge of purine metabolism the evidence presented above clearly supports the concept of purine biosynthesis from non-purine precursors. However, this conclusion was not so obvious to the early workers themselves, who in general tended, for example, to dissociate uric acid synthesis in birds and reptiles from the synthesis of nucleic acid purines. Thus, according to Mendel and Leavenworth (*10*), "the synthetic production of uric acid as an endproduct of nitrogen metabolism in birds and reptiles is a distinctive reaction associated with excretory functions in these species, without a demonstrated parallel in animals."

The studies just described which demonstrated uric acid and allantoin synthesis in adult mammals came relatively late in this period of discovery, and even these developments considerably preceded the introduction in the late 1930s of the concept of the dynamic equilibrium of body constituents. It is not surprising, then, that investigators in the first decade of this century could conclude with some certainty that there was no positive experimental evidence to show that purines could be synthesized in the adult mammalian organism (*10, 16,* p. 185). Uric acid production in fasting subjects and those on low-purine diets was believed to be caused by "some metabolic change like the destruction of tissue nucleoproteins" (*21*), "which must be supposed to be essential to the continuation of life" (*22*).

Identification of the Precursors of the Purine Ring

Early History. Attempts to identify precursors of the purine ring in animals prior to the advent of ^{15}N-, ^{13}C-, and ^{14}C-labeled compounds in the 1950s and '60s were fraught with technical difficulties, and it is not surprising that they led to conflicting conclusions. This work has been reviewed by Fisher (*23*), Edson (*24*), Rose (*25*), and Christman (*26*) and will be only summarized here.

Wiener, Ascoli, and a number of other investigators believed that urea was the source of the nitrogens of the purine ring (plus C-2 and C-8) and that lactate, *via* hydroxymalonate, furnished C-4, C-5, and C-6. This hypothesis was proposed in the period 1898–1901, and although opposing evidence was soon presented it was not until the 1930s that really compelling evidence accumulated against it.

The hypothesis proposed in 1916 by Ackroyd and Hopkins, that arginine, histidine, or both were precursors of the purine ring, was also popular for many years. Different nutritional studies either supported or contradicted it, and studies with labeled amino acids were required to show this proposal to be incorrect.

More progress was made by the studies of purine synthesis in liver slices *in vitro* by Krebs and his associates, and by Schuler and Reindel. Pigeon liver was chosen for such work because, in contrast to livers of most other birds, it lacks xanthine oxidase and hence hypoxanthine accumulates instead of uric acid (*27–30*). Accumulation of hypoxanthine was demonstrated when liver slices were incubated aerobically in the presence of ammonia and lactate or pyruvate (*31*), and Örstrom *et al.* (*32*) subsequently made the very significant observation that hypoxanthine synthesis was stimulated by addition of either oxaloacetate or glutamine. They suggested correctly that glutamine probably acted as an ammonia carrier, but these studies of purine synthesis in liver slices were not pursued.

Studies with Labeled Compounds. The first use of labeled compounds for studying purine biosynthesis *de novo* occurred in 1943. Barnes and Schoenheimer (*33*) showed first that ^{15}N-urea was not incorporated into the uric acid excreted by pigeons. They also observed that the specific activities of arginine and histidine in pigeons which had received ^{15}N-ammonium citrate were not high enough for them to qualify as precursors of the purine ring. Later studies in which ^{15}N-histidine was fed to rats confirmed this conclusion (*34*).

Definitive information regarding the precursors of the purine ring originated in 1946 with the important investigations of Sonne, Buchanan, and Delluva (*35*) and Buchanan and Sonne (*36*). These and subsequent studies in the period 1946–51 showed that the C-4 of the purine ring was derived from the carboxyl carbon of glycine (*37, 38*), C-5 from the α-carbon of glycine (*39*), C-6 from carbon dioxide or bicarbonate (*38, 40*), and C-2 and C-8 from formate or other one-carbon sources (*38–42*). Although it was quickly established that the N-7 of the purine ring was derived from the α-amino group of glycine (*43, 44*), and that N-1, N-3, and N-9 were derived from the general metabolic pool of amino groups (*33*), the proximal ammonia donors for the latter positions could not be established by studies using whole animals. This point was finally cleared up with extracts of pigeon liver which could synthesize inosinate. It was shown that ^{15}N from amide-labeled glutamine labeled predominantly the purine N-3 and N-9 positions whereas ^{15}N from aspartate predominantly labeled N-1 (*45, 46*).

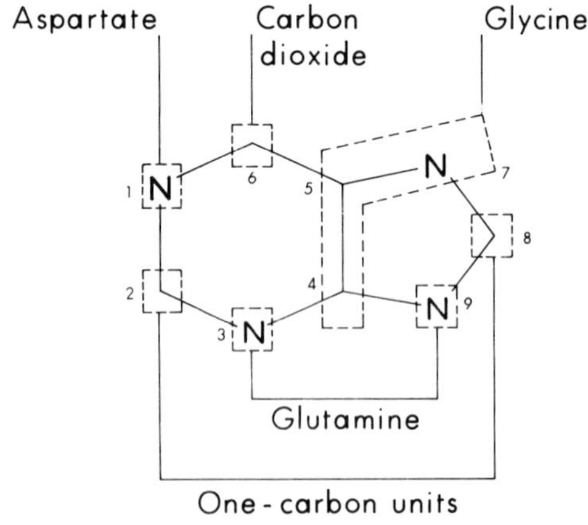

Shortly after glycine was shown to be incorporated into excreted uric acid in pigeons (*40*) and in man (*44*), Abrams *et al.* (*43*) demonstrated, using the yeast *Torulopsis utilis,* that glycine was also incorporated into nucleic acid purines. All subsequent studies have indicated that both excretory and nucleic acid purines are synthesized *de novo* by basically the same pathway. Extensive reviews of this early work with labeled compounds are available (*26, 47–50*). The results of these and many other studies of the precursors of the purine ring may be summarized in the now classic diagram shown on p. 18.

Identification of the Individual Enzymes of Purine Biosynthesis de novo

Reactions of the Purine Biosynthetic Pathway. Between 1951 and 1959 J. M. Buchanan, G. R. Greenberg, and their associates identified all of the enzymes of purine biosynthesis *de novo* using preparations of pigeon and chicken liver. Because this work has been amply reviewed (*47–50*), individual references are not given in the brief description of these enzymes which follows; reference to newer studies may be found in a recent text (*51*) and review (*52*). Enzyme Commission names and numbers of these enzymes are given below.

Phosphoribosylamine is believed to be the product of the reaction of PP-ribose-P and glutamine, catalyzed by PP-ribose-P amidotransferase.

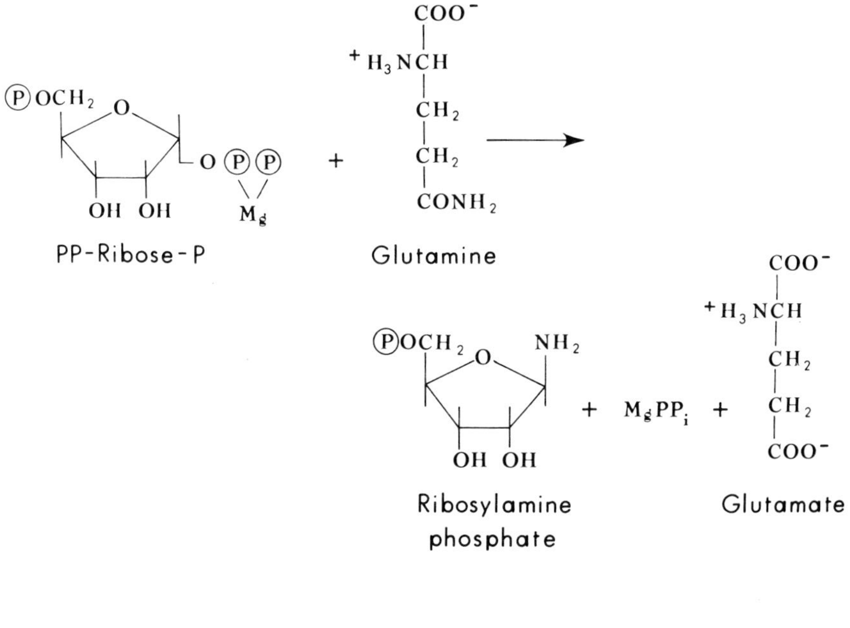

PP-Ribose-P + Glutamine → Ribosylamine phosphate + M_gPP_i + Glutamate

This product is extremely unstable in aqueous solutions, and enzymatically synthesized material has never been isolated and characterized. Its synthesis was first deduced from identification of the other products, pyrophosphate and glutamate; later it was shown that chemically synthesized phosphoribosylamine served as substrate for the subsequent step in the pathway. This reaction is presumed to involve inversion from α-PP-ribose-P to β-phosphoribosylamine.

Ammonia and a number of simple alcohols and amines can replace glutamine as substrates of the PP-ribose-P amidotransferase reaction. The reaction is inhibited by reagents which react with sulfhydryl groups or which chelate iron, and by the glutamine analog 6-diazo-5-oxo-L-norleucine. PP-ribose-P amidotransferase contains 12 atoms of non-heme iron per 200,000-molecular weight unit; the iron has both catalytic and structural functions which are not yet understood. Other properties of this enzyme are discussed in Chapters 3 and 5.

Phosphoribosyl-glycineamide synthetase catalyzes a readily reversible reaction which requires all three components both for product formation and for isotope exchange.

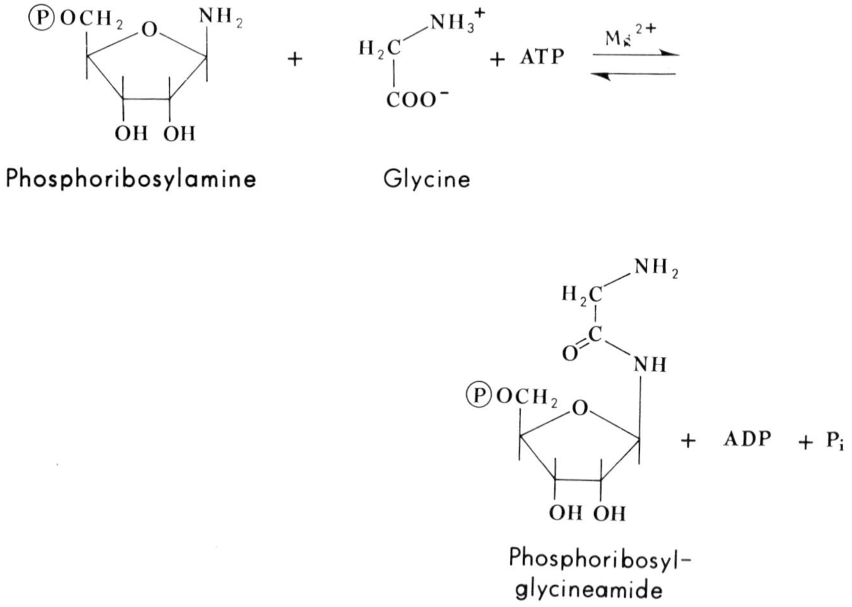

ⓅOCH_2 O NH_2 / OH OH + $H_2C(NH_3^+)COO^-$ + ATP $\xrightleftharpoons{Mg^{2+}}$

Phosphoribosylamine Glycine

ⓅOCH_2 O NH–C(=O)–CH_2–NH_2 / OH OH + ADP + P_i

Phosphoribosyl-glycineamide

The molecular weight of this enzyme is approximately 48,000.

Phosphoribosyl-glycineamide formyltransferase catalyzes the transfer of a one-carbon unit at the oxidation level of formate from 5,10-methenyl H_4-folate to phosphoribosyl-glycineamide. This reaction has been little studied.

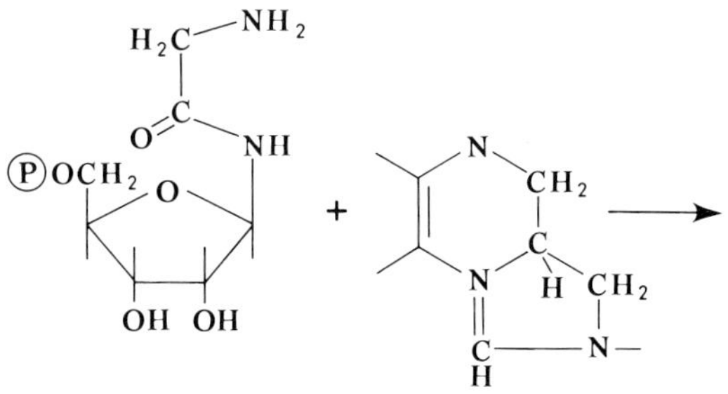

Phosphoribosyl-glycineamide + 5, 10-Methenyl H_4-folate →

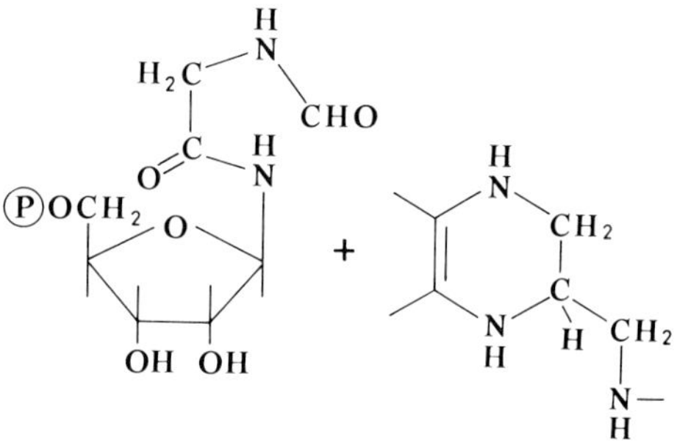

Phosphoribosyl-formylglycineamide + H_4-Folate

A second glutamine amide-transfer reaction adds what will be N-3 in the completed purine ring (p. 22, top). Phosphoribosyl-formylglycine-amidine synthetase has a molecular weight of about 135,000 and is inhibited by a number of glutamine analogs including diazo-oxo-norleucine and azaserine, which react covalently with a sulfhydryl group of the enzyme. The enzyme from chicken liver appears to have a sequential mechanism in which glutamine binds first, followed randomly by the other substrates; a quaternary complex is formed (*53*). In contrast, the enzyme from Ehrlich ascites tumor cells catalyzes a strictly ordered ping-pong reaction in which substrates bind in the order: glutamine, Mg-ATP, phosphoribosyl-formyl-glycineamide (*54*). Although the enzymes from chicken liver and Ehrlich ascites tumor cells (*54*) can use ammonia as an alternative substrate, it is a poor substrate for that from *Salmonella typhimurium*. This reaction requires (*54*), or is stimulated by (*55*), potassium ion.

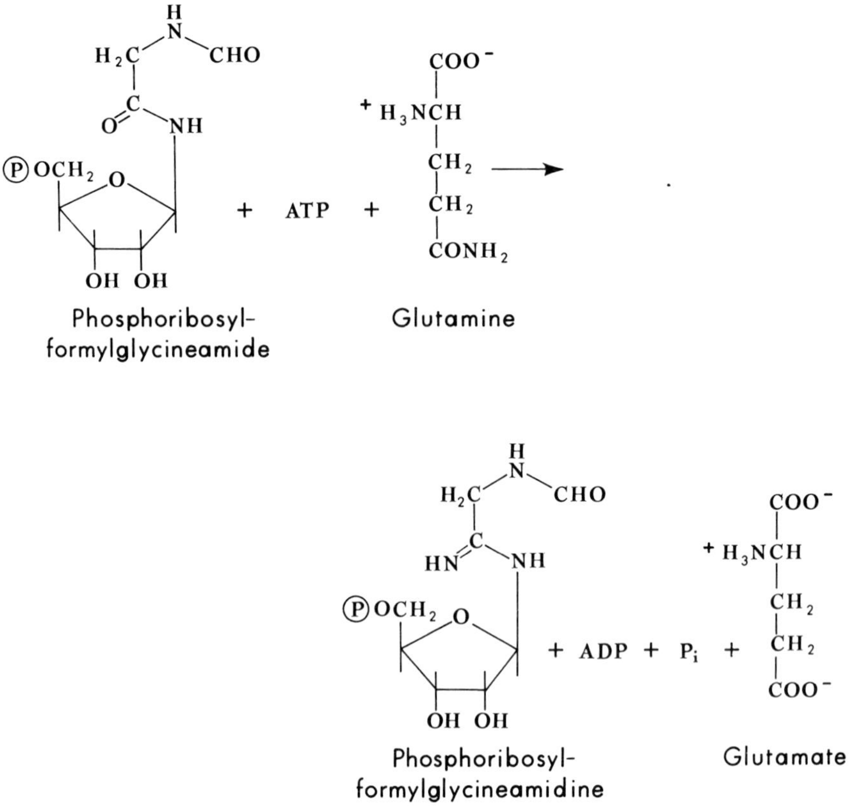

Phosphoribosyl-formylglycineamide + ATP + Glutamine →

Phosphoribosyl-formylglycineamidine + ADP + P_i + Glutamate

The formation of what will be the imidazole moiety of the completed purine ring is catalyzed by phosphoribosyl-aminoimidazole synthetase and requires Mg-ATP and potassium ion in addition to phosphoribosyl-formylglycineamidine.

$$\text{Phosphoribosyl-formylglycineamidine} + \text{ATP} \xrightarrow[K^+]{Mg^{2+}} \text{Phosphoribosyl-aminoimidazole} + \text{ADP} + P_i$$

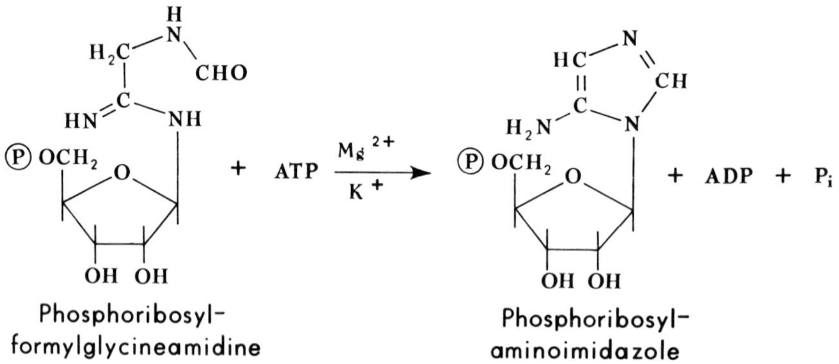

The fixation of bicarbonate or carbon dioxide (it is not known which is the real substrate) leads to the formation of phosphoribosyl-aminoimidazole carboxylate *via* the readily reversible carboxylase reaction.

Phosphoribosyl-aminoimidazole + HCO_3^- ⇌ Phosphoribosyl-aminoimidazole carboxylate

It has not been studied in any detail.

The N-1 of the completed purine ring is introduced in a two-step procedure. Phosphoribosyl-aminoimidazole succinocarboxamide synthetase catalyzes the ATP-supported combination of L-aspartate with phosphoribosyl-aminoimidazole carboxylate.

Phosphoribosyl-aminoimidazole carboxylate + Aspartate + ATP $\xrightarrow{Mg^{2+}}$ ADP + P_i + Phosphoribosyl-aminoimidazole succinocarboxamide

The product is then cleaved (by displacement rather than by hydrolysis) to form fumarate and phosphoribosyl-aminoimidazole carboxamide.

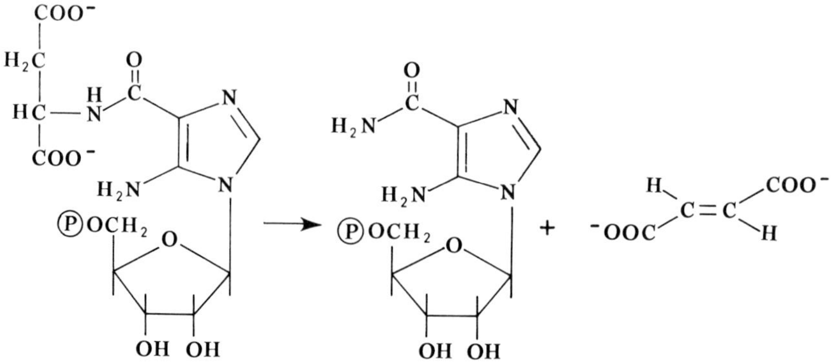

Phosphoribosyl-aminoimidazole succinocarboxamide → Phosphoribosyl-aminoimidazole carboxamide + Fumarate

The enzyme that catalyzes this reaction is called adenylosuccinate lyase because it is the same enzyme which converts adenylosuccinate to adenylate.

Phosphoribosyl-aminoimidazole carboxamide formyltransferase catalyzes the introduction of another formyl group, from 10-formyl H_4-folate, into what will be the C-2 position of the completed purine ring.

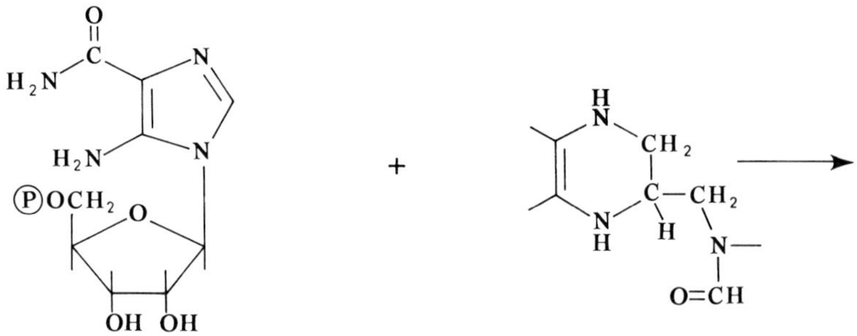

Phosphoribosyl- aminoimidazole carboxamide + 10-Formyl H_4-folate →

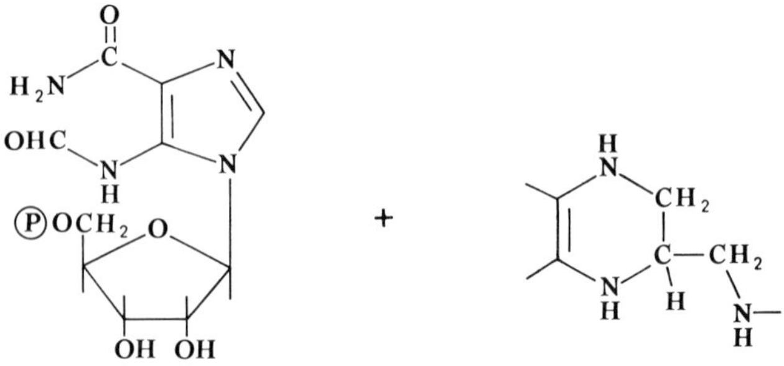

Phosphoribosyl-formamido-imidazole carboxamide + H_4-Folate

The final step in the process of purine biosynthesis *de novo* is the cyclization of phosphoribosyl-formamido-imidazole carboxamide to form inosinate;

Phosphoribosyl-formamido-aminoimidazole carboxamide → Inosinate

this is catalyzed by inosinate cyclohydrolase. Trivial and official names of the enzymes of purine biosynthesis *de novo* are given in Table 2-1.

The reactions of the pathway of purine biosynthesis are given, with the structures of the intermediates, in Figure 2-1; an abbreviated scheme is shown in Figure 2-2.

With the possible exception of one enzyme discussed below, all of the reactions of purine biosynthesis *de novo* identified in avian liver have also been found in microorganisms. The older studies with microorganisms have been reviewed by Moat and Friedman (*56*) and by Magasanik (*57*). Far fewer studies of the enzymes of this pathway have been conducted using other organisms, but the uniformity of results of isotope incorporation studies have led to the generally accepted conclusion that the enzymes listed above must be universally present wherever the pathway can be detected. The occurrence of branches leading off or into the main pathway of purine biosynthesis does vary considerably among organisms, however; this subject is discussed in Chapter 7.

Current Studies. Most questions regarding the basic outline of the pathway of purine biosynthesis and identification of substrates and reactions were settled by the early 1960s. However, a number of more recent studies have investigated the possible use of alternative substrates and the enzymatic nature of certain of the reactions. These are discussed below.

Use of Alternative Nitrogen Sources. Glutamine, glycine, and aspartate are usually considered to furnish the nitrogen atoms of the purine ring, and there is certainly ample evidence that this is usually the case. Several studies, however, have also shown or suggested that, at least under certain conditions, other sources of nitrogen may replace glutamine as the origin of N-9 and perhaps of N-3 as well. This field is still somewhat unsettled, but the relevant studies are reviewed here.

Table 2-1. Enzymes of Purine Biosynthesis *de novo*

Enzyme Commission Number	*Systematic Name*	*Trivial Name*
2.4.2.14	Ribosylamine-5-phosphate:pyrophosphate phosphoribosyl transferase (glutamate-amidating)	PP-Ribose-P amidotransferase
6.3.1.3	Ribosylamine-5-phosphate:glycine ligase (ADP)	Phosphoribosyl-glycineamide synthetase
2.1.2.2	5′-Phosphoribosyl-*N*-formylglycine-amide:tetrahydrofolate 5,10-formyl-transferase	Phosphoribosyl-glycineamide formyltransferase
6.3.5.3	5′-Phosphoribosyl-formylglycine-amide:L-glutamine amido-ligase (ADP)	Phosphoribosyl-formylglycineamidine synthetase
6.3.3.1	5′-Phosphoribosyl-formylglycine-amidine cyclo-ligase (ADP)	Phosphoribosyl-aminoimidazole synthetase
4.1.1.21	5′-Phosphoribosyl-5-amino-4-imidazole-carboxylate carboxy-lyase	Phosphoribosyl-aminoimidazole carboxylase
6.3.2.6	5′-Phosphoribosyl-4-carboxy-5-amino-imidazole:L-aspartate ligase (ADP)	Phosphoribosyl-amino-imidazole succinocar-boxamide synthetase
4.3.2.2	Adenylosuccinate AMP-lyase	Adenylosuccinate lyase
2.1.2.3	5′-Phosphoribosyl-5-formamido-4-imi-dazolecarboxamide:tetrahydrofolate 10-formyltransferase	Phosphoribosyl-aminoimi-dazole carboxamide formyltransferase
3.5.4.10	IMP 1,2-hydrolase (decyclizing)	Inosinate cyclohydrolase

Phosphoribosylamine Synthesis. Although the first reaction in the pathway of purine biosynthesis *de novo* is usually considered to be the PP-ribose-P amidotransferase–mediated reaction of PP-ribose-P and glutamine, several alternative routes to phosphoribosylamine have been either demonstrated or proposed.

In the original studies of the early steps of purine biosynthesis in suitably fortified extracts of pigeon liver Hartman *et al.* (*58*) reported that asparagine, ammonium salts, aspartate, and glutamate would not replace glutamine in the synthesis of phosphoribosyl-glycineamide; no details were given. Goldthwait *et al.* (*59*) did not try to replace glutamine in a similar system although their blank values were quite high. Goldthwait (*60*) also showed that ribose-

5-P plus ATP plus either glutamine or ammonium ion would not support phosphoribosyl-glycineamide synthesis in a system that would use PP-ribose-P and glutamine for this process. In a later study with a highly purified PP-ribose-P amidotransferase from chicken liver, however, Hartman (*61*) showed that ammonium chloride could replace glutamine as substrate. The Michaelis constant for ammonium chloride at pH 8 was 0.4M whereas that for glutamine was $2 \times 10^{-5}M$. The product of this reaction presumably was phosphoribosylamine because it would support the synthesis of phosphoribosyl-glycineamide in a suitable system. Because of the high concentrations of ammonium ion needed its use was thought to have no physiological significance.

In 1961 Nierlich and Magasanik (*62*) reported that phosphoribosylamine could be synthesized from ribose-5-P, ATP, and ammonium ion, as indicated by the ability of the product to support phosphoribosyl-glycineamide synthesis when the appropriate enzymes and substrates were supplied; extracts of chicken liver, *Aerobacter aerogenes*, and *Escherichia coli* were used. Although in relatively crude extracts of *Aerobacter aerogenes* combinations of PP-ribose-P and glutamine, and of PP-ribose-P and ammonium ion, were active, a more purified preparation was obtained which used predominantly ribose-5-P and ammonium ion. It was concluded that there were two alternative pathways of phosphoribosylamine synthesis in these organisms. In 1965, however, the same authors (*63*) reported that this synthesis of phosphoribosylamine from ribose-5-P, ATP, and ammonium ion was non-enzymatic in nature; ATP was in fact not required. The chemical synthesis and stability of phosphoribosylamine were studied in some detail (*cf. 60*), and it was concluded that concentrations of ribose-5-P and ammonium might be attained in bacteria such that this reaction could be of potential physiological significance although such concentrations of ammonium ions would be toxic in animals.

This was not the end of the story, however. Kapoor and Waygood (*64*) reported in 1962 that extracts of wheat embryos would use not only glutamine but also asparagine and carbamyl-phosphate to support the synthesis of phosphoribosyl-glycineamide when PP-ribose-P was present; ammonium ion was a poor substrate. When ribose-5-P was used in place of PP-ribose-P, however, ammonium ion was the best substrate although asparagine was almost as active. Somewhat similar studies were later reported by LeGal *et al.* (*65*), using extracts of *Escherichia coli* B. In this case, glutamine, carbamyl-phosphate, and (to a lesser extent) ammonium ion appeared to react with PP-ribose-P whereas ammonium ion was by far the best substrate when ribose-5-P was used. The reaction of ammonium ion and ribose-5-P was not retarded by methionine sulfoximine, an inhibitor of glutamine synthetase, but was inhibited strongly by adenylate and guanylate; the reaction was heat labile

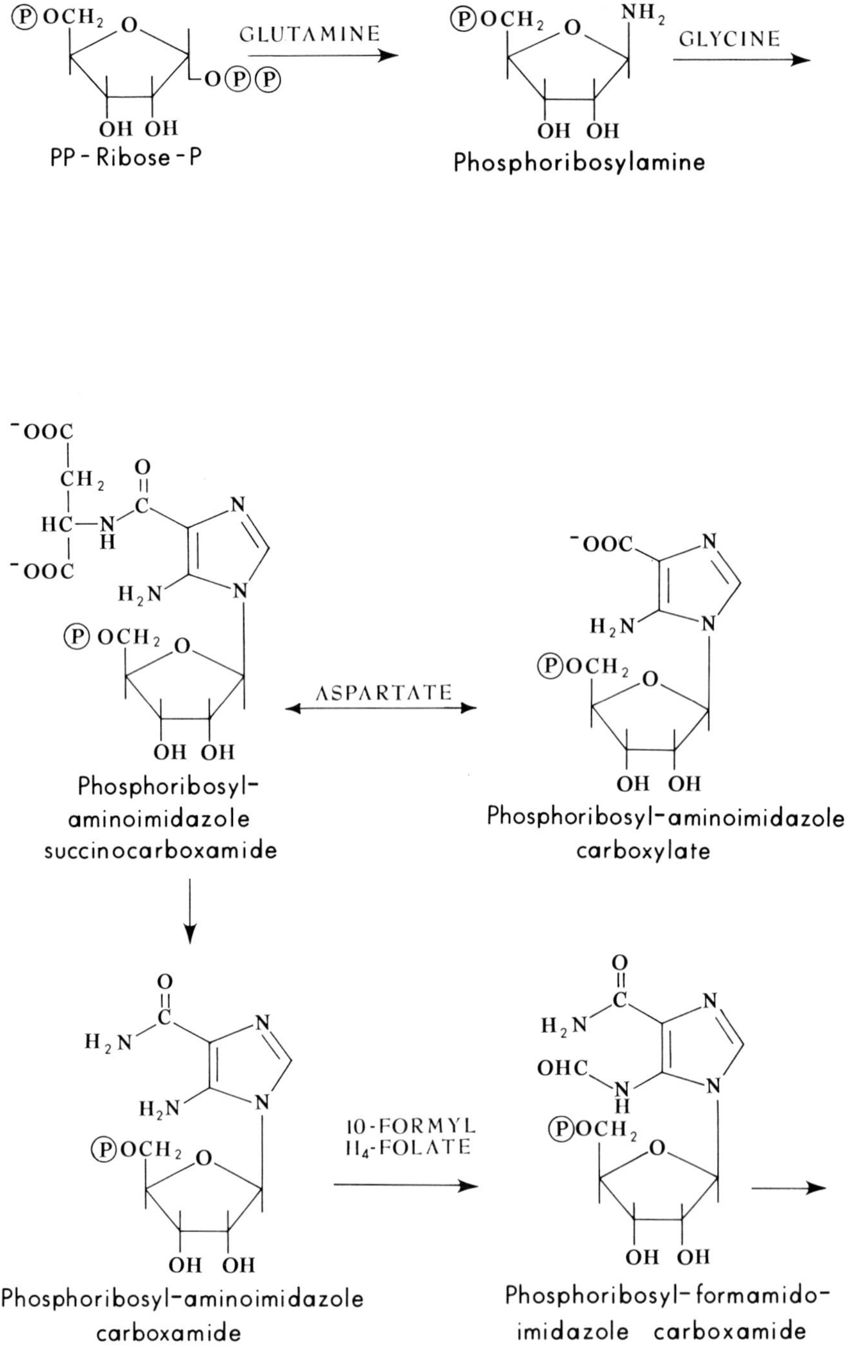

ⓅOCH$_2$ O —O ⓅⓅ OH OH

PP - Ribose - P

GLUTAMINE →

ⓅOCH$_2$ O NH$_2$ OH OH

Phosphoribosylamine

GLYCINE →

$^-$OOC CH$_2$ O C HC—N H $^-$OOC N H$_2$N N Ⓟ OCH$_2$ O OH OH

Phosphoribosyl-aminoimidazole succinocarboxamide

ASPARTATE ⟷

$^-$OOC N H$_2$N N ⓅOCH$_2$ O OH OH

Phosphoribosyl-aminoimidazole carboxylate

↓

O C H$_2$N N H$_2$N N ⓅOCH$_2$ O OH OH

Phosphoribosyl-aminoimidazole carboxamide

10-FORMYL H$_4$-FOLATE →

O C H$_2$N N OHC N H N ⓅOCH$_2$ O OH OH

Phosphoribosyl-formamido-imidazole carboxamide

→

Figure 2-1. Reactions of

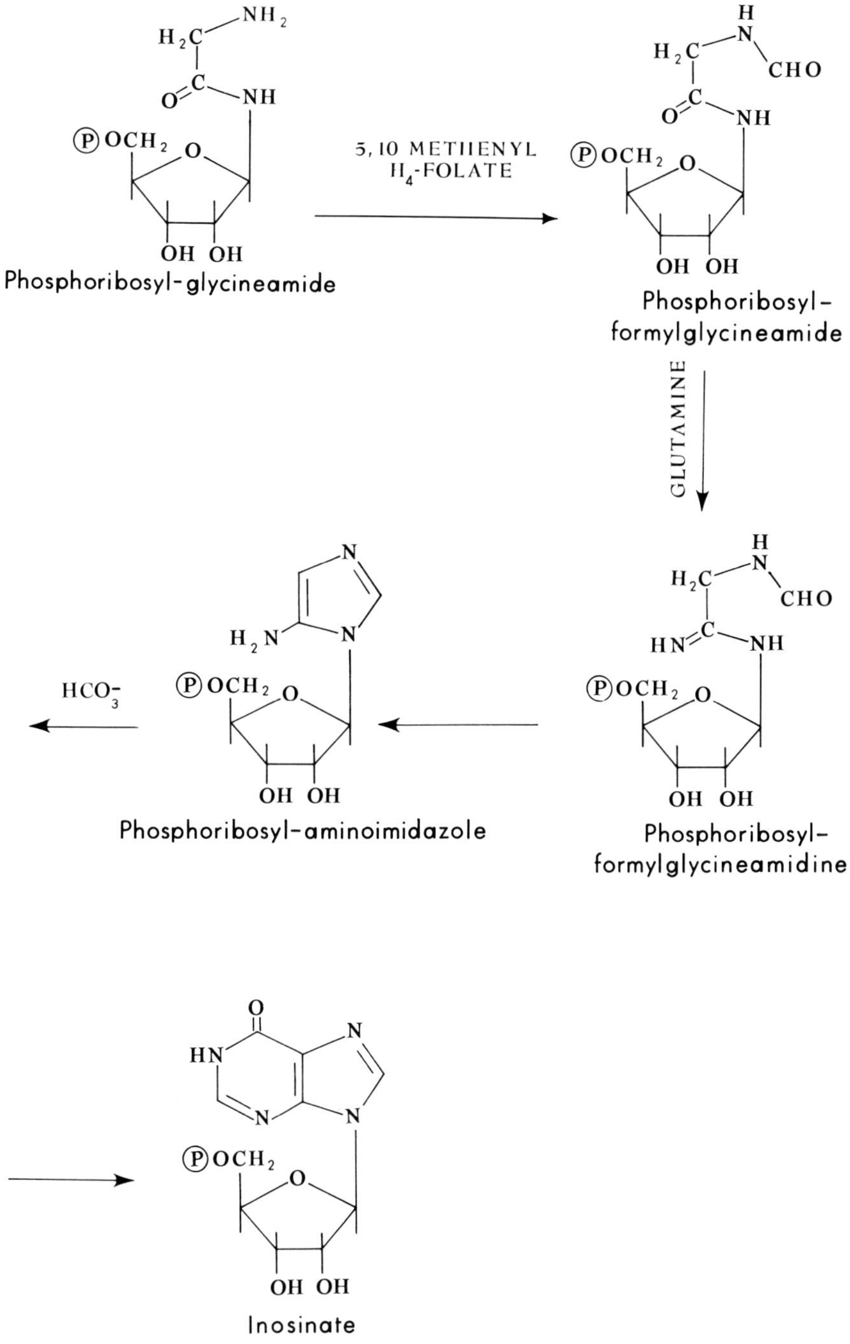

H_2C—NH_2

$O{=}C$—NH

ⓅOCH_2 O

OH OH

Phosphoribosyl-glycineamide

5,10 METHENYL H_4-FOLATE

→

H

H_2C—N—CHO

$O{=}C$—NH

ⓅOCH_2 O

OH OH

Phosphoribosyl-formylglycineamide

GLUTAMINE ↓

H

H_2C—N—CHO

HN=C—NH

ⓅOCH_2 O

OH OH

Phosphoribosyl-formylglycineamidine

←

N

H_2N N

ⓅOCH_2 O

OH OH

Phosphoribosyl-aminoimidazole

HCO_3^- ←

→

O

HN N

N N

ⓅOCH_2 O

OH OH

Inosinate

purine biosynthesis de novo

and depended on enzyme amount and ammonium ion concentration in a manner characteristic of an enzyme reaction.

Another apparently enzymatic reaction of ribose-5-P and ammonium ion was demonstrated by Johnstone and her students (*66, 67*) using unfractionated extracts of Ehrlich ascites tumor cells. The rate of synthesis of phosphoribosyl-formylglycineamide was twice as fast when ribose-5-P and ammonium ion were used as when PP-ribose-P and glutamine were present, at equimolar concentrations. Glutamine appeared also to react with ribose-5-P, and ammonium ion with PP-ribose-P. The fact that ammonium ion did not participate through conversion to glutamine was demonstrated by the use of methionine sulfoximine. Both reactions of phosphoribosylamine synthesis were inhibited by purine nucleotides.

Perhaps the most detailed study of the apparently enzymatic synthesis of phosphoribosylamine from ribose-5-P and ammonium ion was done by Reem (*68*). She separated the PP-ribose-P amidotransferase and phosphoribosyl-glycineamide synthetase activities of chicken liver extracts, and she found that the latter fraction contained what was termed "ribose-5-P amidotransferase" activity. (The phosphoribosyl-glycineamide synthetase fraction from mouse spleens infected with Friend leukemia virus did not have this additional activity.) The "ribose-5-P amidotransferase" was purified about 100-fold, and its apparent Michaelis constants were determined to be $6.3 \times 10^{-3}M$ for ammonium ion at pH 9.0 and $1.8 \times 10^{-3}M$ for ribose-5-P. Glutamine reacted at about one-fourth the rate of ammonium ion whereas asparagine and carbamyl-phosphate were virtually inactive. ATP and magnesium ion were required, but the stoichiometry of the reaction was not determined. The reaction was heat labile, followed hyperbolic substrate kinetics, and was inhibited by excess ribose-5-P, and to a small degree, by adenylate and guanylate.

The physiological significance of the proposed alternative pathway of phosphoribosylamine synthesis from ribose-5-P and ammonium ions is very difficult to evaluate. In each system studied so far, PP-ribose-P amidotransferase activity has also been present, and in most cases its maximum velocity has been greater than that of "ribose-5-P amidotransferase." Certainly, the concentrations of ammonium ion required seem to restrict the potential physiological use of this reaction.

Studies with intact Ehrlich ascites tumor cells incubated *in vitro* (*69, 70*) have definitely shown that ammonium ion can support phosphoribosyl-formylglycineamide synthesis and that this process is not inhibited by methionine sulfoximine; initial extracellular ammonium ion concentrations of 5 to 10 mM are required to achieve reasonable rates. Under similar incubation conditions, but in the absence of any nitrogen source, concentrations of PP-ribose-P have been reported to range from 1 to 3 μmoles per gram of cells (*71, 72, 73*) whereas that of ribose-5-P (*73*) or total pentose monophos-

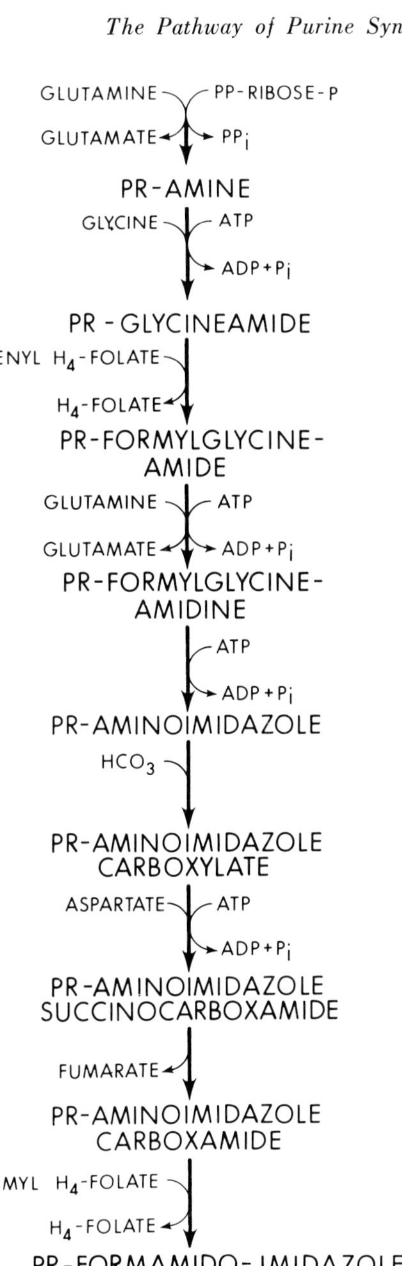

Figure 2-2. Abbreviated scheme of the reactions of purine biosynthesis de novo

phates (*72*) have been reported to range from 1 to 4 μmoles per gram; sufficient sugar phosphate for either reaction would appear to be available. Henderson (*69*), however, concluded that ammonium ion was reacting with PP-ribose-P *via* the PP-ribose-P amidotransferase reaction because both glutamine-supported and ammonium ion-supported reactions were inhibited upon addition of purine bases to the media with the same dose-response and structure-activity relationships. In addition, ammonium ion inhibited the use of glutamine as might be expected if both were substrates for the same enzyme. Somewhat similar results were observed by LeGal *et al.* (*74*) using non-proliferating suspensions of *Escherichia coli* B cells. Again ammonium ion could be used for the first reaction in the *de novo* pathway, but it appeared to compete with glutamine.

The most recent studies of LeGal *et al.* (*75*), however, provide another suggestion of the independent nature of the "ribose-5-P amidotransferase" reaction. These workers showed that whereas certain pyrimidine ribonucleotides stimulated the reaction of PP-ribose-P and glutamine, other pyrimidine ribonucleotides inhibited the reaction of ribose-5-P and ammonium ion; extracts of *Escherichia coli* B were used. Again, the physiological significance of these observations remains to be studied.

This subject requires further study. It remains to be established whether two parallel pathways to phosphoribosylamine do exist in cells, whether both are of physiological significance, what function each reaction has, and to what extent and under what conditions each contributes to purine biosynthesis. Hartman (*52*) has also concluded that "owing to the complexity of the system used, the indirect nature of the assay systems, and the relatively low amounts of synthesis observed, one might still question how well this proposed alternative reaction for phosphoribosylamine synthesis has been documented." Our understanding of the regulation of purine biosynthesis will be strongly influenced by the answers to these questions. The possible use of the imino nitrogen of formiminoglutamate and related compounds for one or both amidotransferase reactions is discussed below.

Phosphoribosyl-Formylglycineamidine Synthesis. Like PP-ribose-P amidotransferase, phosphoribosyl-formylglycineamidine synthetase can use ammonium salts as substrate in place of glutamine. The Michaelis constants for glutamine and ammonium ion are 1 to 3 $\times$ $10^{-4}M$ and 8 to 10 $\times$ $10^{-2}M$, respectively, for the enzyme from chicken liver (*76*), and 1.1 $\times$ $10^{-4}M$ and 7.5 $\times$ $10^{-3}M$, respectively, for the enzyme from Ehrlich ascites tumor cells (*54*). In both cases measurements were done at pH 8, and it can be calculated that the Michaelis constant for ammonia, the probable true substrate, would be 4 $\times$ $10^{-4}M$, quite close to that for glutamine. The initial velocity of the chicken liver enzyme, when ammonium ion was substrate, and the maximum velocity of the tumor cell enzyme were both about 2% of the values obtained when glutamine was used (*54, 76*).

Studies both with Ehrlich ascites tumor cells and with *Escherichia coli* B (*70, 74, 77*) have, however, shown that ammonium ion is not used to any extent for the phosphoribosyl-formylglycineamidine synthetase reaction in intact cells and, in fact, seems to inhibit the use of glutamine for this reaction at low glutamine concentrations.

The use of the imino nitrogen of formiminoglutamate, a metabolite of histidine, and of such related compounds as formiminoaspartate and formiminoglycine has been demonstrated in a number of studies by Hedegaard, LeGal, and their associates (*77–82*). The ^{15}N derived from these compounds is incorporated into the ribosyl-aminoimidazole carboxamide that accumulates in cultures of *Escherichia coli* B that are partially inhibited by sulfadiazine. This incorporation is enhanced by the addition of glutamine whereas that of ammonium ion is decreased by glutamine. These results are interpreted as indicating that neither glutamine nor free ammonium ion is an intermediate in the utilization of the imino nitrogen for purine synthesis, and it is suggested that the formimino derivatives may be substrates of the PP-ribose-P or ribose-5-P amidotransferase.

In other experiments resting cell suspensions were treated with azaserine to give maximal inhibition of phosphoribosyl-formylglycineamidine synthetase. Stimulation by glutamine and formiminoglutamate of incorporation of glycine-^{14}C into phosphoribosyl-formylglycineamide was observed, supporting the conclusions reached above. However, addition of these nitrogen sources also stimulates glycine-^{14}C incorporation into nucleic acid adenine and guanine. These workers suggest that these compounds reverse the inhibition produced by azaserine and that both are therefore substrates of phosphoribosyl-formylglycineamidine synthetase. Although this may be true, this interpretation is clouded by previous observations (*83, 84, 85*) that amino acids such as phenylalanine, tryptophan, tyrosine, and methionine, as well as glutamate and glutamine, may reverse the inhibitory action of azaserine in bacteria. It must be concluded that the enzymatic mechanism or mechanisms by which imino nitrogen is utilized for purine biosynthesis and the physiological significance of this process remain unclear at present.

FORMATION OF PHOSPHORIBOSYL-FORMYLGLYCINEAMIDE. Buchanan and Schulman (*86*) reported in 1953 that addition of 5-formyl H_4-folate to extracts or homogenates of pigeon liver which were capable of synthesizing inosinate slightly and somewhat erratically stimulated formate-^{14}C incorporation into position 8 of the purine ring. Later, Goldthwait *et al.* (*59, 87*) removed endogenous folate cofactors from pigeon liver extracts with Dowex-1 and showed that only phosphoribosyl-glycineamide was synthesized; when 5-formyl H_4-folate and formate were added, only phosphoribosyl-formylglycineamide was formed. The 58-fold-purified pigeon liver phosphoribosyl-glycineamide formyltransferase of Warren and Buchanan (*88*) showed an absolute dependence on 5,10-methenyl H_4-folate. However, studies with certain microorganisms (*see below*) suggest at least the possibility that phosphoribosyl-glycineamide and phosphoribosyl-glycineamide formyltransferase may in some cases not be obligatory in the pathway of purine biosynthesis *de novo.* This question has not yet been settled.

Phosphoribosyl-glycineamide has been reported to accumulate in pea seedlings which were made folate-deficient with 5-methyl-3-sulfanilamide isoxazole (*89*), and it is usually also found in cells or cell extracts treated with glutamine antimetabolites when large amounts of phosphoribosyl-formylglycineamide accumulate (*e.g., 58, 90, 91*).

Buchanan (*47*) mentioned in a review that mutants of *Neurospora crassa* lacking phosphoribosyl-glycineamide formyltransferase had been isolated, and abstracts (*92, 93*) have appeared which report mutants of *Saccharomyces cerevisiae* which also lack this enzyme. Details of these studies have not been published, however, and Westby and Gots (*94*) have been unable to identify any such mutants of *Salmonella typhimurium* despite an extensive search for them.

These workers were also unable to procure any significant accumulation of phosphoribosyl-glycineamide under any conditions of incubation of extracts or in extracts of cells grown under conditions of folate deficiency. They did demonstrate, however, a folate coenzyme-dependent formylation of this substrate in extracts. It was suggested that phosphoribosyl-glycineamide may represent a reversible side reaction branching out from the phosphoribosyl-formylglycineamide which is a true intermediate of the pathway of purine biosynthesis. Such a situation would require that a new and as yet unrecognized reaction exists for the conversion of phosphoribosylamine to phosphoribosyl-formylglycineamide in *Salmonella typhimurium.* It is well documented that the closely related organism, *Aerobacter aerogenes,* has a functioning phosphoribosyl-glycineamide synthetase, which would either have to be absent or without a function if such an alternative pathway were to exist.

Other evidence that the phosphoribosyl-glycineamide formyltransferase reaction of many cells behaves in a somewhat peculiar manner is reviewed in Chapter 4. Until more definitive evidence to the contrary is obtained, it must be assumed that it is also present—and unusual—in *Salmonella typhimurium.*

CONVERSION OF PHOSPHORIBOSYL-AMINOIMIDAZOLE CARBOXAMIDE TO INOSINATE. The original studies (*95*) of the reversible conversion of phosphoribosyl-aminoimidazole carboxamide to inosinate did not succeed in separating the enzyme responsible for the transformylation step from that which catalyzes the subsequent ring closure; at first there was some question whether a single enzyme catalyzed both reactions (*57*). In any case the common intermediate, phosphoribosyl-formamido-imidazole carboxamide, did not accumulate under any conditions tried. Genetic studies with *Escherichia coli* K_{12} (*96*), *Schizosaccharomyces pombe* (*97, 98*) and *Salmonella typhimurium* (*cf.* *99*) also supported the idea that only one enzyme might be involved in these two reactions.

Levin and Magasanik (*100*), however, reported studies in 1961 of a mutant of *Escherichia coli,* HP-1, which had no measureable formyltransferase activity but 15% of normal cyclohydrolase activity. This observation was not followed up, however, until 1969, when Gots *et al.* (*101*) showed conclusively that mutants at the *purH* locus of *Salmonella typhimurium* could be divided into two complementation groups. In appropriate mutants the two enzyme activities could be measured separately, and they were present in equal amounts.

Recent studies have shown that phosphoribosyl-formamido-imidazole carboxamide accumulates in *Salmonella typhimurium* mutants lacking the cyclohydrolase (*101*); Mazlen and Eaton (*102*) also had previously reported indirect evidence for the occurrence of this compound, using mutants of *Saccharomyces cerevisiae.* Baxter-Gabbard and Pattee (*103*) have isolated mutants of *Staphylococcus aureus* which could utilize formamido-aminoimidazole carboxamide but not aminoimidazole carboxamide; this may imply mutational separation of the formyltransferase and cyclohydrolase.

Accumulation of Intermediates. Some or all of the intermediates of the pathway of purine biosynthesis may accumulate in microbial mutants, microbial and animal cells treated with certain drugs, or microbial and animal cells grown or incubated under certain conditions of nutritional deficiency. These phenomena are studied in detail in later chapters, but it may be pointed out here that in many cases the real intermediates of the pathway are not detected or isolated, but rather their various metabolites.

Dephosphorylation of these compounds is a particularly common fate and appears to be required for their passage across cell membranes. It is usually the ribonucleosides of the intermediates of the purine biosynthetic pathway, therefore, which are found in microbial growth media or in media in which microorganisms or animal cells have been incubated. In some cases the sugars are removed also. Compounds extracted from the cells themselves usually are the true phosphorylated intermediates, therefore, although there are some exceptions.

Derivatives of Phosphoribosyl-Aminoimidazole. As discussed in later chapters, a purple, red, or pink pigment often accumulates in cells (and the media in which they are grown) which lack the enzymes phosphoribosyl-aminoimidazole succinocarboxamide synthetase or phosphoribosyl-aminoimidazole carboxylase. The pigment found in the medium is presumably derived from aminoimidazole or phosphoribosyl-aminoimidazole and may result from the reaction of two such molecules to form a dimer (*104*). Smirnov *et al.* (*105*) have recently shown that the intracellular pigment in *Saccharomyces cerevisiae* is a mixture of poly(ribosyl-aminoimidazole) molecules to which various amino acids are attached through amide bonds to the amino group of the imidazole. Whether or not this type of pigment molecule also occurs in growth media is not clear. In yeast, the pigment is localized in large vacuoles (*106*).

Derivatives of Phosphoribosyl-Aminoimidazole Carboxamide. In 1942 Fox (*107*) reported that a previously undescribed aromatic amine accumulated in bacterial cultures under conditions of sulfonamide bacteriostasis; it could be diazotized but not acetylated, and this compound was later identified by Shive *et al.* (*108*) as aminoimidazole carboxamide. Greenberg (*109, 110*) and Gots (*111*) subsequently demonstrated that the material which accumulated was predominantly the ribosyl derivative with some free base and a small amount of the phosphoribosyl derivative; the conditions required for isolation probably result in the formation of free aminoimidazole carboxamide.

References

1. Scheele, C. W., *Kongl. Vetenskaps Academiens Handlingar (Stockholm)* (1776) **37,** 327; "Opuscula," (1776) **ii,** 73; Eng. tr., "The Chemical Essays," p. 145, Scott, Greenwood and Co., London, 1907.
2. Bergmann, T., *Kongl. Vetenskaps Academiens Handlingar (Stockholm)* (1776) **37,** 333; "Opuscula," (1776) **iv,** 232; Eng. tr., Scheele, C. W., "The Chemical Essays," p. 151, Scott, Greenwood and Co., London, 1907.
3. Minkowski, O., *Arch. Exp. Pathol. Pharmakol.* (1886) **21,** 41.
4. Minkowski, O., *Arch. Exp. Pathol. Pharmakol.* (1892) **31,** 214.
5. Lang, S., *Z. Physiol. Chem.* (1901) **32,** 320.
6. Kowalewski, K., Salaskin, S., *Z. Physiol. Chem.* (1901) **33**, 210.
7. Miescher, F., *Verh. Naturforsch. Ges. Basel* (1874) **6,** 138.
8. Tichomiroff, A., *Z. Physiol. Chem.* (1885) **9,** 518.
9. Kossel, A., *Z. Physiol. Chem.* (1886) **10,** 248.
10. Mendel, L. B., Leavenworth, C. S., *Amer. J. Physiol.* (1908) **21**, 77.
11. Socin, C. A., *Z. Physiol. Chem.* (1890) **15,** 93.
12. McCollum, E. V., *Amer. J. Physiol.* (1909) **25,** 120.
13. Osborne, T. B., Mendel, L. B., *Z. Physiol. Chem.* (1912) **80**, 307.
14. Abderhalden, E., *Z. Physiol. Chem.* (1912) **77,** 22.
15. Burian, R., Schur, H., *Z. Physiol. Chem.* (1897) **23,** 55.
16. McCrudden, F. H., "Uric Acid. The Chemistry, Physiology, and Pathology of Uric Acid and the Physiologically Important Purine Bodies with a Discussion of the Metabolism of Gout," Fort Hill Press, Boston, 1905.
17. Benedict, S. R., *J. Lab. Clin. Med.* (1916) **2,** 1.
18. Kapeller-Adler, R., Lauda, E., von Megay, K., *Biochem. Z.* (1934) **269,** 254.
19. Rockwood, E. W., *Amer. J. Physiol.* (1904) **12,** 38.
20. Kollmann, G., *Biochem. Z.* (1921) **123,** 235.
21. Mendel, L. B., *Harvey Lect.* (1905) **1**, 195.
22. Folin, O., *Amer. J. Physiol.* (1905) **13,** 66.
23. Fisher, R. B., *Biochem. J.* (1935) **29,** 2198.
24. Edson, N. L., *Aust. J. Sci.* (1946) **9,** 102.
25. Rose, W. C., *Physiol. Rev.* (1923) **3,** 544.
26. Christman, A. A., *Physiol. Rev.* (1952) **32,** 303.
27. Benzinger, T., Krebs, H. A., *Klin. Wochenschr.* (1933) **12,** 1206.
28. Schuler, W., Reindel, W., *Z. Physiol. Chem.* (1933) **221**, 209.
29. Schuler, W., Reindel, W., *Z. Physiol. Chem.* (1933) **221,** 232.

30. Edson, N. L., Krebs, H. A., Model, A., *Biochem. J.* (1936) **30,** 1380.
31. Örstrom, A., Örstrom, M., Krebs, H. A., *Biochem. J.* (1939) **33,** 990.
32. Örstrom, A., Örstrom, M., Krebs, H. A., Eggleston, L. V., *Biochem. J.* (1939) **33,** 995.
33. Barnes, F. W., Jr., Schoenheimer, R., *J. Biol. Chem.* (1943) **151,** 123.
34. Tesar, C., Rittenberg, D., *J. Biol. Chem.* (1947) **170,** 35.
35. Sonne, J. C., Buchanan, J. M., Delluva, A. M., *J. Biol. Chem.* (1946) **166,** 395.
36. Buchanan, J. M., Sonne, J. C., *J. Biol. Chem.* (1946) **166,** 781.
37. Buchanan, J. M., Sonne, J. C., Delluva, A. M., *J. Biol. Chem.* (1948) **173,** 81.
38. Heinrich, M. R., Wilson, D. W., *J. Biol. Chem.* (1950) **186,** 447.
39. Karlsson, J. L., Barker, H. A., *J. Biol. Chem.* (1949) **177,** 597.
40. Sonne, J. C., Buchanan, J. M., Delluva, A. M., *J. Biol. Chem.* (1948) **173,** 69.
41. Elwyn, D., Sprinson, D. B., *J. Biol. Chem.* (1950) **184,** 465.
42. Marsh, W. H., *J. Biol. Chem.* (1951) **190**, 633.
43. Abrams, R., Hammarsten, E., Shemin, D., *J. Biol. Chem.* (1948) **173,** 429.
44. Shemin, D., Rittenberg, D., *J. Biol. Chem.* (1947) **167,** 875.
45. Sonne, J. C., Lin, I., Buchanan, J. M., *J. Biol. Chem.* (1956) **220,** 369.
46. Levenberg, B., Hartman, S. C., Buchanan, J. M., *J. Biol. Chem.* (1956) **220,** 379.
47. Buchanan, J. M., *Harvey Lect.* (1959) **54,** 104.
48. Buchanan, J. M., "The Nucleic Acids," Chargaff, E., Davidson, J. N., Eds., Vol. 3, p. 303, Academic, New York, 1960.
49. Buchanan, J. M., Hartman, S. C., *Advan. Enzymol. Relat. Areas Mol. Biol.* (1960) **21,** 199.
50. Hartman, S. C., Buchanan, J. M., *Ergeb. Physiol. Biol. Chem. Exp. Pharmakol.* (1959) **50**, 75.
51. Henderson, J. F., Paterson, A. R. P., "Nucleotide Metabolism," Academic, New York, in press.
52. Hartman, S. C., "Metabolic Pathways," Greenberg, G. R., Ed., 3rd ed., Vol. 4, p. 1, Academic, New York, 1970.
53. Li, H.-C., Buchanan, J. M., *J. Biol. Chem.* (1971) **246,** 4720.
54. Chu, S. Y., Ph.D. Thesis, University of Alberta, 1971.
55. Li, H.-C., Buchanan, J. M., *J. Biol. Chem.* (1971) **246,** 4713.
56. Moat, A. G., Friedman, H., *Bacteriol. Rev.* (1960) **24,** 309.
57. Magasanik, B., "The Bacteria; a Treatise on Structure and Function," Gunsalus, I. C., Stanier, R. Y., Eds., Vol. 3, p. 295, Academic, New York, 1963.
58. Hartman, S. C., Levenberg, G., Buchanan, J. M., *J. Biol. Chem.* (1956) **221,** 1057.
59. Goldthwait, D. A., Peabody, R. A., Greenberg, G. R., *J. Biol. Chem.* (1956) **221,** 569.
60. Goldthwait, D. A., *J. Biol. Chem.* (1956) **222,** 1051.
61. Hartman, S. C., *J. Biol. Chem.* (1963) **238**, 3024.
62. Nierlich, D. P., Magasanik, B., *J. Biol. Chem.* (1961) **236,** PC 32.
63. Nierlich, D. P., Magasanik, B., *J. Biol. Chem.* (1965) **240,** 366.
64. Kapoor, M., Waygood, E. R., *Biochem. Biophys. Res. Commun.* (1962) **9,** 7.
65. LeGal, M.-L., LeGal, Y., Roche, J., Hedegaard, J., *Biochem. Biophys. Res. Commun.* (1967) **27,** 618.
66. Herscovics, A., Johnstone, R. M., *Biochim. Biophys. Acta* (1964) **93,** 251.
67. Trachewsky, D., Johnstone, R. M., *Can. J. Biochem.* (1969) **47,** 839.
68. Reem, G. H., *J. Biol. Chem.* (1968) **243**, 5695.
69. Henderson, J. F., *Biochim. Biophys. Acta* (1963) **76,** 173.
70. Fontenelle, L. J., Henderson, J. F., *Biochim. Biophys. Acta* (1969) **177,** 88.
71. Henderson, J. F., Khoo, M. K. Y., *J. Biol. Chem.* (1965) **240,** 2349.
72. Gumaa, K. A., McLean, P., *Biochem. J.* (1969) **115,** 1009.

73. Wong, P. C. L., Ph.D. Thesis, Flinders University of South Australia, 1970.
74. LeGal, Y., Hedegaard, J., Roche, J., *C. R. Soc. Biol.* (1967) **161,** 2408.
75. LeGal, M.-L., Hedegaard, J., LeGal, Y., *C.R. Acad. Sci. Ser. D* (1971) **272 D,** 488.
76. Mizobuchi, K., Buchanan, J. M., *J. Biol. Chem.* (1968) **243**, 4842.
77. LeGal, Y., Hedegaard, J., Cittadini, D., Roche, J., *C. R. Soc. Biol.* (1966) **160,** 299.
78. Hedegaard, J., Thoai, N.-V., Roche, J., *Arch. Biochem. Biophys.* (1959) **83,** 183.
79. Hedegaard, J., Maspero-Sergre, S., Thoai, N.-V., Roche, J., *C. R. Soc. Biol.* (1959) **153,** 954.
80. Roche, J., LeGal, Y., LeGal, M.-L., Cittadini, D., Hedegaard, J., *C. R. Soc. Biol.* (1963) **157,** 1764.
81. Hedegaard, J., LeGal, Y., Roche, J., *Biochim. Biophys. Acta* (1965) **100,** 308.
82. LeGal, Y., Hedegaard, J., Roche, J., *Biochim. Biophys. Acta* (1967) **149,** 325.
83. Gots, J. S., Gollub, E. G., *J. Bacteriol.* (1956) **72**, 858.
84. Bennett, L. L., Jr., Schabel, F. M., Jr., Skipper, H. E., *Arch. Biochem. Biophys.* (1956) **64,** 423.
85. Tomisek, A. J., Reid, M. R., Skipper, H. E., *Cancer Res.* (1959) **19,** 489.
86. Buchanan, J. M., Schulman, M. P., *J. Biol. Chem.* (1953) **202,** 241.
87. Goldthwait, D. A., Peabody, R. A., Greenberg, G. R., *J. Biol. Chem.* (1956) **221,** 555.
88. Warren, L., Buchanan, J. M., *J. Biol. Chem.* (1957) **229,** 613.
89. Iwai, K., Nakagawa, S., Okinaka, O., *Biochim. Biophys. Acta* (1963) **68,** 152.
90. LePage, G. A., Jones, M., *Cancer Res.* (1961) **21**, 642.
91. Henderson, J. F., *J. Biol. Chem.* (1962) **237,** 2631.
92. Levinthal, M., Fogel, S., Hurst, D. D., *Genetics* (1962) **47,** 967.
93. Silver, J. M., Eaton, N. R., *Genetics* (1968) **60,** 225.
94. Westby, C. A., Gots, J. S., *J. Biol. Chem.* (1969) **244,** 2095.
95. Flaks, J. G., Erwin, M. J., Buchanan, J. M., *J. Biol. Chem.* (1957) **229,** 603.
96. Stouthamer, A. H., deHaan, P. G., Nykamp, H. J., *Genet. Res.* (1965) **6,** 442.
97. Whitehead, E., Nagy, M., Heslot, H., *C. R. Acad. Sci.* (1966) **263**, 819.
98. Nagy, M., Heslot, H., Poirier, L., *C. R. Acad. Sci.* (1969) **269,** 1268.
99. Sanderson, K. E., *Bacteriol. Rev.* (1967) **31,** 354.
100. Levin, A. P., Magasanik, B., *J. Biol. Chem.* (1961) **236,** 184.
101. Gots, J. S., Dalal, F. R., Shumas, S. R., *J. Bacteriol.* (1969) **99,** 441.
102. Mazlen, A. S., Eaton, N. R., *Biochem. Biophys. Res. Commun.* (1967) **26,** 590.
103. Baxter-Gabbard, K. L., Pattee, P. A., *Arch. Mikrobiol. Z.* (1970) **71,** 40.
104. Hunter, G., Hlynka, I., *Can. J. Res. Sect. B* (1941) **19B,** 305.
105. Smirnov, M. N., Smirnov, V. N., Budowsky, E. I., Inge-Vechtomov, S. G., Serebrjakov, N. G., *Biochem. Biophys. Res. Commun.* (1967) **27,** 299.
106. Dorfman, B. Z., *Genetics* (1969) **61,** 377.
107. Fox, C. L., Jr., *Proc. Soc. Exp. Biol. Med.* (1942) **51,** 102.
108. Shive, W., Ackerman, W. W., Gordon, M., Getzendander, M. E., Eakin, R. E., *J. Amer. Chem. Soc.* (1947) **69,** 725.
109. Greenberg, G. R., *J. Amer. Chem. Soc.* (1952) **74,** 6307.
110. Greenberg, G. R., Spilman, E., *J. Biol. Chem.* (1956) **219,** 411.
111. Gots, J. S., *Nature (London)* (1953) **172**, 256.

Chapter

3

Properties of Individual Enzymes of Purine Biosynthesis Relevant to Regulation

AMONG THE FIRST factors that should be considered in this study of the regulation of purine biosynthesis are the physical and kinetic properties of the individual constituent enzymes of this pathway. Unfortunately, most of these enzymes have not been studied in sufficient detail to provide much information on this subject. In addition, the first enzyme of the pathway, PP-ribose-P amidotransferase, is of such regulatory significance that it must be treated separately (Chapter 5). At this point, then, those properties of the other enzymes of purine biosynthesis which may participate in the regulation of the pathway are summarized and discussed briefly. For the most part, however, the precise physiological significance of these properties is not yet known.

Physical Properties

Subunit Structure. Rowe and Wyngaarden (*1*) have shown that the PP-ribose-P amidotransferase of pigeon liver, which has a molecular weight of approximately 200,000, readily and reversibly dissociates into two 100,000-molecular weight subunits. Upon further treatment with mercaptoethanol or similar reagents subunits of 50,000 molecular weight can be produced. It would appear, therefore, that the 200,000-molecular weight enzyme is composed of four subunits, pairs of which are held together by disulfide bonds. The potential regulatory significance of these observations is discussed in Chapter 5.

Genetic studies have shown that the phosphoribosyl-aminoimidazole carboxylases of *Neurospora crassa* (*ade3* locus) (*2, 3*), *Saccharomyces cerevisiae* (*ade2* locus) (*4*), *Schizosaccharomyces pombe* (*ade6* locus) (*5, 6*), and *Salmonella typhimurium* (*purE* locus) (J. S. Gots as quoted in Ref. *4*) are composed of subunits. This conclusion is based in all cases on the phenomenon of interallelic complementation, which tests for hybridization between differentially defective subunits and hence requires that the subunits be identical. No direct physical studies of the subunit structure of this enzyme have yet been reported.

Studies of interallelic complementation in *Neurospora crassa* (*ade4* locus) (*7*), *Schizosaccharomyces pombe* (*ade8* locus) (*8*), *Saccharomyces cerevisiae* (*ade8* locus) (*9*), and *Aspergillus nidulans* (*adeA* locus) (*10*), have provided evidence that adenylosuccinate lyase also consists of identical subunits. Physical and chemical studies of the enzyme from *Neurospora crassa* (*11, 12*) have shown that its active form has a molecular weight of about 200,000 daltons and consists of six to eight identical subunits.

There is as yet no evidence that the subunit structures of adenylosuccinate lyase and phosphoribosyl-aminoimidazole carboxylase play any special role in the regulation of the activity of these enzymes or of the pathway of purine biosynthesis as a whole. However, this subject has hardly been investigated.

Multienzyme Complexes. Gots *et al.* (*13*) have demonstrated that the *purH* locus in *Salmonella typhimurium* is "a genetic duplex comprised of two contiguous but functionally different genes," which code for phosphoribosyl-aminoimidazole carboxamide formyltransferase and inosinate cyclohydrolase. Mutations in either gene affect the activity of both enzymes, and these investigators suggested that normally the two activities would function as some kind of bifunctional complex. Physical studies of this complex and its constituent enzymes have not yet been reported.

The possibility that the first four enzymes of the purine biosynthetic pathway might comprise some kind of complex in the cell has been suggested on the basis of the observation (*1*) that these activities remained in the same fraction throughout treatment of pigeon liver extracts with ammonium sulfate and Sephadex G-150. Similarly, phosphoribosyl-formylglycineamidine synthetase and phosphoribosyl-aminoimidazole synthetase activities could not be separated in extracts of Ehrlich ascites tumor cells whereas they were readily separable in extracts of chicken liver (*14*). Whether these observations really do reflect the existence of complexes of enzymes of purine biosynthesis remains to be seen.

Genetic and biochemical studies of *Schizosaccharomyces pombe* mutants blocked at early steps of the purine biosynthetic pathway have led Flury *et al.* (*15*) to suggest that phosphoribosyl-glycineamide synthetase and phosphoribosyl-aminoimidazole synthetase activities reside in a single polyfunctional protein molecule and that mutational events at the single locus can affect either enzyme activity or both. Results compatible with this suggestion have also been obtained with *Saccharomyces cerevisiae* by Gross and Woods (*16*). Physical studies of this entity have not yet been reported.

Kinetic Properties

Reversibility. The first reaction in the pathway of purine biosynthesis *de novo,* PP-ribose-P amidotransferase, is essentially irreversible (*17*), as are phosphoribosyl-glycineamide formyltransferase (*18*), phosphoribosyl-formylglycineamidine synthetase (*14, 19*), and phosphoribosyl-aminoimidazole synthetase (*20*). However, the second reaction in the pathway, phosphoribosyl-glycineamide synthetase, is reversible (*21*). The reactions that convert phosphoribosyl-aminoimidazole to inosinate are mostly reversible—phosphoribosyl-aminoimidazole succinocarboxamide synthetase (*22, 23, 24*), adenylosuccinate lyase (*25*), inosinate cyclohydrolase (*13, 26*), and phosphoribosyl-aminoimidazole carboxylase (*27*).

The reversibility of the last two reactions in this pathway in cells under certain conditions is discussed in Chapter 4.

Michaelis Constants. Table 3-1 lists what little information is available regarding the Michaelis constants of the enzymes of purine biosynthesis *de novo.* These data must be used with caution because they have been obtained using enzymes from a variety of sources; except in the cases of the

Table 3-1. Michaelis Constants

	Apparent Michaelis Constant (M)	*Reference*
PP-ribose-P amidotransferase		
PP-ribose-P	2×10^{-5} to 2×10^{-4}	(*1, 28–33*)
glutamine	1×10^{-3}	
Phosphoribosyl-glycineamide synthetase		
phosphoribosylamine	8×10^{-6}	(*31*)
glycine	2×10^{-4}	
ATP	5.6×10^{-5}	
Phosphoribosyl-glycineamide formyltransferase		
phosphoribosyl-glycineamide	5.2×10^{-5}	(*18*)
5,10-methenyl H_4-folate	5.8×10^{-5}	
Phosphoribosyl-formylglycineamidine synthetase		(*14, 19*)
phosphoribosyl-formylglycineamide	1×10^{-4}	
glutamine	1 to 3×10^{-4}	
ATP	1.5×10^{-3}	
Phosphoribosyl-aminoimidazole succinocarboxamide synthetase (reverse action)		(*24*)
phosphoribosyl-aminoimidazole succinocarboxamide	1.25×10^{-4}	
Adenylosuccinate lyase		(*25*)
phosphoribosyl-aminoimidazole succinocarboxamide	1.1 to 1.9×10^{-4}	

one-substrate reactions (*24, 25*) and the phosphoribosyl-formylglycineamidine synthetase of Ehrlich ascites tumor cells (*14*) the values given are only apparent Michaelis constants.

Ionic Requirements. Three reactions require potassium ion for maximal activity. The optimum K^+ concentrations for phosphoribosyl-aminoimidazole carboxamide formyltransferase were between 8×10^{-3} and $3 \times 10^{-2}M$ (*26*), and that for phosphoribosyl-aminoimidazole synthetase was $5 \times 10^{-2}M$ (*34*). These concentrations are considerably less than the potassium ion concentration of most cells although in a few cases this factor may be of some regulatory significance. The phosphoribosyl-formylglycineamidine synthetase of Ehrlich ascites tumor cells requires only about $2 \times 10^{-3}M$ K^+ for maximum activity, and NH_4^+ will replace both K^+ as activator and glutamine as substrate (*14*). The optimum K^+ concentration for the chicken liver synthetase was about $6 \times 10^{-2}M$ (*35*).

Adenylosuccinate lyase has been reported to require an ionic strength of 0.06*M* for optimum activity (*27*).

The pH optima of most of the enzymes studied seem to be between 7 and 8 although that for phosphoribosyl-aminoimidazole succinocarboxamide synthetase in the reverse direction was pH 6.0 (*24*).

References

1. Rowe, P. B., Wyngaarden, J. B., *J. Biol. Chem.* (1968) **243,** 6373.
2. Giles, N. H., *Proc. Int. Congr. Genet. 10th* (1958) **I,** 261.
3. DeSerres, F. J., *Genetics* (1963) **48,** 351.
4. Woods, R. A., Bevan, E. A., *Heredity* (1966) **21,** 121.
5. Leupold, U., *Arch. Julius Klaus-Stift. Vererbungsforsch. Sozialanthropol. Rassenhyg.* (1961) **36,** 89.
6. Leupold, U., Gutz, H., *Proc. Int. Congr. Genet. 11th* (1965) **2,** 31.
7. Giles, N. H., Partridge, C. W. H., Nelson, N. J., *Proc. Nat. Acad. Sci.* (1957) **43,** 305.
8. Megnet, R., *Genetics* (1959) **44,** 526.
9. Esposito, M. S., *Genetics* (1968) **58,** 507.
10. Foley, J. M., Giles, N. H., Roberts, C. F., *Genetics* (1965) **52,** 1247.
11. Partridge, C. W. H., Giles, N. H., *Nature (London)* (1963) **199,** 304.
12. Woodward, D. O., Braymer, H. D., *J. Biol. Chem.* (1966) **241,** 580.
13. Gots, J. S., Dalal, F. R., Shumas, S. R., *J. Bacteriol.* (1969) **99,** 441.
14. Chu, S. Y., Ph.D. Thesis, University of Alberta, 1971.
15. Flury, R., Flury, U., Coddington, A., *Heredity* (1971) **27,** 311.
16. Gross, T. S., Woods, R. A., *J. Bacteriol.,* in press.
17. Goldthwait, D. A., *J. Biol. Chem.* (1956) **222,** 1051.
18. Warren, L., Buchanan, J. M., *J. Biol. Chem.* (1957) **229,** 613.
19. Mizobuchi, K., Buchanan, J. M., *J. Biol. Chem.* (1968) **243,** 4842.
20. Levenberg, B., Buchanan, J. M., *J. Biol. Chem.* (1957) **224,** 1005.
21. Hartman, S. C., Buchanan, J. M., *J. Biol. Chem.* (1958) **233,** 456.
22. Lukens, L. N., Buchanan, J. M., *J. Biol. Chem.* (1959) **234,** 1791.
23. Miller, R. W., Buchanan, J. M., *J. Biol. Chem.* (1962) **237,** 485.
24. Fisher, C. R., *Biochim. Biophys. Acta* (1969) **178,** 380.
25. Miller, R. W., Lukens, L. N., Buchanan, J. M., *J. Biol. Chem.* (1959) **234,** 1806.

26. Flaks, J. G., Erwin, M. J., Buchanan, J. M., *J. Biol. Chem.* (1957) **229,** 603.
27. Lukens, L. N., Buchanan, J. M., *J. Biol. Chem.* (1959) **234,** 1799.
28. Hartman, S. C., *J. Biol. Chem.* (1963) **238,** 3024.
29. Wyngaarden, J. B., Ashton, D. M., *J. Biol. Chem.* (1959) **234,** 1492.
30. Rottman, F., Guarino, A. J., *Biochim. Biophys. Acta* (1964) **89**, 465.
31. Nierlich, D. P., Magasanik, B., *J. Biol. Chem.* (1965) **240,** 358.
32. Shiio, I., Ishii, K., *J. Biochem. (Tokyo)* (1969) **66,** 175.
33. Hill, D. L., Bennett, L. L., Jr., *Biochemistry* (1969) **8,** 122.
34. Melnick, I., Buchanan, J. M., *J. Biol. Chem.* (1957) **225,** 157.
35. Li, H.-C., Buchanan, J. M., *J. Biol. Chem.* (1971) **246,** 4713.

Chapter

4

Substrate Concentrations

THE PATHWAY of purine biosynthesis *de novo* requires as substrates the amino acids glutamine, glycine, and aspartate; the single-carbon units 5,10-methenyl H_4-folate, 10-formyl H_4-folate, and carbon dioxide (or bicarbonate); PP-ribose-P; and ATP. Evidence will be presented in this chapter that, in one biological system or another, the concentrations of each of these substrates may limit the rate of this pathway. The recognition of this fact began with studies of effects of various kinds of diets on the excretion of endproducts of purine metabolism by animals; however, the conclusions that can be drawn from such investigations are necessarily somewhat limited because of the complexity of the system. After a survey of the effect of nutrition in general on purine metabolism specific attention will be paid to the effect of each of the above-mentioned substrates on purine biosynthesis. In most cases this must include consideration of the regulation of the synthesis of the substrate in question as well as a study of other routes of its metabolism.

Effects of Diet on Purine Biosynthesis de novo

Nutrition of Uricotelic Animals. In the middle of the 19th century, recognition of the fact that uric acid was the major endproduct of nitrogen metabolism in birds was soon followed by measurements of the amounts of this purine which were excreted by birds fed different diets. The first such study seems to have been that of von Knierem (*1*) in 1877, in which the feeding of ammonium salts, glycine, leucine, aspartate, or asparagine to hens resulted in increased uric acid excretion. For example when glycine containing 0.70 gram of nitrogen was fed, additional uric acid was formed which contained 0.66 gram of nitrogen. Taurine was used by Cech (*2*), urea by Meyer and Jaffe (*3*), and ammonium salts by von Schröder (*4*) in similar experiments; in all cases the excretion of uric acid, rather than that of urea or ammonia, was increased.

Later investigators studied the effects of diets in which the major source of nitrogen was grain or purified proteins. Thus in a precise and critical study of uric acid excretion by adult homing pigeons Fisher (*5*) fed different levels of grain and found that there was a linear relationship between nitrogen intake and uric acid excretion over a wide range of dietary nitrogen levels. On all of the diets used, excretion of uric acid nitrogen equalled 42 to 50% of the nitrogen ingested. In later studies Tasaki and Okumura (*6*) and Teekel *et al.* (*7*) varied the protein content of the diets of young cockerels and hens, respectively, with results similar to those obtained by Fisher. In a study with 5- to 6-week-old chicks fed a variety of diets O'Dell *et al.* (*8*) found that uric acid was 75 to 81% of the total urinary nitrogen. However, the total urinary nitrogen ranged from 814 mg per day with a 22% protein diet to 1208 mg per day with a diet of 35% casein plus 1% arginine.

Okumura and Tasaki (*9*) found that the uric acid nitrogen content of chicken liver and kidneys increased from about 2 mg per gram of tissue on a very low protein diet to 4 mg per gram when the diet contained 40% casein. These workers also noted that plasma uric acid concentrations rose sharply after feeding, and that the maximum level was proportional to the amount of nitrogen absorbed. Similar results have been reported by Rostagno and Featherton (*10*), and Featherton (*11*) has shown that plasma uric acid concentrations rose from 4.8 mg per 100 ml on a 25% soybean protein diet to 19.7 mg per 100 ml when the protein content was increased to 75%. When ammonium acetate was also given, plasma uric acid concentrations rose to 12.2 mg per 100 ml when the 25% protein diet was used but did not significantly change from this figure when 75% protein was fed.

Krakoff and Karnofsky (*12*) intravenously infused 3- to 6-month-old chickens with nitrogen-free solutions and with solutions containing glucose plus ammonium acetate. Plasma uric acid concentrations rose from 4.7 to 11.1 mg per 100 ml, and urinary uric acid excretion increased from 56 to 118 mg per kg per hour when the high-nitrogen infusions were used instead of the control. Treatment with azaserine and diazo-oxo-norleucine, inhibitors of purine biosynthesis *de novo*, reduced plasma uric acid to 2.4 mg per 100 ml and urinary uric acid excretion to 2.6 mg per kg per hour.

In some cases ingestion of high-protein diets by uricotelic animals has lead to deposition of uric acid crystals and to gout. Tournut and Montlaur-Ferradou (*13*) have related the predisposition of young chicks to gout both to the elevated blood uric acid concentrations which occur during the first four weeks of life and to the protein content of the diet. Lloyd *et al.* (*14*) specifically studied the toxic effects of feeding high-protein diets to chicks and turkey poults. Ingestion of low-purine diets that contained 36% protein resulted in the precipitation of uric acid in the feet; poults appeared to be more sensitive than chicks. These deposits of uric acid gradually disappeared when the protein content of the diet was reduced.

Recent studies by Peterson *et al.* (*15*) have shown that the susceptibility of different strains of chickens to dietary induction of gout is inherited. Thus while the plasma uric acid concentration of apparently normal chickens fed a diet containing 80% protein was 27.4 mg per 100 ml, that of a susceptible strain on the same diet was 95.8 mg per 100 ml. The incidence of gout was proportional to plasma uric acid concentration in several strains.

These and other studies clearly demonstrate the sensitivity of the rate of purine biosynthesis *de novo* in uricotelic animals to the availability of nitrogenous precursors. However, they have generally been disregarded in considerations of the regulation of this pathway, particularly in ureotelic animals.

Nutrition of Ureotelic Animals. The rate of purine biosynthesis is, in general, lower in ureotelic than in uricotelic animals, and this pathway does not have an important role in excretion of nitrogen in ureotelic animals; in addition most laboratory mammals do not excrete uric acid even as an endproduct of nucleic acid purine metabolism. These facts make it both less likely that dietary nitrogen will influence the rate of purine biosynthesis and more difficult to detect those changes which might occur on different diets. The following review of the studies which have been done in this regard clearly shows how difficult it is to interpret the results obtained. Nevertheless, it appears that diet does influence the rate of purine biosynthesis in ureotelic animals to some extent.

EFFECT OF DIETARY NITROGEN CONTENT. Burian and Schur (*16*) and Siven (*17*) concluded in 1900–01 that the excretion of purines is constant from day to day in the same individual on a purine-free diet and does not depend on the total amount of nitrogen ingested or excreted. This idea was generally accepted, and although evidence against it was soon presented, it remained popular for many years. The following quotation from Rose's 1923 review (*18*) is of interest not only in this connection but also as an early statement regarding the control of metabolic pathways in adult animals. After a discussion of the possible role of arginine and histidine as precursors of purines he added ". . . even if it be admitted that tissue purines have their ultimate origin in arginine and histidine, this fact does not warrant the assumption that the extent of purine synthesis is proportional to the arginine-histidine supply. On the contrary, it seems reasonable to suppose that the synthesis of a tissue component is limited quantitatively to the anabolic needs of the organism for that particular ingredient. As soon as a diet contains sufficient precursors of a given anabolite, synthesis probably proceeds at the optimum rate. If this conception is correct, one should not expect an increase in uric acid excretion to follow the feeding of purine precursors, unless the preceding diet were deficient in these precursors. It therefore seems unreasonable to assume a stimulated formation of purines following food ingestion, unless a second assumption is also made, namely, that part of the uric acid in man as in birds is an *endproduct of protein catabolism* [Rose's emphasis].

We know of no experiments which justify the second proposition." This statement has a very modern ring to it, and the following discussion attempts in part to evaluate its validity.

Although Hopkins and Hope (*19*) had noted in 1898 that uric acid excretion in man increased slightly following a meal and had suggested that this was probably the result of increased synthesis, the idea that uric acid synthesis in man might be affected by the quality or quantity of low-purine diets is usually attributed to Folin (*20*). He reported in 1905 that ingestion of a low-nitrogen starch and cream diet led to the excretion of 50 to 80% less uric acid than that excreted using a diet of milk and eggs. Subsequent studies were usually conducted in either of two ways, one of which was to measure hourly rates of uric acid excretion during the course of a day, both before and after ingestion of a test meal. Diuresis was usually induced by a large water intake. Under such circumstances some increase in uric acid excretion following purine-free but high-nitrogen diets was observed in man by a number of workers (*21–26*). Although protein mixtures or purified proteins were used as the nitrogen supplement in most cases, single amino acids or ammonium salts were used in a few studies. Thus Lewis *et al.* (*25*) observed that ingestion of glycine, alanine, glutamate, or aspartate led to marked increases in uric acid excretion, and Borsook and Keighley (*26*) found a similar result following feeding of amino acids or of ammonium carbonate. Some of these studies may be criticized for not taking into account the effects of the test meals on urine volume, the effects of amino acids, lactate, and so forth on the handling of uric acid by the kidney and on basal metabolic rate and the like [*see*, for example, the critical reviews of Folin *et al.* (*27*), Bröchner-Mortensen (*28*), and Bishop and Talbott (*29*)]. However, at least some of these factors were indeed controlled in many of these investigations. The present tendency is to discount these results as indications of increased purine biosynthesis in man; this is probably not entirely justified, and it is unfortunate that there have been no studies with labeled precursors which might adequately confirm or allay such suspicion.

A second type of experiment has measured daily urinary uric acid excretion for varying periods after the start of test dietary regimens. For example, Taylor and Rose (*30*) used starch and sugar as the low-nitrogen diet (4.6 to 7.4 grams of nitrogen per day) and egg white and sugar as an isocaloric high-nitrogen diet (18.6 to 30.2 grams nitrogen per day); daily uric acid excretion was threefold higher on the latter diet (0.48 to 0.82 gram uric acid per day). Similar results were obtained by others (*31, 32*). In later studies which included measurements of blood uric acid concentrations (*33, 34, 35*) it was concluded that at least part of the effect of high-nitrogen diets was exerted at the level of renal excretion of uric acid.

Animal studies of similar design also provided evidence that uric acid excretion in mammals reflected to some degree the amount of nitrogen ingested. Benedict observed in his original studies of the Dalmation coach hound (*36*) that although uric acid excretion did not respond to increased dietary nitrogen the amount of allantoin excreted did. Hence, the total excretion of endproducts of purine metabolism did increase. This was later confirmed by Young *et al.* (*37*), who also (*38*) observed that allantoin excretion in mongrel dogs varied with varying protein intake.

Two recent studies along these lines may also be mentioned. Calloway and her associates (*39, 40*) first increased the daily nitrogen intake of men from 12 to 96 grams by feeding increasing amounts of egg albumin; daily uric acid excretion rose from 366 mg to 1253 mg. In a more detailed study the daily nitrogen intake of men on isocaloric diets was varied from 0.9 to 62 grams, and the diets were consumed for 15–18 days. Although there was no change in serum uric acid levels or in the miscible body pool of uric acid, the daily urinary excretion of uric acid rose from 306 mg to 1095 mg. These investigators were reluctant to conclude that the tremendous increases in uric acid excretion observed on high-nitrogen diets were in any measure the result of increased purine biosynthesis *de novo*. There seems little reason to doubt, however, that increased synthesis must have been at least partly the basis of these observations.

That such a conclusion is justified is also supported by the study of Bien *et al.* (*41*) of the incorporation of glycine-^{15}N into urinary uric acid in men on low-purine diets whose daily nitrogen intake was adjusted to 48 or 84 grams by supplementation with dry skimmed milk powder. Despite a greater dilution of the labeled amino acid in men on the higher nitrogen diet there was roughly a 50% increase in the incorporation of ^{15}N into uric acid in these subjects.

Effect of Dietary Carbohydrate. Studies similar to those just discussed also suggest that the caloric value of the diet is important in determining the amount of uric acid excreted and that, as a calorie source, carbohydrate is definitely superior to fat. Cathcart (*42*) apparently was the first to note that uric acid excretion in man increased on a high carbohydrate diet, and this conclusion was confirmed by other investigators (*26, 43, 44, 45*). Ingestion of fats did not alter uric acid excretion (*24, 46, 47*).

Both Höst (*48*) and Rose (*32*) studied the interaction of caloric and nitrogen intake with regard to uric acid excretion; the latter observed, for example, that at a constant nitrogen intake an increase from 1780 to 3433 calories was accompanied by an increase in uric acid excretion.

These studies are much more difficult to interpret than those in which only dietary nitrogen levels were varied. Some are subject to criticism regarding various uricosuric effects (*49, 50*) and so forth. In most cases, as suggested by Rose (*32*), the protein-sparing action of carbohydrates underlies the observed effects. Whether in fact increased availability of PP-ribose-P may result from ingestion of high carbohydrate diets has never been studied directly.

Summary of Effects of Diet. The studies discussed above demonstrate that the rate of purine biosynthesis *de novo* in uricotelic animals reflects the availability of one or more of the nitrogenous substrates of this pathway and that the supply of the latter depends on the level of nitrogen intake. A similar effect is observed in ureotelic animals although it is much smaller in magnitude. These findings lead naturally to the following sections of this chapter, in which the factors affecting the availability of each of the substrates of the purine biosynthetic pathway are examined in turn. The possibility that the intracellular concentrations of one or more of these compounds might limit the rate of purine synthesis in various tissues or organisms is discussed and evaluated.

Phosphoribosyl Pyrophosphate

Use of PP-Ribose-P for Purine Biosynthesis *de novo*. The ribose phosphate moiety of purine ribonucleotides is introduced at the first step of the pathway of their biosynthesis *de novo*, through the donor PP-ribose-P.

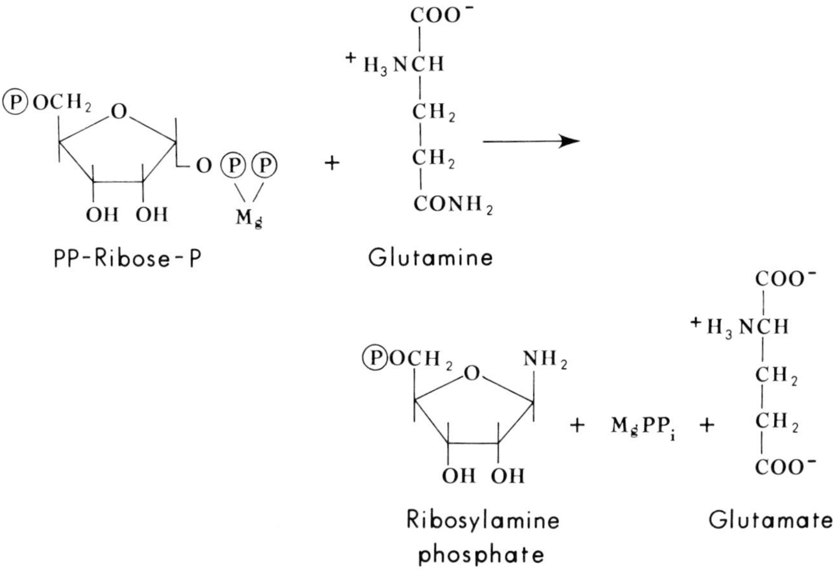

ⓅOCH_2 O — OH OH — O ⓅⓅ Mg

PP-Ribose-P

+

COO^- | ^+H_3NCH | CH_2 | CH_2 | $CONH_2$

Glutamine

→

ⓅOCH_2 O NH_2 — OH OH

Ribosylamine phosphate

+ $MgPP_i$ +

COO^- | ^+H_3NCH | CH_2 | CH_2 | COO^-

Glutamate

Concentrations of this substrate in some cells and tissues under certain conditions are rate limiting for purine biosynthesis; both increased and decreased rates of this process have consequently been observed upon corresponding alterations in the concentration of PP-ribose-P.

PP-ribose-P is most commonly synthesized from glucose by the oxidative or nonoxidative branches, or both, of the pentose phosphate pathway. Alternatively, in some systems it is formed from pentoses or from the ribose of ribonucleosides. The routes of synthesis of ribose 5-phosphate from most distal precursors are subject to a number of potential regulatory mechanisms, as is the synthesis of PP-ribose-P from ribose 5-phosphate itself.

The factors that regulate concentrations of PP-ribose-P are considered here, and the general pathways of PP-ribose-P synthesis and utilization may be summarized as follows:

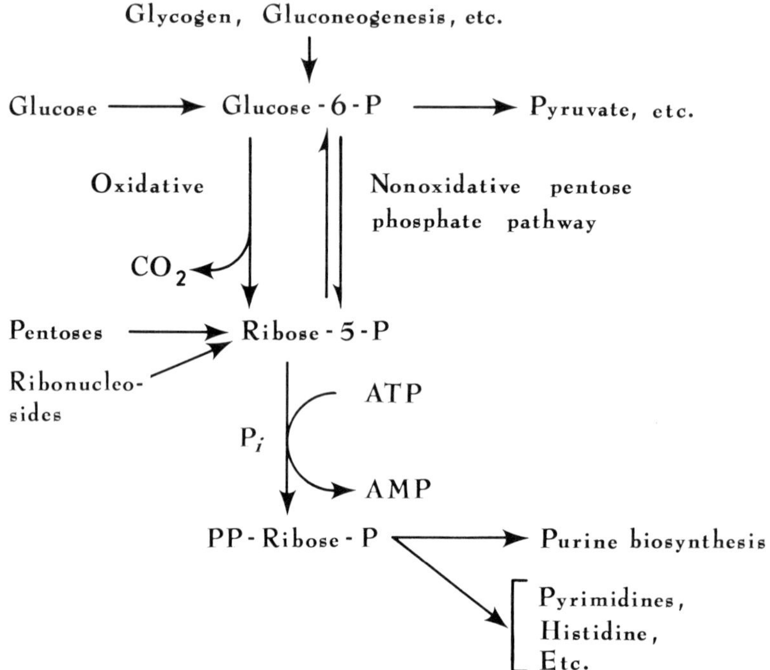

Stimulation of Purine Biosynthesis by Exogenous Glucose. Stimulation of purine biosynthesis upon addition of glucose to cells is generally considered to be because of its conversion to PP-ribose-P, which itself does not readily enter cells.

MICROORGANISMS. A number of studies of adenine-requiring *Saccharomyces cerevisiae* strains have demonstrated the importance of glucose for purine biosynthesis, although they were designed for quite different purposes. *Ade1* and *ade2* mutants produce a pink or red pigment (*51, 52, 53*), which probably results from polymerization of 4-aminoimidazole, which in turn is formed following the accumulation of its phosphoribosyl derivative. White variants, some of which are defective in carbohydrate metabolism, have been noted (*51, 52, 54*). Reaume and Tatum (*55*) observed that although these would not produce pigment (*i.e.*, synthesize phosphoribosyl-aminoimidazole) when grown in a standard medium containing 1% glucose, pigment was produced on media in which the glucose concentration was 8%. Tavlitzki (*56*) also studied *ade2* mutants whose colonies were white when grown with 1% glucose but red when grown with 2% glucose. He also showed that pigment was not produced anaerobically.

Love and Gots (*57*) also noted that the accumulation of ribosyl-amino-imidazole in cultures of *Escherichia coli* mutant W-11 was increased by glucose and aeration.

Glucose was also required for the accumulation of aminoimidazole carboxamide in sulfadiazine-inhibited cultures of *Escherichia coli* B grown in a medium containing casein hydrolysate (*58*); intense aeration prevented this glucose-supported accumulation (*59*). The latter point has not been studied further. Accumulation of aminoimidazole carboxamide in *Escherichia coli* B-96, which lacks phosphoribosyl-aminoimidazole carboxamide formyltransferase, also required glucose (*60*). Gluconate and galactose could replace glucose, but little or no accumulation occurred when the culture was supplied with glucose 6-phosphate, uridine, or glucose 1-phosphate. Arabinose could be used after adaptation. Slotnick and Sevag (*61*) detected small amounts of aminoimidazole carboxamide in culture media following growth of a number of wild-type strains of *Escherichia coli*, but only when glucose had been added to the media. Stimulation of glycine-^{14}C incorporation into nucleic acid purines of *Pasteurella multicida* by glucose has also been reported (*62*).

Animal Cells *in vitro*. In a number of early studies of purine biosynthesis *de novo* in animal cells *in vitro* glucose was included in the incubation media without any special study of the effect of its absence (*e.g.*, *63–68*). Totter (*64*), however, did show that purine synthesis in rabbit bone marrow slices was reduced in its absence. In 1958 Thomson *et al.* (*69*) showed that at least part of the activity of liver extracts that had been shown to stimulate purine biosynthesis (*70*) could be replaced by glucose. Later Henderson and LePage (*71*) found that glucose plus glutamine could completely replace the liver extract. Harrington (*72*) and others (*73–76*) later showed clearly that the added glucose exerted its stimulatory effect by furnishing the ribose of PP-ribose-P, and these conclusions were confirmed by direct measurements of the synthesis of PP-ribose-P from glucose (*77*).

Regulation of Ribose 5-Phosphate Synthesis From Sugar Phosphates. The major route of ribose 5-phosphate synthesis, and hence that of PP-ribose-P as well, is from sugar phosphates—glucose 6-phosphate, fructose 6-phosphate, and glyceraldehyde 3-phosphate—*via* the oxidative and nonoxidative branches of the pentose phosphate pathway. These key sugar phosphates may in turn be formed (a) by phosphorylation of glucose and fructose, (b) by phosphorolysis of glycogen or starch, and (c) from amino and keto acids *via* gluconeogenesis. The sugar phosphates themselves are interconverted by the enzymes of the glycolytic and gluconeogenic pathways.

All of these reactions and pathways are subject to a multitude of regulatory mechanisms of a complexity that is only beginning to be appreciated. Unfortunately, however, the relationship of these controls to the regulation of ribose 5-phosphate synthesis has not been studied in any detail.

OXIDATIVE PATHWAY OF RIBOSE PHOSPHATE SYNTHESIS. Glucose 6-phosphate, whether formed from free glucose, from glycogen, or through gluconeogenesis, may be converted to ribose 5-phosphate *via* either oxidative or nonoxidative pathways. The oxidative route, which is irreversible, proceeds by way of 6-phosphogluconate and ribulose 5-phosphate.

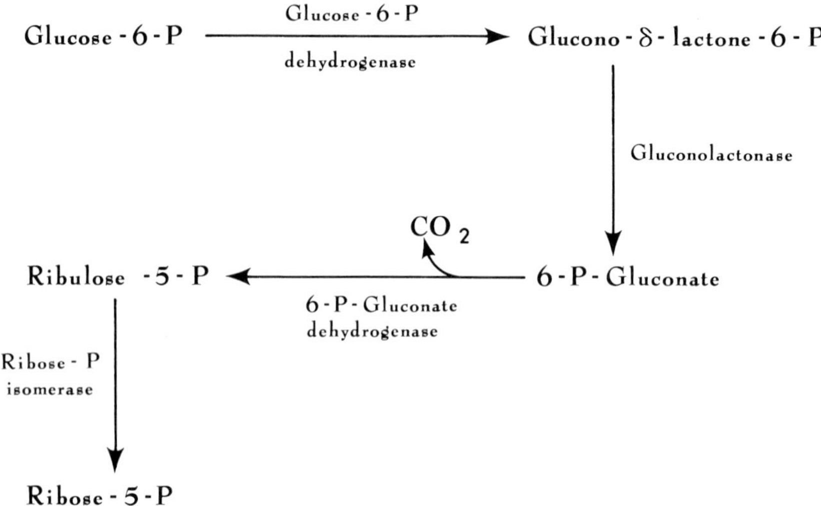

Control of Dehydrogenase Activities. The rate-limiting enzyme in this pathway may vary from cell to cell or under different conditions, but it is usually believed to be one of the two dehydrogenases. Greatest attention is usually paid to glucose 6-phosphate dehydrogenase because of its irreversibility and position at a branch point in glucose metabolism.

The activities of both glucose 6-phosphate dehydrogenase and 6-phosphogluconate dehydrogenase are inhibited by a wide variety of intermediary metabolites, but there is little direct information available concerning the relationship between the regulation of these enzymes and the availability of ribose 5-phosphate for PP-ribose-P synthesis. Of interest, however, are Scholefield's observations (*78, 79*) that the addition of adenine to Ehrlich ascites tumor cells *in vitro* not only increased the conversion of radioactive glucose to nucleotides but also stimulated the oxidation of glucose-1-^{14}C. These results suggest that the rapid removal of PP-ribose-P *via* the adenine phosphoribosyltransferase reaction caused an increase in the rate of the oxidative pentose phosphate pathway in such a way as to produce more PP-ribose-P. The mechanism by which this is accomplished has not been investigated.

Specific glucose 6-phosphate dehydrogenases in endocrine target organs appear to be stimulated by such trophic hormones as adrenalcorticotrophic hormone, thyroid-stimulating hormone, chorionic gonadotrophin, and perhaps others. Such stimulation may be observed even when the hormones are added in low concentrations to homogenates of the appropriate tissue and so can act without necessarily increasing the total amount of dehydrogenase present. This work has been reviewed by McKerns (*80, 81, 82*).

Hall (*83, 84*) found in 1963 that addition of thyroid-stimulating hormone to calf thyroid slices incubated *in vitro* led to increased incorporation of formate, glycine, and adenine into RNA purines. Although stimulation was also produced by addition of glucose, the hormone had additional effects. These were believed to be in part at the level of nucleotide synthesis, although the hormone also appears to increase nucleic acid synthesis directly. Using a similar system, Lindsay *et al.* (*85, 86*) showed that thyroid-stimulating hormone increased the conversion of orotate to uridylate. This process depends on PP-ribose-P, and it has been concluded that stimulation of glucose 6-phosphate dehydrogenase activity by this hormone increases PP-ribose-P synthesis and hence nucleotide synthesis. Dehydrogenase activity also appears to be rate limiting for PP-ribose-P synthesis because the stimulatory effects of glucose and of thyroid-stimulating hormone were not observable when ribose was present; apparently ribose 5-phosphate synthesis from ribose is relatively rapid in this tissue.

McKerns (*82, 87*) has shown that addition of adrenalcorticotropin to homogenates of adrenal cortex supplemented with ATP, NADP, and glucose 6-phosphate stimulated oxidation of the C-1 position of glucose and conversion of orotate to uridylate; addition of PP-ribose-P in the absence of hormone also stimulated the latter process. He concluded that although the potential activity of the oxidative pentose phosphate pathway is high in adrenal cortex, this potential may not be realized at normal tissue levels of substrates in the absence of activation of glucose 6-phosphate dehydrogenase activity by adrenalcorticotropin.

Effects similar to those described above have also been observed when human chorionic gonadotrophin was added to homogenates of ovaries of rats pretreated with follicle-stimulating hormone (*81, 87*).

Although these studies with homogenates are intriguing, their physiological significance with respect to control of PP-ribose-P synthesis in hormone target tissues *in vivo* remains to be established.

Availability of NADPH. The activities of glucose 6-phosphate and 6-phosphogluconate dehydrogenases are also limited by the availability of

NADPH, reoxidation of which can be accelerated by electron acceptors such as methylene blue and phenazine methosulfate.

Uppin and Scholefield (*79*) observed in 1965 that addition of methylene blue stimulated glucose-1-^{14}C oxidation fivefold in Ehrlich ascites tumor cells incubated with adenine and caused a 35% decrease in the amount of radioactivity from glucose-1-^{14}C which was incorporated into nucleotides. Under the same conditions the amounts of radioactivity from glucose-2-^{14}C and glucose-6-^{14}C which were converted into nucleotides were increased somewhat.

Henderson and Khoo (*77*) showed that incubation of Ehrlich ascites tumor cells with methylene blue stimulated the synthesis of PP-ribose-P about twofold; under the same conditions the formation of $^{14}CO_2$ from glucose-1-^{14}C was increased 10-fold. Addition of methylene blue also stimulated nucleotide synthesis from purine bases, under conditions where PP-ribose-P concentrations were rate limiting for this process (*88*). That merely an increase in pentose phosphate produced *via* the oxidative pathway was not alone sufficient to cause an increase in PP-ribose-P synthesis was indicated by the lack of response to methylene blue in another line of these cells, even though $^{14}CO_2$ formation still was increased. Similarly, the line of Ehrlich ascites tumor used by Wong (*89*) for his studies of PP-ribose-P synthesis was not stimulated by methylene blue. Methylene blue also did not stimulate nucleotide synthesis from adenine in slices of mouse brain under conditions where this process was dependent upon PP-ribose-P (P. C. L. Wong and J. F. Henderson, unpublished observations).

Kelley *et al.* (*90*) have reported that incubation with methylene blue also stimulated PP-ribose-P synthesis from glucose in cultured human skin fibroblasts. However, these workers also found that intravenous injection of this electron acceptor did not increase PP-ribose-P concentrations in human erythrocytes *in vivo* (*91*).

The activation of PP-ribose-P synthetase by phosphate will be described below. Hershko *et al.* (*92, 93*) found that the stimulation of PP-ribose-P synthesis attained upon addition of methylene blue to human erythrocytes depended greatly upon the degree of activation of the synthetase by phosphate. Thus methylene blue treatment increased the rate of the oxidative pentose pathway 30- to 40-fold and the concentrations of ribose 5-phosphate five- to 10-fold whether or not the phosphate concentration of the medium was 10 or 60 m*M*. However, only at the latter concentration were elevated concentrations of PP-ribose-P (up to five times normal) observed. It was concluded that in erythrocytes, at least under these conditions, increased ribose 5-phosphate synthesis *via* the oxidative pathway results in increased formation of PP-ribose-P only when the mechanisms regulating PP-ribose-P synthetase are adjusted to favor synthesis.

Variations in Amounts of Dehydrogenases. The amounts of the two dehydrogenases of the oxidative pentose phosphate pathway vary greatly in different cells and can be markedly influenced in animal cells by nutritional conditions and hormonal stimulation or deprivation.

Several forms of human disease associated with erythrocyte glucose 6-phosphate dehydrogenase deficiency are known (*94*). In most cases the deficiency is only partial, and the condition is usually not harmful if the patient is not stressed by certain drugs, foods, or other metabolic alterations. Hershko *et al.* (*93*) have shown that at least in human erythrocytes, in which the rate of the oxidative pentose phosphate pathway is normally low, rates of PP-ribose-P synthesis are normal in the absence of glucose 6-phosphate dehydrogenase.

The rates of glucose-1-^{14}C oxidation, and hence presumably of the whole oxidative pentose phosphate pathway, have frequently been noted to be greater in growing than in nongrowing tissues (*e.g.*, *95–98*), and this has been related to increased rates of isotope incorporation into nucleic acids (*95, 98*). In the case of adipose tissue, Benjamin and Gellhorn (*99*) showed that fasting decreased RNA synthesis, and this was resumed upon re-feeding with glucose. Under similar conditions many investigators have found corresponding changes in glucose-1-^{14}C oxidation and in the total activities of the dehydrogenases of this pathway. These studies have been reviewed by Gumaa *et al.* (*100*).

Similarly, de la Garza *et al.* (*101*) found that fasting led to a 50% reduction in RNA synthesis in rat liver; this was restored by re-feeding a high-protein carbohydrate-free diet. RNA synthesis was only slightly increased over the fasting value when a high-carbohydrate protein-free diet was re-fed. The high-protein carbohydrate-free diet also caused a 3.5-fold increase in glucose 6-phosphate oxidation *via* the oxidative pentose phosphate pathway in liver homogenates together with an increase in the conversion of glucose-1-^{14}C to acid-soluble nucleotides *via* the nonoxidative pentose phosphate pathway. It was suggested that the oxidative pathway was of particular importance for ribose phosphate synthesis on the high-protein diet whereas the nonoxidative pathway was more important when the high-carbohydrate diet was re-fed.

Although these findings are intriguing, direct studies of the relationship of variations in the amounts of glucose 6-phosphate and 6-phosphogluconate dehydrogenase to PP-ribose-P synthesis have not yet been made.

Both the amount and activity of ribose 5-phosphate isomerase can also be controlled by various metabolites and nutritional conditions, but the relationship of such control mechanisms to the availability of ribose 5-phosphate for PP-ribose-P synthesis has not been studied directly.

NONOXIDATIVE PATHWAY OF RIBOSE PHOSPHATE SYNTHESIS. Glucose 6-phosphate may also be converted to ribose 5-phosphate *via* the reversible nonoxidative pentose phosphate pathway. After conversion to fructose 6-phosphate and glyceraldehyde 3-phosphate by glycolytic enzymes the enzymes transketolase (EC 2.2.1.1) and transaldolase (EC 2.2.1.2) form ribose 5-phosphate and xylulose 5-phosphate.

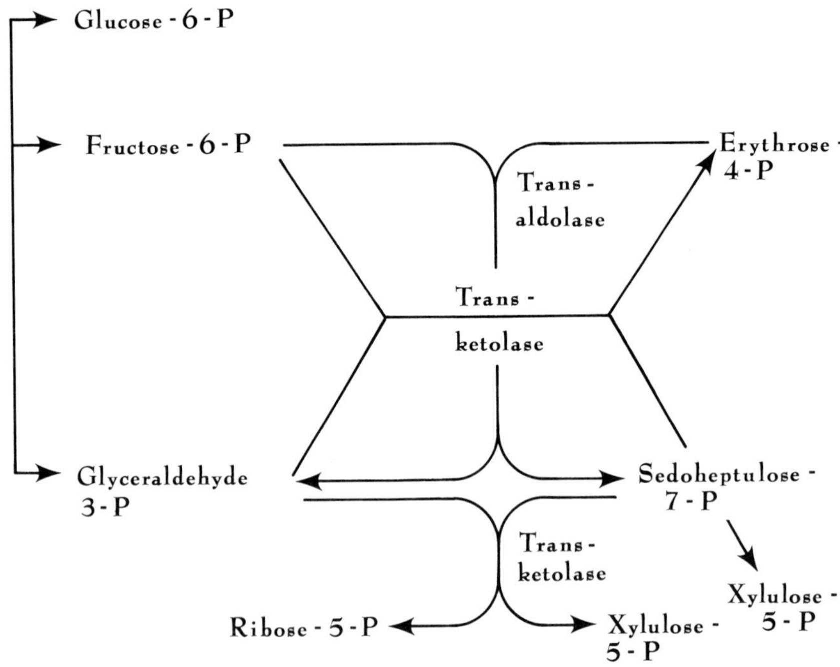

Erythrose 4-phosphate and sedoheptulose 7-phosphate are intermediates which are both formed and reutilized in this process, and the overall stoichiometry is the following:

$$\text{2 Fructose 6-phosphate} + \text{Glyceraldehyde 3-phosphate} \longrightarrow \text{2 Xylulose 5-phosphate} + \text{Ribose 5-phosphate}$$

Xylulose 5-phosphate may be converted to ribose 5-phosphate *via* the readily reversible ribulose 5-phosphate 3-epimerase (EC 5.1.3.1) and ribose 5-phosphate isomerase (EC 5.3.1.6) reactions:

$$\text{Ribose-5-P} \xrightleftharpoons[]{\text{Ribose-P isomerase}} \text{Ribulose-5-P} \xrightleftharpoons[]{\text{Ribulose phosphate epimerase}} \text{Xylulose-5-P}$$

The same series of reactions also serves to convert the ribulose 5-phosphate produced oxidatively back to glycolytic intermediates.

Although the nonoxidative pentose phosphate pathway is more important for PP-ribose-P synthesis in many animal cells (*e.g.*, *100, 102, 103, 104*) than is the oxidative pathway, little is known about the control of the former process.

The synthesis of PP-ribose-P from glucose in Ehrlich ascites tumor cells *in vitro* was found by Henderson and Khoo (*77*) to be strongly inhibited under anaerobic conditions and in the presence of iodoacetate and of dinitrophenol. In the same system, anaerobiosis and the same inhibitors decreased PP-ribose-P synthesis from uridine, although not to the same extent as from glucose (*105*). Glycolysis was also inhibited in Ehrlich ascites tumor cells incubated with formimino-L-glutamate; apparently a metabolite of this compound inhibits triose phosphate isomerase (EC 5.3.1.1) (*106*). The synthesis of PP-ribose-P from glucose is also inhibited under these conditions, and this leads to a marked decrease in the rate of purine biosynthesis *de novo*. The exact cause of inhibition of PP-ribose-P synthesis from glucose and ribonucleosides under these various conditions is not known, but it would appear that changes in the concentrations of fructose 6-phosphate or glyceraldehyde 3-phosphate may cause a shift in the equilibria of the nonoxidative pentose phosphate pathway so that the formation of glycolytic intermediates is favored over that of ribose 5-phosphate.

Control of Enzyme Activities. Little is known about the regulation of the activities of the individual enzymes of the nonoxidative pathway. The equilibrium constants of most of these enzymes are close to unity, and changes in concentrations of any of the substrates might affect the entire sequence of reactions.

Dische and Ingals (*107*) have observed that phosphate (*ca.* 0.1*M*) could strongly inhibit transketolase activity in lysates of human erythrocytes. Hershko *et al.* (*92*) subsequently demonstrated that this enzyme was inhibited in intact erythrocytes incubated *in vitro* in a medium containing 60 m*M* phosphate; compared with a control medium having 10 m*M* phosphate up to 70% inhibition was observed. Despite such inhibition, PP-ribose-P synthesis from glucose both in normal human erythrocytes and in those deficient in glucose 6-phosphate dehydrogenase was not affected. These results would suggest that transketolase activity in erythrocytes is in great excess, and the supposed rate-limiting character of this enzyme may be more apparent than real.

Ribose 5-phosphate isomerase participates in this pathway as well as in the oxidative synthesis of ribose 5-phosphate; it has already been discussed.

Thiamine Deficiency. Thiamine pyrophosphate is the tightly bound cofactor for transketolase, and deficiencies caused by dietary lack of thiamine or by administration of thiamine analogs such as oxythiamine or pyrithiamine

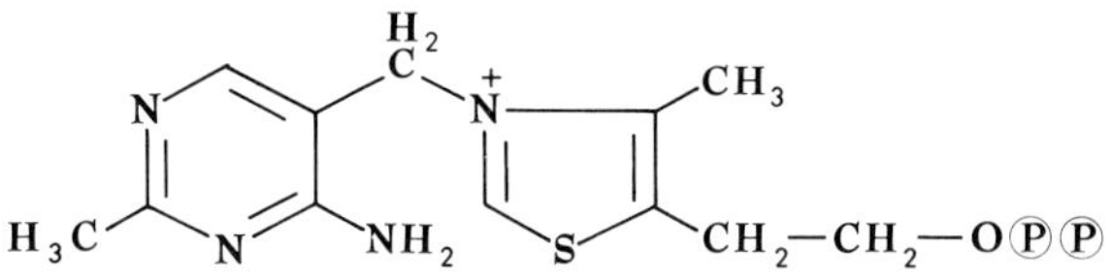

Thiamine pyrophosphate

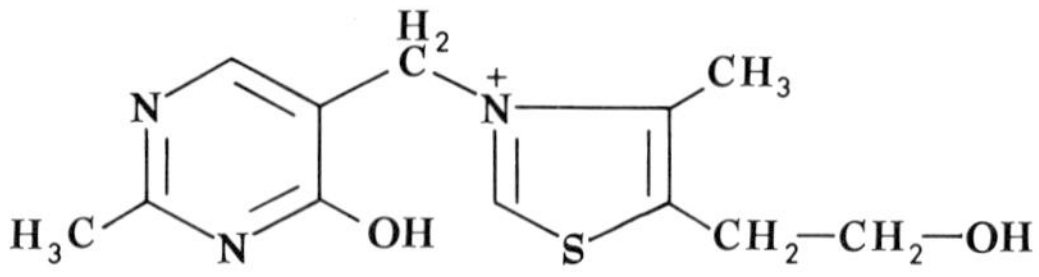

Oxythiamine

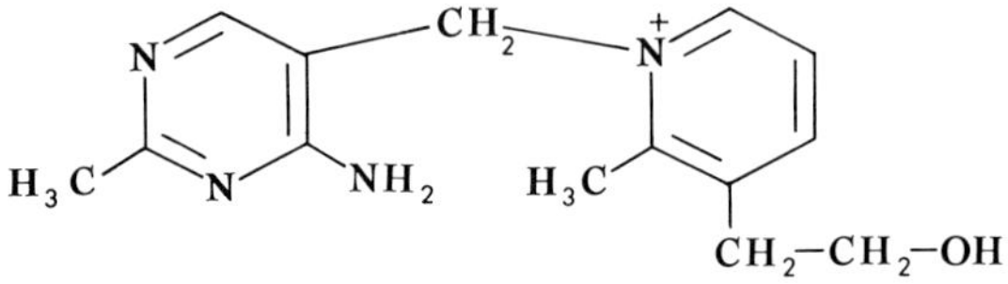

Pyrithiamine

may alter pentose phosphate metabolism and possibly purine biosynthesis *de novo.*

Brin *et al.* (*108, 109*) and Sie *et al.* (*110*) have demonstrated that the conversions in tissue homogenates of ribose 5-phosphate to hexose phosphate and of ribose 5-phosphate, ribonucleosides, and fructose 6-phosphate to sedoheptulose 7-phosphate are inhibited by thiamine deficiency. The recycling of glucose-2-^{14}C in intact erythrocytes in the presence of methylene blue was also markedly decreased after as little as a week on a thiamine-deficient diet.

Although thiamine deficiency would be expected to retard pentose phosphate synthesis *via* the nonoxidative pentose phosphate pathway, the concentrations of those compounds synthesized oxidatively might tend to increase because their conversion back to glycolytic intermediates is inhibited under these conditions. Brin (*111*) indeed did observe an almost threefold increase in pentose phosphates in rat erythrocytes following two to three months on a thiamine-deficient diet; transketolase activity in the intact cells was inhibited by 80 to 85% under the same conditions. Pyrithiamine treatment of rats also produced a 2.5-fold increase in the concentration of xylulose 5-phosphate in the brain, as well as a twofold increase in ATP concentration (*112*); transketolase activity was inhibited 50%.

Coordination of Oxidative and Nonoxidative Pathways and Regulation of the Pathway as a Whole. The relative rates of the oxidative and nonoxidative branches of the pentose phosphate pathway, the predominant direction of the nonoxidative pathway, and hence the overall regulation of these reactions vary greatly from one cell or tissue to another. However, two extreme types of cells may be postulated with regard to the function of the pentose phosphate pathway. In one case the two branches are directed to pentose phosphate (and PP-ribose-P) synthesis and hence operate as two alternative pathways to the same endproduct. In the other case the primary product is the NADPH produced by the oxidative branch, and the nonoxidative branch serves mainly to convert ribulose 5-phosphate back into the mainstream of glycolysis. Many cells probably take an intermediate position, in which both NADPH and ribose 5-phosphate are, in varying proportion, physiologically significant products and in which the nonoxidative branch acts both to form ribose 5-phosphate from glycolytic intermediates and to convert oxidatively formed ribulose 5-phosphate back to fructose 6-phosphate and glyceraldehyde 3-phosphate. Of course, in some cells intermediates of the nonoxidative pathway are also starting products for aromatic amino acid synthesis. As yet, unfortunately, there is little really firm evidence regarding the coordination of the oxidative and nonoxidative branches, and of the regulation of the pentose phosphate pathway as a whole.

Regulation of Ribose 5-Phosphate and PP-Ribose-P Synthesis from Ribonucleosides. Reactions that cleave various purine, pyrimidine, and pyridine ribonucleosides to free ribose or (more commonly) to ribose 1-phosphate have been known for many years. These products may be converted to glycolytic intermediates by the nonoxidative pentose phosphate pathway and thence used in energy yielding reactions. However, as shown in this section, ribose 1-phosphate may also be converted to PP-ribose-P and used for purine biosynthesis and other reactions.

Stimulation of Purine Biosynthesis by Ribonucleosides. In 1958 Harrington (*72*) demonstrated that the incorporation of formate-^{14}C into acid-soluble and RNA purine nucleotides in Ehrlich ascites tumor cells incubated *in vitro* was stimulated not only by glucose but also by cytidine and uridine. Cytidine and glucose both gave approximately eightfold stimulations of this process whereas uridine was somewhat less effective. These observations were confirmed by Thomson *et al.* (*73*), who also showed that the stimulation of formate-^{14}C incorporation into purines induced by uridine in rabbit bone marrow slices was actually greater than that produced by glucose. Stimulation by uridine of purine biosynthesis in Ehrlich ascites tumor cells has also been detected by Shantz and Henderson (unpublished observations). Pyrimidine ribonucleosides had no effect on this aspect of formate-^{14}C metabolism in Leukemia L5178Y cells (*73*) or rat bone marrow slices (*113*), however.

Metabolism of Ribonucleoside Ribose. The ribose moiety of ribonucleosides can be converted into PP-ribose-P in most cells by the sequential action of one of the several ribonucleoside phosphorylases, phosphoribomutase, and PP-ribose-P synthetase, as:

$$\text{Uridine} + P_i \xrightarrow{\text{Phosphorylase}} \text{Uracil} + \text{Ribose-1-P}$$

$$\text{Ribose-1-P} \xrightarrow{\text{Phosphoribomutase}} \text{Ribose-5-P}$$

$$\text{Ribose-5-P} + \text{ATP} \xrightarrow[\text{synthetase}]{\text{PP-Ribose-P}} \text{PP-Ribose-P} + \text{AMP}$$

Administration of uniformly labeled pyrimidine ribonucleosides to rats (*114*) and to cultures of *Neurospora crassa* (*115*) was reported in 1958 to lead to small but significant labeling of nucleic acid and acid-soluble purine nucleotides. Larger amounts of radioactive nucleoside ribose were transferred in Ehrlich ascites tumor cells incubated *in vitro* (*116, 117*) and in homogenates of the Novikoff hepatoma (*118*). Most recently, ribose-labeled inosine was shown to transfer its ribose to adenine nucleotides, *via* PP-ribose-P, in Ehrlich ascites tumor cells (*89*).

SYNTHESIS OF PP-RIBOSE-P FROM RIBONUCLEOSIDES. Henderson and Khoo (*105*) demonstrated in 1965 that the ribose of a number of purine and pyrimidine ribonucleosides was converted to PP-ribose-P in Ehrlich ascites tumor cells incubated *in vitro*. Uridine was the best precursor under these conditions, but the resultant PP-ribose-P concentrations were only about 10% of those attained when glucose was used. Even when PP-ribose-P was trapped by addition of adenine, that formed from inosine and guanosine was only about 75% of that synthesized from glucose; uridine produced about 50% as much as glucose. It would appear that in the absence of adenine considerable amounts of the ribose 5-phosphate formed from uridine was diverted to the glycolytic pathway instead of towards PP-ribose-P.

Although no more PP-ribose-P was formed from combinations of high concentrations of glucose plus nucleosides than from glucose alone, combinations of high concentrations of nucleoside plus low concentrations of glucose gave additive or more than additive effects on PP-ribose-P synthesis.

It may be concluded that substantial amounts of PP-ribose-P can be synthesized from the ribose of ribonucleosides in at least some cells. The physiological significance of this pathway remains quite uncertain, however, in part because most cells usually have a substantial supply of glucose and in part because the supply of ribonucleosides is probably small under normal conditions.

Regulation of PP-Ribose-P Synthetase. At the focus of all of these diverse pathways for the synthesis of ribose 5-phosphate is its conversion to PP-ribose-P by PP-ribose-P synthetase.

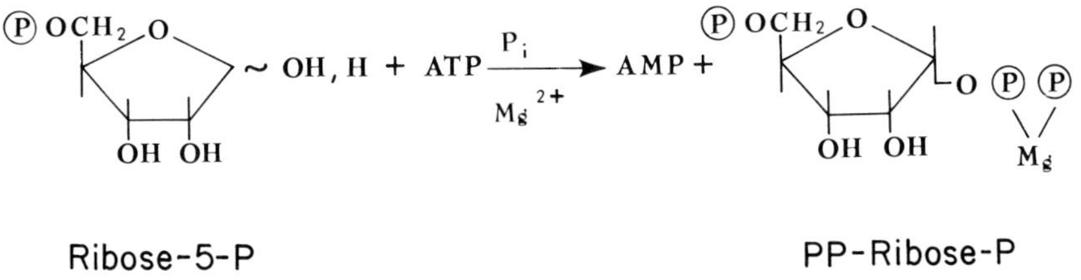

$$\text{Ribose-5-P} + ATP \xrightarrow[Mg^{2+}]{P_i} AMP + \text{PP-Ribose-P}$$

Ribose-5-P PP-Ribose-P

This reaction is subject to a number of regulatory mechanisms of potential physiological significance and is just beginning to receive the careful study it deserves.

PROPERTIES OF PP-RIBOSE-P SYNTHETASE. Switzer (*119*) has partially purified PP-ribose-P synthetase from wild-type *Salmonella typhimurium* and estimates that its molecular weight is roughly 540,000 daltons and that it is composed of subunits. The apparent optimum pH is 8.1 to 8.6, and it is not stimulated by addition of sulfhydryl compounds. He has shown that the reaction is reversible, with an equilibrium constant of about 29.

The human erythrocyte enzyme has been highly purified by Fox and Kelly (*120*). In the absence of ATP its molecular weight is about 60,000 daltons, but in the presence of this substrate and Mg^{2+} it aggregates to forms of 720,000 and 1,200,000 daltons. The pH optimum is about 7.3.

Studies of isotope exchange between adenylate and ATP and between ribose 5-phosphate and PP-ribose-P led to the conclusion that a pyrophosphoryl-enzyme complex participated in the reaction (*121, 122*), and ^{32}P-labeled enzyme has been formed by reaction of ATP-^{32}P and free enzyme. However, it has not yet been possible to convert this to PP-ribose-P upon addition of ribose 5-phosphate.

Switzer (*119*) found that the apparent Michaelis constant for Mg-ATP varied from 0.1 to 2.9 mM, depending on assay conditions. Wong and Murray (*123*) reported Michaelis constants of 0.06 mM for Mg-ATP and 0.05 mM for ribose 5-phosphate for the enzyme from Ehrlich ascites tumor cells, although these also varied with the conditions used. Much lower Michaelis constants have been reported for the human erythrocyte enzyme (*120*): 14 μM for ATP, 33 μM for ribose 5-phosphate.

ACTIVATION BY PHOSPHATE. The absolute dependence of PP-ribose-P synthetase activity on inorganic phosphate has been noted for preparations from human erythrocytes (*120, 124*), pigeon liver (*125*), Ehrlich ascites tumor cells (*123, 126*), and *Salmonella typhimurium* (*119, 127*) although this was not noted in some early studies (*128, 129, 130*) because of the routine use of phosphate buffer. Switzer (*119*) and Fox and Kelley (*120*) found that phosphate stabilized PP-ribose-P synthetase during both heating and freezing.

Wong and Murray (*123, 126*) observed that the apparent Michaelis constant for phosphate for the enzyme from Ehrlich ascites tumor cells was about 3.3 m*M*, but saturation was not achieved until 50 m*M*. The *Salmonella typhimurium* enzyme had apparent Michaelis constants of 2.3 and 40 m*M* at pH 8.4 and pH 7.5, respectively, but only one Michaelis constant of 40 m*M* at pH 6.8; again, 50 m*M* phosphate was saturating (*119, 127*). Phosphate was required for both the forward and reverse actions (*119*).

High (15 to 30 m*M*) phosphate concentrations in incubation media stimulated PP-ribose-P synthesis in erythrocytes (*92, 93*) and Ehrlich ascites tumor cells (*92, 131*), and parallel increases in nucleotide synthesis from purine bases have been measured. The stimulatory effect of phosphate on PP-ribose-P synthesis has been studied in greatest detail by Herschko *et al.* (*92, 93*), using rabbit and human erythrocytes incubated *in vitro.*

Although increased phosphate concentrations in incubation media also led to some increase in glucose uptake and ATP concentrations, PP-ribose-P synthesis was far more sensitive to this stimulus. PP-Ribose-P synthesis from glucose was stimulated by phosphate concentrations only up to about 30 m*M*, but that from inosine or glucose plus methylene blue was stimulated markedly by phosphate levels up to 60 m*M*.

Studies using methylene blue to stimulate ribose 5-phosphate synthesis have led to the conclusion that although increased production of ribose 5-phosphate can lead to a higher rate of PP-ribose-P synthesis the activity of the PP-ribose-P synthetase soon becomes limiting. However, it can be increased by addition of phosphate to the system so that PP-ribose-P synthetase activity now outstrips the capacity of the cell to supply ribose 5-phosphate.

Although extracellular phosphate concentrations of 25 to 60 m*M* were used in these and similar studies, its normal intracellular levels are much lower (1 to 5 m*M*). The regulatory role of small changes in free phosphate concentrations in this range during metabolism *in vivo* remains to be explored.

ACTIVATION BY DIVALENT CATIONS. Wong and Murray (*123, 126*) and Switzer (*119*) have shown that the PP-ribose-P synthetases from Ehrlich ascites tumor cells and *Salmonella typhimurium* not only require Mg^{2+} (or certain other divalent cations) to form Mg-ATP, the true substrate, but that Mg^{2+} also activates the reaction by another mechanism, presumably through the formation of a direct Mg^{2+}-enzyme complex. The exact mechanism of this effect of Mg^{2+} is not known.

INHIBITION BY NUCLEOTIDES AND AMINO ACIDS. As mentioned previously, Mg-ATP is the true substrate of PP-ribose-P synthetase, and free ATP inhibits the enzyme from Ehrlich ascites tumor cells (*123, 126*).

In 1967 Switzer (*132*) reported briefly that the PP-ribose-P synthetase from *Salmonella typhimurium* was inhibited by ADP, CTP, GTP, UTP, and tryptophan but not by histidine, NAD, NADP, or NADPH. Not unexpectedly, the extent of inhibition depended on pH, substrate concentration, and divalent cation concentration. The details of these experiments have not yet been published.

Atkinson and his colleagues (*133, 134*) have studied the effect of the so-called energy charge on the activity of the PP-ribose-P synthetase of *Escherichia coli;* this is a measure of the ratio of ATP concentration to those of ADP and AMP. Atkinson and Fall (*133*) first showed that ADP was a much more potent inhibitor than AMP, GDP, CDP, or tryptophan. Subsequently (*134*) it was found that when the energy charge was about 0.9 (*i.e.*, almost all the adenine nucleotide was in the form of ATP), the reaction was inhibited about 50% on the addition of 1.0 m*M* each of GDP, ITP, or UTP or 0.3 m*M* each of UDP, IDP, ITP, tryptophan, and other compounds.

The PP-ribose-P synthetase of Ehrlich ascites tumor cells was inhibited by nearly all of the nucleoside mono-, di-, and triphosphates tested (*123*). The product, adenylate, was a particularly potent inhibitor, and its kinetics of inhibition differed somewhat from those of guanylate and inosinate. Because of the relatively high concentrations of these compounds required for inhibition, however, it is unlikely that nucleoside monophosphates other than adenylate could take part in the regulation of PP-ribose-P synthesis in intact cells.

Except for ADP, the potent inhibition of which was competitive with respect to ATP, other nucleoside diphosphates showed only weak inhibitory activity. Inhibitions by the various nucleoside triphosphates were competitive with respect to Mg-ATP; however, high concentrations of such compounds never resulted in complete inhibition. PP-ribose-P was not inhibitory at any of the concentrations tested.

That these potential regulatory mechanisms might indeed have physiological significance was demonstrated by the observation that the rate of PP-ribose-P synthesis in Ehrlich ascites tumor cells incubated with glucose and adenine was only about 10% of the maximum rate of PP-ribose-P synthetase activity measured in cell extracts. Wong (*89*) has suggested that inhibition of this enzyme by GTP may be physiologically significant, since addition of 2-deoxyglucose to tumor cells caused a transient increase in PP-ribose-P synthesis with a concomitant decrease in the concentration of this nucleoside triphosphate. Changes in the concentrations of other nucleotides could not be correlated with changes in the rate of PP-ribose-P synthesis.

The PP-ribose-P synthetase activity of erythrocyte hemolysates was inhibited most strongly by ADP, by 2,3-diphosphoglycerate, and by GDP. Other purine and pyrimidine nucleotides were inactive or only weakly inhibitory (*92*). Joint addition of the three active compounds at concentrations approximating those found in erythrocytes, in the presence of 1 to 2 m*M* phosphate, produced 99% inhibition of PP-ribose-P synthetase activity. Measurement of the activity of this enzyme in intact erythrocytes suggests that it normally is under inhibitory control of this magnitude. PP-ribose-P itself was not found to be inhibitory. Inhibition of PP-ribose-P synthetase by ADP was partially relieved by increased phosphate concentration whereas that produced by GDP and 2,3-diphosphoglycerate was not.

These studies show clearly that PP-ribose-P synthetase activity is normally very strongly inhibited in cells and identify a number of potential inhibitory nucleotides. The relationship between the concentrations of these inhibitors and those of substrates and activators in cells under physiological conditions remains virtually unknown.

Regulation of Enzyme Amount. Little is known of the relative activities of PP-ribose-P synthetase in different cells and tissues. The following specific activities were reported in Kornberg's (*128*) original study of this enzyme: chicken liver, 0.29; mouse liver, 0.04; rat liver, 0.01; and *Escherichia coli*, 0.34. Wong (*89*) found these specific activities: rat liver, 0.9; human blood lysate, 0.8; mouse brain, 3.3; mouse lymph nodes, 6.2; Ehrlich ascites tumor cells, 8–15; germinated wheat embryo, 5.3.

Switzer (*132*) reported briefly that the specific activity of PP-ribose-P synthetase in *Salmonella typhimurium* did not vary appreciably when cells were grown with high concentrations of purine, pyrimidine, or amino acid endproducts of PP-ribose-P metabolism, or when they were starved for carbon or nitrogen or were under conditions of high or low rates of histidine metabolism. He concluded that either the enzyme is constitutive, or that nutritional status had little effect on the levels of some co-repressor. Details have not yet been published; however, David and Wiesmeyer (*135*) also found that growth conditions did not affect PP-ribose-P synthetase levels in *Escherichia coli.*

Table 4-1. Reactions of PP-Ribose-P

Phosphoribosyl Acceptor	*Product*	*Enzyme Commission Number*
Glutamine, NH_3	Phosphoribosylamine	2.4.2.14
Adenine	Adenylate	2.4.2.7
Guanine, hypoxanthine	Guanylate, inosinate	2.4.2.8
Xanthine	Xanthylate	
Orotate	Orotidylate	2.4.2.10
Uracil	Uridylate	2.4.2.9
2,4-Diketopyrimidines, 2,6-diketopurines	Uridylate, orotidylate, 3-phosphoribosyl-uric acid, 3-phosphoribosyl-xanthine	
Nicotinate	Nicotinate ribonucleotide	2.4.2.11
Nicotinamide	Nicotinamide ribonucleotide	2.4.2.12
Quinolinate	Quinolinate ribonucleotide + CO_2	
Imidazoleacetate (+ ATP)	Phosphoribosyl-imidazoleacetate (+ ADP + P_i)	
Histamine (+ ATP)	Phosphoribosyl-histamine (+ ADP + P_i)	
Anthranilate	Phosphoribosyl-anthranilate	
ATP	1-(5′-Phosphoribosyl) ATP	

Alternative Pathways of PP-Ribose-P Metabolism. PP-Ribose-P participates in a number of other enzyme reactions in addition to that catalyzed by PP-ribose-P amidotransferase; these are listed in Table 4-1.

PURINE PHOSPHORIBOSYLTRANSFERASES. The possibility that competition for PP-ribose-P between the pathway of purine biosynthesis *de novo* and purine phosphoribosyltransferases might reduce the amount of this substrate which is available for the former process will be considered in Chapters 5 and 8.

The acceleration in purine biosynthesis *de novo* caused by increased availability of PP-ribose-P in cells deficient in hypoxanthine-guanine phosphoribosyltransferase will be discussed in Chapter 9.

OROTATE PHOSPHORIBOSYLTRANSFERASE. There is good evidence that orotate can trap PP-ribose-P *via* the orotate phosphoribosyltransferase (EC 2.4.2.10) reaction and that this process results in a decreased rate of purine biosynthesis *de novo* in several systems.

Orotate + PP-Ribose-P $\xrightarrow{\text{Orotate phosphoribosyltransferase}}$ Orotidylate + Mg - PP_i

Standerfer and Handler (*136*) observed in 1955 that fatty livers were produced in rats by feeding a diet containing 1% orotate, and Handschumacher *et al.* (*137, 138*) later found that addition of 0.25% adenine to these diets nullified the effect of this pyrimidine. A fourfold increase in nucleotides of uracil occurred in liver of rats fed orotate (*139*), and both this increase and accelerated acetate-^{14}C incorporation into triglycerides were prevented when the diet also contained adenine.

The effects of adding various concentrations of orotate to diets were studied by Marchetti *et al.* (*140*). In livers of rats fed 0.001% orotate, concentrations of acid-soluble cytosine and guanine nucleotides were somewhat elevated, but as the amount of orotate fed was increased, uracil nucleotides increased and cytosine and purine nucleotides decreased. RNA synthesis was also accelerated in the livers of the rats fed orotate. Windmueller (*141*) found that feeding 1% orotate led to a fourfold increase in liver uracil nucleotides within 16 hours whereas purine nucleotide concentrations decreased progressively to a minimum after four days. It is interesting that feeding orotate to chicks did not lead to fatty livers, increased uracil nucleotide concentration only slightly, and caused no change in liver adenine nucleotide concentrations (*142, 143*).

Rajalakshmi and Handschumacher (*144*) obtained more direct evidence regarding the mechanism by which feeding of orotate leads to lowered adenine nucleotide concentrations in rat livers. Orotate was found to inhibit the incorporation of glycine-^{14}C into liver acid-soluble adenine nucleotides both *in vivo* and *in vitro*, and evidence was obtained that under these conditions concentrations of PP-ribose-P were limiting for purine biosynthesis *de novo.*

More definitive evidence that orotate phosphoribosyltransferase and PP-ribose-P amidotransferase compete in some cells for a limited supply of PP-ribose-P came from studies of skin fibroblasts by Kelley *et al.* (*145*). Addition of orotate reduced purine biosynthesis *de novo,* as measured with glycine-^{14}C, and also reduced PP-ribose-P concentrations by 15 to 43%. Both effects were nullified when azaorotate, a competitive inhibitor of orotate phosphoribosyltransferase, was added together with the orotate. Finally, similar studies were conducted with fibroblasts which lacked hypoxanthine-guanine phosphoribosyltransferase, in which PP-ribose-P concentrations were elevated fourfold to fivefold (*145*). Although addition of orotate caused 33 to 47% decreases in PP-ribose-P concentrations, these were still above those normally found in control cells, and purine biosynthesis *de novo* was not inhibited.

Intravenous administration of orotate in man led to 21 to 38% decreases in the incorporation of glycine-^{14}C into urinary uric acid and about 40% decreases in erythrocyte PP-ribose-P concentrations *in vivo* (*146*). However, there was no inhibition of purine biosynthesis *de novo* in patients with hypoxanthine-guanine phosphoribosyltransferase deficiency. Although erythrocyte PP-ribose-P concentrations declined following administration of orotate, they still did not drop below normal control levels.

Although it is clear that orotate phosphoribosyltransferase competes for PP-ribose-P with the purine biosynthetic pathway when exogenous orotate is supplied, it is not known if this still happens at endogenous concentrations of this pyrimidine. That such might not be the case was suggested by the observation of Fox and Kelley (*91*) that PP-ribose-P concentrations were not elevated in erythrocytes of patients with oroticaciduria and with only 25% of normal orotate phosphoribosyltransferase.

Adenosine Triphosphate

Use of ATP for Purine Biosynthesis *de novo*. ATP is one of the substrates of four of the reactions of purine biosynthesis: phosphoribosylglycineamide synthetase, phosphoribosyl-formylglycineamidine synthetase, phosphoribosyl-aminoimidazole synthetase, and phosphoribosyl-aminoimidazole succinocarboxamide synthetase. In addition, of course, it is required directly or indirectly for the synthesis of the other substrates of this pathway.

$$\text{Phosphoribosylamine} + \text{ATP} + \text{Glycine} \longrightarrow \text{Phosphoribosyl-glycineamide} + \text{ADP} + P_i$$

$$\text{Phosphoribosyl-formylglycineamide} + \text{ATP} + \text{Glutamine} \longrightarrow \text{Phosphoribosyl-formyl-glycineamidine} + \text{Glutamine} + \text{ADP} + P_i$$

$$\text{Phosphoribosyl-formyl-glycineamidine} + \text{ATP} \longrightarrow \text{Phosphoribosyl-aminoimidazole} + \text{ADP} + P_i$$

$$\text{Phosphoribosyl-aminoimidazole carboxylate} + \text{ATP} + \text{Aspartate} \longrightarrow \text{Phosphoribosyl-amino-imidazole succinocarboxamide} + \text{ADP} + P_i$$

ATP as a Limiting Substrate for Purine Biosynthesis. Because of the central role of ATP in cellular metabolism it is extremely difficult to single out any effect of altered ATP concentrations on the pathway of purine synthesis alone. As discussed in Chapter 5, there are a number of reports that lowered ATP concentrations result in increased purine biosynthesis *de novo* because of decreased feedback inhibition.

However, several investigators (*147, 148, 149*) have shown that whereas treatment of rats with certain doses of ethionine causes an increased rate of purine biosynthesis in liver the use of larger doses of this amino acid analog leads to inhibition of this process. At the lower doses ATP concentrations fall moderately whereas large doses of ethionine cause a substantial depletion of this substrate. In the latter case it has been suggested that ATP concentrations may limit purine biosynthesis. In addition, Rapp and Sacks (*150*) have noted both lowered ATP concentrations and reduced formate-^{14}C incorporation into liver purine nucleotides in alloxan diabetic rats.

Abrams (*151, 152*) in 1951–52 reported studies of an interesting mutant of *Saccharomyces cerevisiae* that required either hypoxanthine or adenine for growth and yet was capable of synthesizing purines from glycine-^{14}C. Addition of adenine (up to a certain concentration) increased the rate of glycine-^{14}C incorporation into purines whereas in wild-type yeast addition of adenine decreased such incorporation, presumably by feedback inhibition. It was noted that the mutant contained no detectable acid-soluble purine compounds whereas those in the wild-type cells amounted to five times the purine content of the DNA. It was suggested that nucleic acid synthesis scavenged all of the acid-soluble purines of the mutant and that purine biosynthesis *de novo* (and presumably other cellular processes) were in fact limited by ATP and related coenzymes. Thus the addition of small amounts of adenine increased the ATP and supported increased purine synthesis.

A similar mutant of *Saccharomyces cerevisiae*, which requires small amounts of adenine for growth and yet still synthesizes purines *de novo*, has also been reported by Takahashi *et al.* (*153*).

Glutamine

Use of Glutamine for Purine Biosynthesis. The amide nitrogen of glutamine provides N-9 of purines by reaction of this amino acid with PP-ribose-P to form phosphoribosylamine.

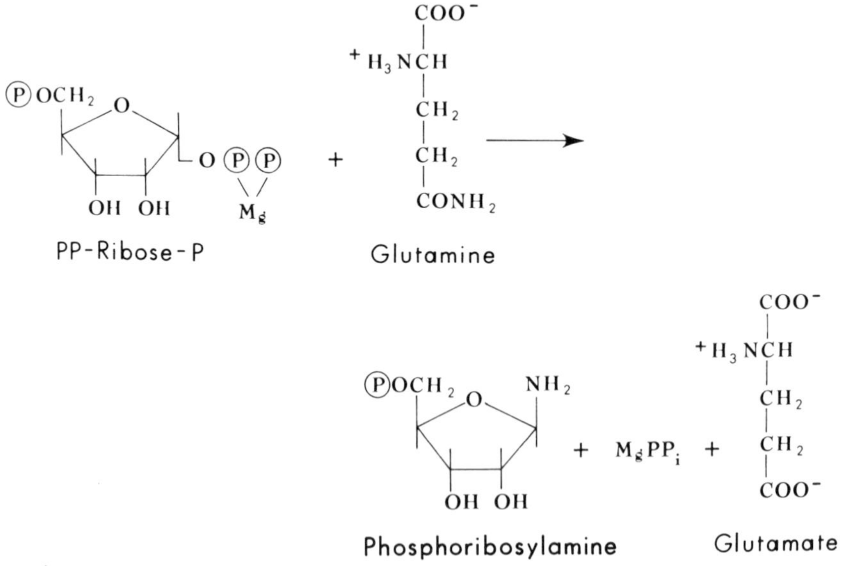

ⓅOCH_2 … O … OⓅⓅ (Mg); OH OH — PP-Ribose-P

+

COO^- / ^+H_3NCH / CH_2 / CH_2 / $CONH_2$ — Glutamine

→

ⓅOCH_2 … O … NH_2; OH OH — Phosphoribosylamine

+ $MgPP_i$ +

COO^- / ^+H_3NCH / CH_2 / CH_2 / COO^- — Glutamate

The reaction of glutamine with phosphoribosyl-formylglycineamide to form the corresponding amidine provides N-3.

$$\text{Phosphoribosyl-formylglycineamide} + \text{ATP} + {}^{+}H_3NCH(COO^-)CH_2CH_2CONH_2 \longrightarrow$$

Phosphoribosyl-formylglycineamide — Glutamine

$$\text{Phosphoribosyl-formylglycineamidine} + \text{ADP} + P_i + {}^{+}H_3NCH(COO^-)CH_2CH_2COO^-$$

Phosphoribosyl-formylglycineamidine — Glutamate

Glutamine concentrations in some cells and tissues are rate limiting for purine biosynthesis *de novo*, and both increased and decreased rates of this process have been observed following corresponding alterations in the concentrations of this precursor. Evidence for these conclusions is presented in this section.

The factors that regulate glutamine concentrations are also considered here, and the general pathways of glutamine synthesis and utilization may be summarized as shown in the diagram on p. 70.

Meister has published several reviews of glutamine metabolism (*154, 155, 156*, p. 617).

RANDOMIZATION OF LABEL FROM GLUTAMINE. Ammonia formed from the amide group of glutamine by hydrolysis may be introduced into the amino group of glutamate *via* the glutamate dehydrogenase reaction, as shown above. By means of transamination reactions this nitrogen may then be converted into the amino groups of aspartate and glycine. Hence, ^{15}N from the amide group of glutamine may be found in significant amounts in all purine

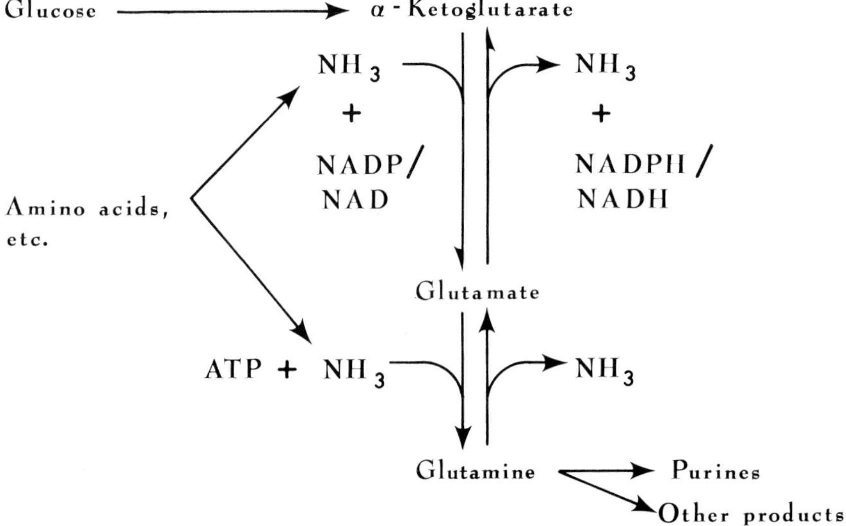

nitrogens. Even with pigeon liver extracts *in vitro*, amide-^{15}N was found to some extent in N-1 and N-7 although most was in N-3 and N-9 (*157, 158*).

In contrast, measurements of the incorporation of glutamine-amide-^{15}N into nucleic acid purines of HeLa cells growing in tissue culture suggested that little randomization had taken place, although the purine rings were not degraded (*159*).

Stimulation of Purine Synthesis by Exogenous Glutamine. Several studies have considered animal cells *in vitro*. Purine biosynthesis *de novo* in Ehrlich ascites tumor cells was stimulated in early studies by addition of plasma or serum (*71, 73*), or of extracts of liver (*70, 160, 161, 162*). Although such effects were caused in part by the glucose content of these preparations, Henderson and LePage (*71*) showed that liver extracts could be replaced completely as a stimulant by a combination of glutamine plus glucose. That at least one stimulatory effect of plasma was caused by glutamine was also suggested by the observation that plasma appeared to counteract the inhibitory effect of azaserine (*162*) as glutamine is known to do.

Glutamine did not increase the rate of purine biosynthesis *de novo* in rabbit bone marrow slices incubated *in vitro* (*64*), but Greenlees and LePage (*160*) showed in 1956 that it did stimulate this process in Ehrlich ascites tumor cells *in vitro*. Later studies with these cells have repeatedly confirmed this observation (*71, 163, 164*), and the PP-ribose-P amidotransferase reaction has been assayed in intact Ehrlich ascites tumor cells by measuring the decline in intracellular concentrations of PP-ribose-P upon the addition of glutamine to incubation media (*88, 165, 166*).

Purine synthesis in brain slices incubated *in vitro* was not stimulated by addition of glutamine (unpublished observations), but it is known that the concentrations of this amino acid are relatively high in this tissue whereas they are virtually undetectable in Ehrlich ascites tumor cells. The effect on purine biosynthesis of supplementation with glutamine may therefore be expected to vary, depending on the glutamine metabolism of each cell or tissue studied.

Herscovics and Johnstone (*76*) have observed that incubation of Ehrlich ascites tumor cells with uridine or glucose leads to a twofold to fourfold increase in intracellular glutamate concentrations. Addition of glutamate or glutamine stimulated formate-^{14}C incorporation into purines, and methionine sulfoximine largely (though not entirely) inhibited the effects of glutamine and glucose on formate-^{14}C incorporation. The authors concluded, therefore, that a major effect of addition of uridine was stimulation of glutamine synthesis. Belkhode *et al.* (*167*) have similarly shown that increased glutamine synthesis in cells incubated with glucose or pyrimidine ribonucleosides also accounts in part for the observed nucleoside-induced stimulation of amino acid incorporation into proteins in Ehrlich ascites tumor cells.

A few studies using animal cells *in vivo* have been performed. Feigelson and Feigelson (*168, 169*) measured the effect of injecting glutamine on the incorporation of glycine-^{14}C into acid-soluble purine derivatives in the livers of adrenalectomized rats; they observed that this process was stimulated threefold. The intraperitoneal injection of glutamine into mice caused a 2.5-fold increase in glycine-^{14}C incorporation into purines in kidney and a 1.7-fold increase in liver (*164*). These results indicate that glutamine concentrations can be a limiting factor for purine nucleotide synthesis *de novo* even in tissues which have high activities of glutamine synthetase (*170, 171*).

Stimulation of purine synthesis in microorganisms by addition of glutamine to media has apparently not been reported. However, Dunn *et al.* (*172*) observed that purines could spare the requirement of *Lactobacillus arabinosus* for glutamine.

Glutamine Synthesis and Its Regulation. The glutamine synthetase (EC 6.3.1.2) reaction is the only known process by which this amino acid can be synthesized.

$$\text{Glutamate} + NH_3 + \text{ATP} \xrightarrow[\text{Synthetase}]{\text{Glutamine}} \text{Glutamine} + \text{ADP} + P_i$$

Its activity can be regulated both by availability of the substrates and by endproduct inhibition and repression. These factors will now be examined, and their importance for the control of purine biosynthesis will be evaluated wherever possible.

Ammonia Concentration. The major source of ammonia in animals is the gastrointestinal tract, where it is produced in part by bacterial action on the urea present in intestinal secretions. Bacterial decomposition of amino acids (particularly glutamine) derived from the diet, intestinal secretions, and cell loss also produces ammonia. The portal blood is therefore relatively high in ammonia, but most of this is normally removed by the liver, leaving a normal peripheral blood concentration of between 0.5 and 1.0 μg per ml. A second source of ammonia is the kidney. Ammonia derived from glutamine and other amino acids is used in acid-base balance, and some diffuses from tubule cells into the renal venous outflow (*173*). Ammonia is also produced in muscle by the deamination of adenylate during muscle contraction; blood levels may rise to 2 to 3 μg per ml during exercise. Ammonia metabolism in general is reviewed by Meister (*156*, p. 284) and Bessman (*174*).

On the basis of studies of glutamine synthetase activity in extracts of rat tissues and of measurements of tissue concentrations of its substrates Lund (*175*) concluded that there is likely to be little glutamine synthesis in most animal tissues that do contain glutamine synthetase. Normal physiological levels of glutamate were reported to be 2.75, 3.0, and 10.4 μmole per gram in liver, kidney, and brain, respectively, whereas the concentrations of ammonia were 0.71, 0.88, and 0.34 μmole per gram in liver, kidney, and brain, respectively. On the basis of these and other data, she concluded that glutamine synthesis can occur if a low, continuous supply of ammonia is available; this is probably true at least of liver and kidney. The reaction probably does not come to equilibrium in any tissue *in vivo*.

Stimulation of Glutamine Synthesis by Exogenous Ammonia. The fact that glutamine synthesis is very responsive to increased ammonia concentrations in animals is confirmed by numerous investigations, and it is generally accepted that glutamine serves an important function in the storage and transport of ammonia in animals (*155*, *156*, p. 286). In early studies Tigerman and MacVicar (*176*) observed only small increases in tissue levels of glutamine after feeding ammonium carbonate to rats and no effect at all when it was injected intraperitoneally. Relatively small amounts of ammonia were used in these experiments, however, and du Ruisseau *et al.* (*177*) found quite different results when they used 10.8 mmoles ammonia per gram, a dose which was an $LD_{99.9}$ in rats. Thus they found a 300% increase in the glutamine content of brain, a 400% increase in testis, and smaller increases in muscle shortly after injection of such a dose.

More detailed studies were performed by Duda and Handler (*178*). Twenty minutes after injection of 58.5 μmoles of ammonium lactate-^{15}N to rats, the specific activity of liver glutamine was seven times those of urea or glutamate. In the total body, however, 80% of the fixed ammonia was in urea. In other experiments they injected amounts of ammonia varying between 50 and 1680 μmoles. At the lower dose 54% of the ^{15}N fixed was in glutamine; this figure was 15% at the higher dose. They concluded that although the total capacities of the glutamine and urea synthesizing systems were equal in the rat, glutamine synthetase was the more efficient means of trapping low concentrations of ammonia. Similar results were obtained by Letter (*143*) when these experiments were repeated with chickens.

Effects of Abnormalities of Ammonia Metabolism on Glutamine Concentrations. The liver is the main site of ammonia detoxication in animals, and several types of hepatic diseases can lead to increased blood levels of ammonia; this in turn often leads to neurological conditions known as hepatic coma or ammoniogenic coma. Other causes of increased blood ammonia levels also exist, including hemorrhagic shock, amino acid toxicity, and some types of cardiac failure; these are reviewed by Bessman (*174*).

When blood concentrations of ammonia rise above a certain level, ammonia is taken up in substantial amounts by brain and muscle, where it may be used for glutamate synthesis, glutamine synthesis, or both (*179*). In experimental animals total hepatectomy leads to elevated glutamine concentrations in brain, muscle, and plasma (*180*). Some of the glutamine that appears in the plasma is formed in the brain (*181*) and skeletal muscle (*182, 183*). Walshe was the first to show that cerebrospinal fluid glutamine concentrations were elevated in cases of hepatic coma (*184*), and later studies (*e.g., 185*) have usually confirmed this although plasma glutamine concentrations are usually normal (*186*). Cerebrospinal fluid glutamine concentrations are not necessarily elevated in case of hepatic disease without coma (*187, 188*). An elevation in cerebrospinal fluid glutamine concentration following administration of a loading dose of ammonium chloride has also been used as a liver function test (*189*).

Inherited hyperammonionemia caused by defects in the biosynthesis of urea may also result in high concentrations of glutamine in cerebrospinal fluid and excretion of considerable amounts of glutamine in urine (*e.g., 190, 191*).

Stimulation of Purine Synthesis by Exogenous Ammonia. The relationship between dietary nitrogen intake and purine biosynthesis and uric acid excretion in birds has already been discussed. The ammonia formed as endproduct of protein metabolism in uricotelic animals is presumably converted to glutamine (together with aspartate and glycine), and the rapid response of uric acid synthesis to increased ingestion of protein suggests both that glutamine synthesis is regulated primarily by the concentrations of the substrates of glutamine synthetase and that the purine biosynthetic pathway is very responsive to glutamine concentrations.

Feigelson and Feigelson (*168 169*) injected ammonium salts into adrenalectomized rats and found that the rate of incorporation of glycine-^{14}C into liver acid-soluble purine nucleotides increased threefold to fourfold.

Henderson (*192*) studied the effect of ammonium chloride on the rate of purine biosynthesis in Ehrlich ascites tumor cells incubated *in vitro*. Ammonia both stimulated the rate of this process and inhibited to some degree the much more potent effect of glutamine in this system. It was concluded that ammonia could replace glutamine as substrate for PP-ribose-P amidotransferase. A later study (*164*) confirmed these observations but showed that some of the ammonia added could be converted to glutamine, especially if glutamate were also supplied to the cells.

It is apparent that the possible role of ammonia concentrations in the regulation of purine synthesis has been little studied. However, there is ample evidence that increased ammonia concentrations lead to accelerated glutamine synthesis and that elevated glutamine levels stimulate purine biosynthesis. It may be expected, therefore, that careful investigation would show that purine synthesis increases, at least to some degree, whenever ammonia concentrations in cells increase.

Glutamate Concentration. The main route of glutamate synthesis in most cells is believed to be the glutamate dehydrogenase (EC 1.4.1.3) reaction. Different forms of this enzyme are specific for NAD, for NADP, or are nonspecific in this respect.

$$\begin{array}{l} COO^- \\ | \\ C{=}O \\ | \\ CH_2 \\ | \\ CH_2 \\ | \\ COO^- \end{array} + NH_3 + \underset{(NADPH)}{NADH} \underset{\text{dehydrogenase}}{\overset{\text{Glutamate}}{\rightleftharpoons}} \begin{array}{l} \quad\;\; COO^- \\ \quad\;\; | \\ {}^+H_3N{-}CH \\ \quad\;\; | \\ \quad\;\; CH_2 \\ \quad\;\; | \\ \quad\;\; CH_2 \\ \quad\;\; | \\ \quad\;\; COO^- \end{array} + \underset{(NADP^+)}{NAD^+} + H_2O$$

α-Ketoglutarate　　　　　Glutamate

However, glutamate may also be formed *via* transamination, from the deamidation of glutamine, and during the catabolism of histidine, proline, and hydroxyproline. In certain microorganisms it may also be formed from β-methylaspartate (*156*, p. 617).

Regulation of Glutamate Dehydrogenase Activity. In general, glutamate dehydrogenases from bacteria, yeast, fungi, and plants are not inhibited or stimulated by purine ribonucleotides (*193, 194*) although a few exceptions have been reported. This enzyme activity from all animal tissues studied is inhibited by guanine nucleotides and activated by adenine nucleotides (*193, 195*) although enzymes from livers of uricotelic animals respond somewhat differently than do those from livers of ureotelic animals (*193*). Even within a single species the properties of glutamate dehydrogenases differ somewhat (*196*). Finally, some glutamate dehydrogenases are specific for NAD, others are specific for NADP, and some will use either.

The relationship of these potential regulatory mechanisms to the actual physiological control of glutamate concentration, and their possible role in the regulation of purine biosynthesis *de novo*, is not yet clear. However, in one of his early studies of the inhibition and stimulation of glutamate dehydrogenase by purine ribonucleotides Frieden (*195*) speculated ". . . that the effects of purine nucleotides on the glutamate dehydrogenase reaction may be important in the rate of synthesis of purine nucleotides and there may be a certain amount of 'feedback' control." This possibility remains to be investigated.

Herscovics and Johnstone (*76*) have shown that glutamate concentrations increase markedly in Ehrlich ascites tumor cells incubated with glucose, and they and Belkhode *et al.* (*167*) have demonstrated that this also occurs when nucleosides are substituted for glucose. In both cases, apparently, α-ketoglutarate formation is accelerated, and this is concomitantly reflected in the synthesis of glutamate. Rates of purine and protein synthesis accelerate under these conditions, and it has been concluded (*76*) that this is due to an increased availability of glutamine.

Stimulation of Glutamine Synthesis by Exogenous Glutamate. Christensen *et al.* (*197*) demonstrated in 1948 that the concentration of glutamine in liver doubled following ingestion of glutamate by rats. Later, Schwerin *et al.* (*198*) found that whereas glutamate was taken up by rat liver and kidney following intravenous administration, it was not taken up by brain; in contrast, glutamine was taken up by all tissues. This is of interest because glutamate concentrations are higher than those of glutamine in brain and kidney whereas the opposite is true of liver. Tigerman and MacVicar (*176*) observed approximately 50% increases in tissue glutamine levels in rats fed glutamate plus ammonia whereas little (ammonia) or no (glutamate) effect was observed when either was fed by itself.

Plasma concentrations of glutamine rose as much as twofold when rats, cats, and man ingested glutamate, depending on the amount of glutamate eaten and the time at which the measurements were made (*199, 200*).

Sapirstein (*201*) showed in 1943 that administration of glutamate to rabbits prevented the convulsant effects of ammonia ingestion, and numerous attempts have since been made in animals and in man to use glutamate, alone or in combination with arginine, to lower blood ammonia levels, reduce toxicity, and quite secondarily, to raise tissue glutamine concentrations.

Thus when glycine was infused to increase blood ammonia levels in dogs, simultaneous administration of glutamate caused a 50% decrease in blood ammonia whereas arginine caused a 90% drop (*202*). Winitz *et al.* (*203*) found that the combination of a subprotective dose of arginine with a non-protective dose of glutamate gave good protection against $LD_{99.9}$ doses of ammonium acetate and lowered blood ammonia levels substantially. In dogs with Eck fistulas, which remove the liver from the circulation, administration of glutamate or arginine-glutamate helped to reduce blood ammonia levels; arginine had little effect (*204*). In this case, where only extrahepatic tissues are involved in the removal of ammonia, glutamate was clearly superior to arginine.

In 1953 Walshe (*185*) introduced glutamate into clinical practice as a treatment for hepatic coma. Although he and some others (*e.g. 205*) found that glutamate treatment did reduce blood ammonia in patients with liver disease, still other workers (*e.g. 206*) did not, and clinical results have been quite variable (*205, 206*). A detailed study of the relative merits of glutamate and arginine in 10 patients with elevated blood ammonia and neurological abnormalities (*207*) showed that intravenous glutamate produced an immediate drop in blood ammonia and a rise in glutamine; intravenous arginine did not have an immediate effect but led to a steady fall in blood ammonia, with a consistent clinical improvement. Najarian *et al.* (*208*) concluded that although glutamate reacted rapidly with ammonia, this reaction appeared to become saturated so that in the presence of a continuing rate of ammonia production addition of glutamate became ineffective.

Stimulation of Purine Biosynthesis by Exogenous Glutamate. Feigelson and Feigelson (*168, 169*) have shown that injection of glutamate into adrenalectomized rats resulted in 1.6- to 2.6-fold increases in glycine-^{14}C incorporation into liver acid-soluble purine nucleotides. Incubation of Ehrlich ascites tumor cells *in vitro* with glutamate also increased the rate of purine synthesis, in this case, threefold to fivefold (*164*).

Ravel *et al.* (*209*) observed that although addition of glutamate alone had no effect on the accumulation of aminoimidazole carboxamide in sulfonamide-inhibited cultures of *Escherichia coli,* it significantly increased the stimulatory effects of glycine and threonine on this process. For example, the amount of conversion of glycine to aminoimidazole carboxamide rose from 35% to 50% when glutamate was added. Addition of glutamate also increased the stimulatory effect of glycine on this process in mutants of *Escherichia coli* which required *p*-aminobenzoate (*210, 211*). Gots and Love (*60*) found that glutamate was one of three amino acids responsible for the observed increase in accumulation of aminoimidazole carboxamide when casein hydrolysate was added to the culture medium. Glutamate also increased the glycine-stimulated accumulation of aminoimidazole (and its ribosyl derivative) in *Escherichia coli* W-11 (*57*) and in biotin-deficient *Saccharomyces cerevisiae* (*212*).

Effect of Adrenocorticotrophic Hormone and Cortisone on Glutamine and Purine Synthesis. Cortisone treatment has long been known to cause (among other things) an increase in the conversion of amino acids to carbohydrate and a consequent increase in the urinary excretion of nitrogen. An early effect of such treatment is the induction in liver of transaminases and other enzymes of amino acid catabolism. Because glutamate is the main channel through which, *via* glutamate dehydrogenase, free ammonia is produced from amino acids, it is not surprising that the content of this amino acid in liver (as well as those of aspartate and alanine) increases. Betheil *et al.* (*213*), for example, found that liver glutamate increased from 164 to 218 μmoles per gram four hours after cortisone treatments.

Feigelson and Feigelson (*168, 169, 214*) have shown that increased purine biosynthesis *de novo* in liver was a consequence of cortisone treatment of adrenalectomized rats. It was shown that this was probably due to increased glutamine synthesis secondary to the primary rise in the concentration of glutamate and probably also of ammonia. One result of increased purine biosynthesis was a 60% increase in liver ATP concentrations compared with the adrenalectomized controls (*168, 215*). These workers observed that the two- to threefold increase in incorporation of glycine-^{14}C into acid-soluble purine nucleotides observed following administration of cortisone could also be produced by injection of glutamate, ammonium salts, and to some extent by other D- and L-amino acids.

Administration of adrenocorticotrophic hormone to normal subjects and patients with adrenal insufficiency has been shown to increase the urinary excretion of uric acid as much as twofold (*216–221*). Serum uric acid levels have been reported both to rise (*218*) and to decrease (*219*) following such treatment. Although Benedict *et al.* (*222*) believed that ACTH acted only by increasing the renal clearance of uric acid, Bishop *et al.* (*221*) have reported that treatment both with this hormone and with cortisone did not alter the body pool of uric acid but increased its turnover rate. They and others (*217, 218*) have concluded that although these hormones also alter the handling of uric acid by the kidney, there is still reason to believe that uric acid synthesis itself is increased. Appropriate experiments to substantiate this conclusion directly have apparently not been performed.

Glutamine synthesis does not appear to be quite as responsive to increased glutamate concentrations as to a greater availability of ammonia. However, purine biosynthesis, presumably *via* glutamine, certainly does increase in response to increased glutamate concentrations under a number of conditions. It may be expected that more detailed study of glutamate metabolism and purine biosynthesis together would discover more examples of a close relationship between these processes.

Regulation of Glutamine Synthetase Activity. There is apparently only one route to glutamine in nature, the glutamine synthetase (EC 6.3.1.2)

$$\underset{\text{Glutamate}}{{}^{+}H_3N{-}CH(COO^-){-}CH_2{-}CH_2{-}COO^-} + NH_3 + ATP \xrightarrow[\text{synthetase}]{\text{Glutamine}} \underset{\text{Glutamine}}{{}^{+}H_3N{-}CH(COO^-){-}CH_2{-}CH_2{-}CONH_2} + ADP + P_i$$

reaction. Although a great deal is being learned about this enzyme and about potential mechanisms by which its activity may be regulated, little has been done to relate this information to the possible role of glutamine synthetase in the control of purine biosynthesis.

Regulation of Enzyme Amount. The distribution of glutamine synthetase activity in rat tissues has most recently been studied by Lund (*175*), who also refers to similar earlier studies. Enzyme activity was detected in liver, brain cortex, kidney cortex, spleen, testis, and retina but was undetectable in muscle, intestinal mucosa, pancreas, heart, adrenals, erythrocytes, and lung. Iqbal and Ottaway (*223*) have recently reported the presence of this enzyme in rat skeletal muscle. They also suggest that the glutamine synthetases of rat liver and kidney have quite different properties.

DeMars (*224*) showed in 1958 that the specific activity of glutamine synthetase in HeLa cells grown in culture was much higher in cells grown in the presence of glutamate than in those grown in the usual glutamine-containing medium. He concluded that the synthesis of the enzyme was repressed in the presence of high concentrations of its product; this has been confirmed in several other animal cell lines (*225, 226*). Thus Paul and Fottrell (*226*) showed that glutamine synthetase activity in L cells rose eightfold within 24 hours after transfer to a glutamine-free medium containing glutamate and declined to the original low levels within 24 hours following addition of glutamine. The corresponding decline was much slower in HeLa cells (*224*). Glutamine synthetase was also repressed by glutamine in germinating wheat embryos (*227*), and glutamate partially reversed this effect.

The extensive studies of Stadtman, Holzer, and others on the regulation of glutamine synthetase in *Escherichia coli* have been reviewed (*228, 229, 230, 231*). The total amount of enzyme activity in these cells reflects the availability of glutamate and ammonia in the medium, being elevated in the presence of low ammonia or of high glutamate concentrations and repressed to low levels in the presence of high concentrations of ammonia or of peptone. It has been suggested that this response may be accommodated to the ability of many bacterial glutamine amidotransferases to use ammonia in place of glutamine.

Glutamine synthetase was repressed by glutamine in *Lactobacillus arabinosus* (*232*), *Bacillus subtilis* (*233*), *Aspergillus nidulans*, and *Neurospora crassa* (*234*), although each system has its own distinctive features.

Unfortunately there is as yet no direct evidence of any relationship between the amount of glutamine synthetase in microbial cells and the rate of purine biosynthesis. However, such a correlation has been proposed for glutamine synthetases in animal livers. The specific activity of glutamine synthetase in chicken liver is 12 times that of rat liver when both are fed diets containing 20% casein (*235*). Although this enzyme activity in rat liver does not change with increasing protein content of the diet, that of chicken liver appears to be inducible. Glutamine synthetase activity doubles in the latter case when the protein content of the diet is increased from 5 to 50% and triples when chickens are fasted seven days. In both cases there is a concomitant rise (sixfold to 15-fold) in serum uric acid levels and in the excretion of nitrogen as uric acid. Katunuma *et al.* (*235*) suggest that the activity of glutamine synthetase, together with low glutaminase activity (*see below*), acts in uricotelic animals to regulate the supply of glutamine for purine biosynthesis. In ureotelic animals different regulatory mechanisms apply.

Regulation of Enzyme Activity. Michaelis constants of *ca.* $1.5 \times 10^{-2}M$ for glutamate have been reported for the glutamine synthetase activities in rat and guinea pig tissue extracts (*175, 236, 237*), but those for pigeon liver extracts and the purified sheep brain enzyme were *ca.* $2.5 \times 10^{-3}M$ (*238, 239*). The Michaelis constant for ammonia (at pH 7.4) was 1.8×10^{-4} for the enzyme activity in rat tissue extracts (*175*). As would be expected, the reaction is inhibited by its products, adenosine diphosphate (*204*), and glutamine (*232*).

Lund (*184*) has recently demonstrated that the net synthesis of glutamine by perfused rat liver is very much lower than would be expected from the total amount of glutamine synthetase in the tissue and the concentrations of glutamate and ammonia present. In contrast rat kidney synthesizes glutamine at relatively rapid rates under similar conditions (*170*). Whether the restricted activity in liver is due to glutaminase activity or to direct regulation of glutamine synthetase is not known.

The glutamine synthetase of *Escherichia coli* may exist in an adenylated form and in a form in which adenylate is not covalently bound; mixtures of these types may also exist. These forms have different catalytic activities, are activated optimally by different divalent cations, and are inhibited by different effectors. Among the active effectors for one or the other enzyme form are tryptophan, histidine, cytidylate, adenylate, glucosamine 6-phosphate, carbamyl phosphate, glycine, and alanine. The ratio of adenylated to unadenylated form, and hence the relative potency of the various effectors, is regulated by the amount of ammonia present. There are several reviews of the extensive literature on this subject (*228, 230, 231*). Although only one form of glutamine synthetase has been found in several fungi, it also is inhibited by a similar variety of effectors (*e.g., 234, 241*).

At present the exact role of these potential regulatory mechanisms in the control of glutamine availability for purine biosynthesis in microorganisms remains a matter of speculation. In animal cells the concentrations of the substrates appear to be of prime importance.

Alternative Pathways of Glutamine Metabolism. In addition to its use in purine biosynthesis *de novo* glutamine also supplies its amide nitrogen in the synthesis of a variety of other compounds (Table 4-2). Glutamine may also be used in man to conjugate organic acids such as phenylacetate. Finally, glutamine is incorporated intact into proteins and hydrolyzed to glutamate plus ammonia by glutaminase. Only in the case of glutaminase is there any suggestion of an inverse relationship between the rates of these processes and that of purine biosynthesis.

Table 4-2. Reactions of the Glutamine Amide Group

Amide-Group Acceptor	*Product*	*Enzyme Commission Number*
Phosphoribosyl pyrophosphate	Phosphoribosylamine	2.4.2.14
Phosphoribosyl-formylglycineamide	Phosphoribosyl-formylglycineamidine	6.3.5.3
Xanthylate	Guanylate	6.3.5.2 6.3.4.1
Uridine triphosphate	Cytidine triphosphate	6.3.4.2
Deamido-nicotinamide-adenine dinucleotide	Nicotinamide-adenine dinucleotide	6.3.5.1
Phosphodeoxyribulosyl-formimino-phosphoribosyl-aminoimidazole carboxamide	Phosphodeoxyribulosyl-amidino-phosphoribosyl-aminoimidazole carboxamide	
Fructose 6-phosphate	Glucosamine 6-phosphate	
CO_2 + ATP	Carbamyl phosphate	
Aspartate	Asparagine	
Chorismate	*o*-Aminobenzoate	
Chorismate	*p*-Aminobenzoate	

GLUTAMINASE. Glutamine is hydrolytically cleaved to glutamate plus ammonia by two types of glutaminases (EC 3.5.1.2); one is activated by phosphate or carboxylic acids while the other is not affected by such anions. Glutaminase activity has been extensively studied, but little attempt has been made to relate it to the availability of glutamine for purine biosynthesis. Katunuma *et al.* (*235*), however, have recently reported that liver glutaminase activity in chickens is only 10 to 20% that in rats and that its total activity increased in rats fed high-protein (50% casein) diets whereas it did not rise in chickens on the same diet. Glutaminase activity in mammalian liver was insensitive to high concentrations of glutamate whereas this product was an inhibitor of the glutaminase from chicken liver. In these respects it was different from glutamine synthetase, which is of low activity and is not inducible by high-protein diets in mammalian liver but of high activity and induced by high-protein diets in chicken liver.

These authors suggest that glutaminase and glutamine synthetase in the livers of uricotelic animals are regulated in concert to support glutamine synthesis and hence purine biosynthesis *de novo* in order to excrete nitrogen. In livers of ureotelic animals they are again regulated in couple but with the opposite aim—to maintain glutamine concentrations at relatively low levels.

Carbon Dioxide

Use of Carbon Dioxide for Purine Biosynthesis *de novo*. Carbon dioxide, perhaps as bicarbonate, supplies C-6 of the purine ring. Although the reaction by which it is incorporated into the purine ring was once thought to require biotin, this is now known not to be the case. Presumably the carbon dioxide required for purine biosynthesis is derived from the oxidative decarboxylation reactions of energy metabolism and amino acid catabolism.

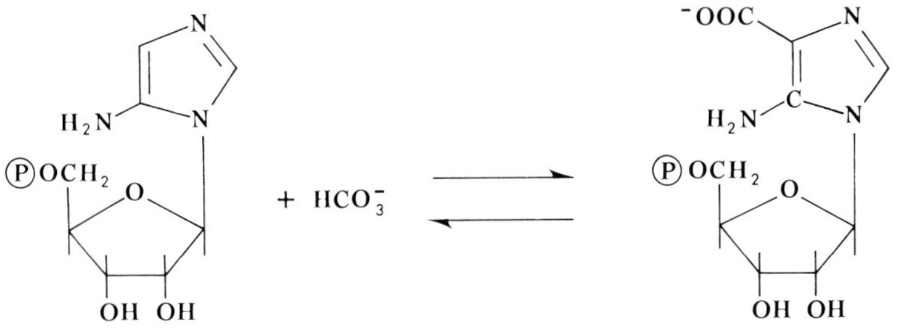

$$\text{Phosphoribosylaminoimidazole} + HCO_3^- \rightleftharpoons \text{Phosphoribosylaminoimidazole carboxylate}$$

Phosphoribosyl-aminoimidazole

Phosphoribosyl-aminoimidazole carboxylate

Carbon Dioxide as a Limiting Substrate for Purine Biosynthesis. The possibility that in cells grown or incubated under anaerobic conditions the concentration of carbon dioxide might limit the rate of purine biosynthesis *de novo* apparently has never been investigated. Several microbial mutants are known, however, in which carbon dioxide becomes limiting for purine biosynthesis even under aerobic conditions. In these cases the production of this substrate is normal, but it is utilized less efficiently than in wild-type strains. Thus mutants of *Neurospora crassa* described by Charles (*242*) required an atmosphere containing 30% carbon dioxide to support optimal growth instead of the much smaller amount found in air. In this and subsequent (*243*) studies it was shown that the carbon dioxide requirement could be replaced in different mutant strains by adenine, arginine, pyrimidines, or combinations of these. DeSerres (*244*) later showed that the carbon dioxide-stimulated, adenine-requiring strains were all leaky mutants at the *ade3B* locus, and they appeared to contain phosphoribosyl-aminoimidazole carboxylases with reduced affinities for bicarbonate. These mutants were among the "purple" adenine mutants because, as mentioned above, the phosphoribosyl-aminoimidazole which accumulates decomposes to form a red or purple pigment. *Ade3B* mutants which were not leaky, and hence which contained no active carboxylase, did not grow in a high carbon dioxide atmosphere.

The growth of some *ade2* (*i.e.*, carboxylase) mutants of *Saccharomyces cerevisiae* was shown by Woods (*245*) also to be stimulated by elevated carbon dioxide concentrations. Most recently Vivian and Charles (*246*) have observed that purines spared the requirement of some mutants of *Streptomyces coelicolor* for 10% carbon dioxide.

The study by Charles and Roberts (*247*) of carbon dioxide-requiring mutants of *Escherichia coli* revealed a more complex situation. Some, as expected, were mutants at the *purE* (carboxylase) locus and produced red or purple pigments; purines could replace their requirement for 20% carbon dioxide in the atmosphere. It was presumed that these strains contained carboxylases with reduced affinities for bicarbonate. Some strains were, however, inhibited by aspartate when growing with the high carbon dioxide atmosphere but not when purines were present. Other mutants were inhibited by purines under various conditions, but the interrelationships indicated by these inhibitions have not been studied further.

Another interesting case has recently been reported by Katz and Rosenberger (*248*). They studied *ade3* mutants of *Aspergillus nidulans* which normally accumulate pigment but which do not do so if extra carbon dioxide is supplied in the atmosphere. A closer examination showed that purine synthesis ordinarily proceeded in the metabolically active hyphae due to their active production of carbon dioxide from glucose. The less active conidia, however, did not produce enough carbon dioxide endogenously and would synthesize purines only when supplied with this substrate.

All of these studies recall the much earlier observation of Pappenheimer and Hottle (*249*) that the purine requirement of certain Group A hemolytic streptococci could be replaced by increasing the carbon dioxide content of the gas phase. This case has not been reexamined in the light of more recent knowledge of purine metabolism.

Carbon dioxide is usually assumed to be in plentiful supply in cells and not to be limiting for any of the reactions which require it. The results obtained with the microbial mutants discussed here suggest that this is indeed probably the case under normal circumstances. However, the possibility that it might limit purine synthesis under conditions where carbon dioxide concentrations are low should be considered more seriously. In addition, the mechanism of the carboxylase reaction and the defects in this enzyme in the above-mentioned mutants deserve careful study.

Aspartate

Use of Aspartate for Purine Biosynthesis *de novo*. The amino group of aspartate contributes the N-1 of the purine ring by reaction of this amino acid with phosphoribosyl-aminoimidazole carboxylate and subsequent disposal of its carbon skeleton as fumarate.

Phosphoribosyl-aminoimidazole carboxylate + Aspartate + ATP $\xrightarrow{Mg^{2+}}$ Phosphoribosyl-aminoimidazole succinocarboxamide + ADP + P_i

Stimulation of Purine Biosynthesis by Exogenous Aspartate. In only a few cases has aspartate been added to growth or incubation media in attempts to increase the rate of purine biosynthesis. In one study Gots and Love (*60*) found that aspartate (with glycine) was one of the amino acids in casein hydrolysate which stimulated the rate of accumulation of aminoimidazole carboxamide in *Escherichia coli* B-96.

Although addition of a low concentration (1 m*M*) of aspartate did not stimulate purine synthesis in Ehrlich ascites tumor cells incubated *in vitro* with glucose (*71*), Fontenelle and Henderson (*164*) later found that 20 m*M* aspartate stimulated this process threefold in the same system. However, its stimulatory effect was much more effective when glutamine was also added to the incubation media. The low permeability of many cells to aspartate both makes experimental supplementation of incubation media for studies of purine biosynthesis rather difficult and also suggests that cells probably do not depend heavily on exogenous supplies of this amino acid. It is readily synthesized endogenously from intermediates of carbohydrate metabolism.

Synthesis of Aspartate. The rate of aspartate synthesis can be decreased in some cells by deficiency of the vitamin biotin, and a decreased rate of purine biosynthesis *de novo* is one consequence of such a deficiency.

PATHWAY OF ASPARTATE SYNTHESIS. Aspartate is synthesized by transamination to oxaloacetate; glutamate is one of the main amino donors.

$$\begin{array}{c}COO^-\\ |\\ C{=}O\\ |\\ CH_2\\ |\\ COO^-\\ \\ \\ \\ \text{Oxalacetate}\end{array} + \begin{array}{r}COO^-\\ |\\ {}^+H_3N\ CH\\ |\\ CH_2\\ |\\ CH_2\\ |\\ COO^-\\ \text{Glutamate}\end{array} \underset{}{\overset{\text{Pyridoxal-phosphate}}{\rightleftharpoons}} \begin{array}{r}COO^-\\ |\\ {}^+H_3N\ CH\\ |\\ CH_2\\ |\\ COO^-\\ \\ \\ \\ \text{Aspartate}\end{array} + \begin{array}{c}COO^-\\ |\\ C{=}O\\ |\\ CH_2\\ |\\ CH_2\\ |\\ COO^-\\ \alpha\text{-Keto-glutarate}\end{array}$$

The oxaloacetate required for aspartate synthesis may be formed both *via* the Krebs cycle and by carbon dioxide fixation into pyruvate or phosphoenolpyruvate. Fixation into pyruvate requires biotin as cofactor; this and other aspects of biotin biochemistry are reviewed by Mistry and Dakshinamurti (*250*).

Following the initial demonstration by Koser *et al.* (*251*) that aspartate would partially replace the biotin requirement for growth of *Torula cremoris*, Stokes *et al.* (*252, 253*) showed in 1947 that optimum growth of several lactobacilli and streptococci required either high concentrations of biotin or low concentrations of this vitamin plus aspartate. Aspartate would not re-

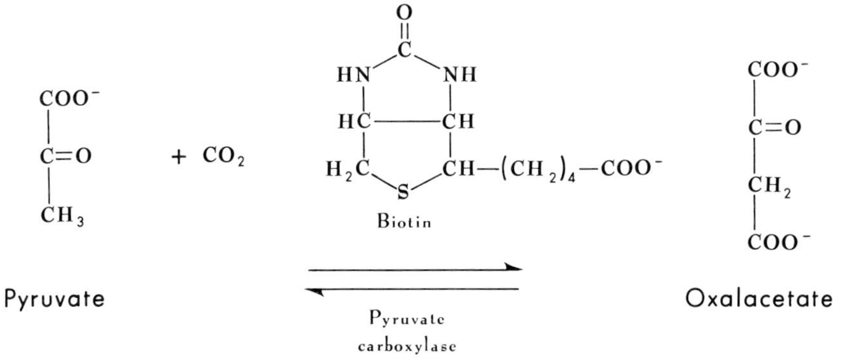

$$\underset{\text{Pyruvate}}{\begin{array}{c} COO^- \\ | \\ C{=}O \\ | \\ CH_3 \end{array}} + CO_2 \xrightleftharpoons[\text{Pyruvate carboxylase}]{\text{Biotin}} \underset{\text{Oxalacetate}}{\begin{array}{c} COO^- \\ | \\ C{=}O \\ | \\ CH_2 \\ | \\ COO^- \end{array}}$$

Biotin: $HN{-}C({=}O){-}NH$ ring fused with $HC{-}CH$; $H_2C{-}S{-}CH{-}(CH_2)_4{-}COO^-$

place biotin for growth of *Leuconostoc mesenteroides* P-60, however. These investigators showed that biotin was not involved in the formation of aspartate by transamination to oxaloacetate and observed that oxaloacetate partially replaced biotin in aspartate-deficient media for the growth of *Lactobacillus casei* and *Lactobacillus arabinosus.* In the same year two other groups also showed that oxaloacetate would replace or spare the biotin requirement for the growth of *Lactobacillus arabinosus* 17-5 (*254, 255*). Later studies confirmed these observations (*256*) and also demonstrated that aspartate could spare the biotin requirement for the growth of *Saccharomyces cerevisiae* (*257*), *Memnoniella echinata* and *Stachybotys atra* (*258*), and *Micrococcus lysodeikticus* (*259*). Using the latter organism, Wessman *et al.* (*259*) showed that carbon dioxide was not fixed into oxaloacetate when the cells were grown under conditions of biotin deficiency. Later studies of pyruvate carboxylase itself confirmed the conclusions of these early nutritional and isotope investigations.

Effects of Biotin Deficiency on Purine Biosynthesis *de novo.* The first indication that biotin might be involved in some way in purine biosynthesis was the report of MacLeod and Lardy (*260*) of decreased incorporation of labeled bicarbonate into visceral nucleic acid purines in biotin-deficient rats; the specific activity of adenine, for example, was reduced to about one-half that of the control. Actually, these results were probably due to quite secondary effects and do not reflect a direct role of biotin in the carbon dioxide fixing reaction of purine synthesis. This was not realized at the time, however.

Reversal of Growth Inhibition. A relationship between biotin, aspartate, and purines was indicated in 1954 in the course of studies of *Lactobacillus arabinosus* 17-5 by Wahba and Shive (*261, 262*). In the absence of added biotin, aspartate promoted growth, and the amount of aspartate required could be decreased by adding purines or aminoimidazole carboxamide. Optimum growth in the absence of aspartate or purines required biotin plus bicarbonate, however. At this time it was still not clear whether biotin was involved only in the synthesis of aspartate or if it also had a direct role in purine biosynthesis. Later Ahmad and Rose (*263*) showed that growth of biotin-deficient *Saccharomyces cerevisiae* was stimulated by addition either of aspartate or of adenine or adenosine. This has also been shown in many of the studies mentioned below.

Accumulation of Aminoimidazole Derivatives. Biotin-requiring mutants of *Saccharomyces cerevisiae* accumulated diazotizable amines and a red pigment, apparently derived from the amines, when they were grown in the presence of sub-optimal amounts of biotin (*212, 264–268*). The amines were identified as aminoimidazole and ribosyl-aminoimidazole (*212, 269, 270*); the pigment is a polymer of these. The accumulation of these compounds decreased when cells were grown either with biotin or with aspartate. However, aspartate did not affect the accumulation of pigment in adenine-requiring organisms which lacked the enzyme required to utilize phosphoribosyl-aminoimidazole.

Phosphoribosyl-aminoimidazole (and its derivatives) accumulates even though it is not the substrate of the reaction in the purine biosynthetic pathway which requires aspartate. Apparently this happens because the carboxylase reaction is readily reversible, and hence phosphoribosyl-aminoimidazole carboxylate is easily decarboxylated.

To show that aminoimidazole was indeed derived from an intermediate of the purine biosynthetic pathway, Moat and Nasuti (*271*) allowed this compound to accumulate in biotin-deficient yeast and then added biotin and amethopterin; the latter compound would cause the accumulation of phosphoribosyl-aminoimidazole carboxamide several steps later in the pathway. In the presence of biotin the aminoimidazole formed in the absence of this vitamin was converted to phosphoribosyl-aminoimidazole carboxamide.

In contrast to these results with yeast, biotin-requiring mutants of *Escherichia coli* did not appear to accumulate aminoimidazole or its derivatives (*57*), perhaps because sufficient oxaloacetate was made by biotin-independent pathways.

Lowered Purine Ribonucleotide Concentrations. Aspartate is required both for purine biosynthesis *de novo* and for the conversion of inosinate to adenylate. Inhibition of these reactions by aspartate deficiency secondary to lack of biotin would be expected to result in lowered concentrations of the various purine ribonucleotides in cells.

Katsuki (*272, 273*) observed that keto acids accumulated in culture media when *Bacillus macerans* and the rice blast fungus *Pericularia oryzae* were grown under conditions of biotin deficiency. Further study showed that the intracellular concentration of ATP was decreased in both cases as were the concentrations of compounds derived from ATP, such as NAD and coenzyme A. The accumulation of keto acids is believed to be caused especially by lack of the latter compound because their metabolism depends on the formation of acyl coenzyme A derivatives.

The concentration of ATP was also reduced in biotin-deficient *Saccharomyces cerevisiae* (M. H. Briggs, quoted in *274*), and such cells also contained less than normal amounts of RNA and DNA (*263, 274*). The addition of aspartate to such cultures stimulated growth and brought about a partial restoration of nucleic acid synthesis (*263*). Yeast grown in methionine-rich media normally has high intracellular concentrations of *S*-adenosylmethionine, and its degradation product, thiomethyladenosine, normally accumulates in the culture media. The accumulation of thiomethyladenosine decreased in biotin deficiency but increased when aspartate was added (*269*). Presumably, the synthesis of *S*-adenosylmethionine was retarded as a consequence of lower ATP concentrations.

Rose and others (*268, 275, 276, 277*) have observed that nicotinate and deamido-NAD accumulated when *Saccharomyces cerevisiae* and other yeasts were grown in biotin-deficient media. Less accumulated when aspartate or adenine was added.

These studies show that in some organisms the synthesis of oxaloacetate is the limiting reaction for aspartate synthesis and for at least some of the processes which depend on aspartate. The several pathways of oxaloacetate synthesis are all regulated in different ways, and the relative importance of these routes undoubtedly varies from one cell and set of conditions to another. Whether oxaloacetate and aspartate synthesis become limiting for purine biosynthesis under conditions other than biotin deficiency remains to be explored.

Glycine

Use of Glycine for Purine Biosynthesis *de novo*. Glycine is incorporated intact into the purine ring, in which it furnishes the C-4, C-5, and N-7 positions.

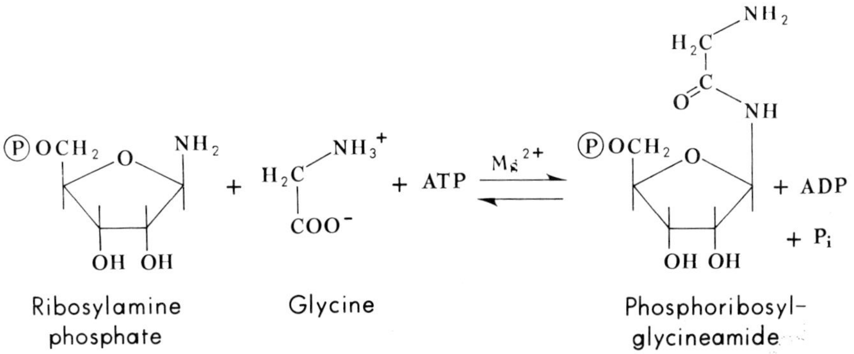

$$\text{Ribosylamine phosphate} + \underset{\text{Glycine}}{H_2C(NH_3^+)COO^-} + \text{ATP} \xrightleftharpoons{Mg^{2+}} \text{Phosphoribosylglycineamide} + \text{ADP} + P_i$$

Ribosylamine phosphate

Glycine

Phosphoribosyl-glycineamide

There is ample evidence that the availability of this amino acid limits purine biosynthesis in some systems. Decreased biosynthesis or lowered nutritional supply of glycine may lead to decreased purine biosynthesis while increased nutritional supply may accelerate this process in some systems. Glycine is, of course, also metabolized by a number of alternative pathways, and changes in their rates may in some cases decrease the availability of glycine for purine biosynthesis. Evidence for these conclusions is presented in this section.

The factors which regulate glycine concentrations are also considered here, and the general pathways of glycine synthesis and utilization may be summarized as follows:

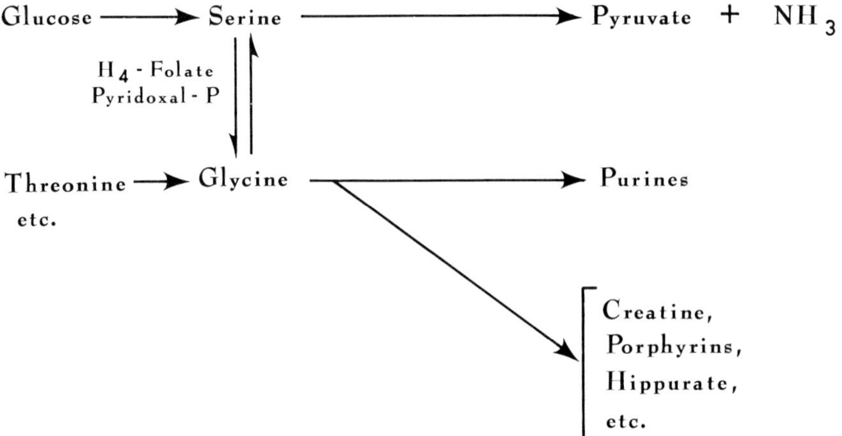

For general discussions of glycine metabolism *see* the reviews of Mitchell and Hamilton (*278,* p. 267), Bach (*279*), Arnstein (*280*), Meister (*156,* p. 636), Blakley (*281,* p. 267), and Greenberg (*282,* p. 111).

RANDOMIZATION OF LABEL FROM GLYCINE. Care must be taken in studies of labeling of purines by glycine to be sure that the label does in fact represent incorporation of the whole glycine molecule and not just reutilization of fragments derived from other routes of glycine metabolism.

Thus although Howell *et al.* (*283*) have shown that more than 90% of the radioactivity in urinary uric acid was in the C-4 position following administration of glycine-1-^{14}C to man, considerable randomization of radioactivity from glycine-2-^{14}C did occur. This results mainly from the conversion of the C-2 of glycine to 5,10-methylene H_4-folate; this process, and its consequences for labeling of purines, will be discussed later. The ^{14}C from glycine is also converted to other amino acids, of course, of which serine, taurine, alanine, aspartate, and glutamate are the most heavily labeled (*e.g., 75*).

The amino group of glycine is converted in significant amounts to the amino group of aspartate and to the amide group of glutamine and is thence incorporated into purines. A number of studies have shown, for example, that when ^{15}N-glycine was fed to man, 20 to 50% of the ^{15}N in urinary uric acid was in N-1, N-3, and N-9 (*283, 284, 285*). The same extent of reutilization of the glycine amino group for uric acid synthesis was observed when ^{15}N-serine (*286*) and ^{15}N-glycine (*157*) were administered to pigeons.

In very early studies of the incorporation of ^{15}N-glycine into nucleic acid purines in rat tissues *in vivo* Reichard (*287*) noted that the amino groups of RNA adenine and guanine contained significant amounts of label. Later studies (*288*) showed that about 80% of the ring ^{15}N of RNA purines labeled from ^{15}N-glycine in regenerating rat liver was in N-7. However, in this case no ^{15}N was detected in the amino group of adenine (derived from aspartate) whereas the amino group of guanine (derived from glutamine) contained as much ^{15}N as did N-1, N-3, and N-9 together. Presumably the amino group of glycine had been converted to the amide group of glutamine but not to the amino group of aspartate.

Stimulation of Purine Biosynthesis by Exogenous Glycine. Studies in a variety of experimental systems have shown that a supply of exogenous glycine may increase the rate of purine biosynthesis.

MICROORGANISMS. Most studies of the effect of exogenous glycine on purine synthesis in microorganisms have been carried out under conditions in which glycine synthesis was retarded; these will be discussed below. However, Gots and Love (*60*) found that resting cell suspensions of *Escherichia coli* B-96 accumulated aminoimidazole carboxamide more rapidly when casein hydrolysate was the nitrogen source than when ammonium salts were used. The active components of the casein hydrolysate were found to be glycine and aspartate. Similarly, more aminoimidazole accumulated in *Escherichia coli* W-11 in the presence of glycine or a casein hydrolysate than in a glucose-salts medium (*57*).

Added glycine did not stimulate the formation of phosphoribosyl-amino-imidazole in *Saccharomyces cerevisiae* in which the further metabolism of this intermediate was blocked by biotin deficiency (*212*). However, these cells were reported already to contain large intracellular pools of this amino acid.

ANIMAL CELLS *in vitro*. Stimulation of purine biosynthesis in animal cells *in vitro* by added glycine was first observed by LePage (*67*) in 1953; Ehrlich ascites tumor cells were used. This observation has been repeatedly confirmed by subsequent investigators (*e.g.*, *75, 163, 164*). In contrast, however, Thomson *et al.* (*70*) were unable to show any effect of addition of an amino acid mixture on purine biosynthesis in this system. The composition of this mixture was said to be based on the composition of casein, which contains little glycine; the amount of glycine actually added may therefore have been small.

In other systems it has been observed that addition of glycine did not stimulate purine synthesis in preparations of rat intestinal mucosa *in vitro*

(*66*) but did increase the rate of this process in rabbit bone marrow preparations (*65*).

A relationship between glycine concentrations and purine biosynthesis has also been demonstrated by Lembach and Charalampous (*289*), using KB cells grown under conditions of *myo*-inositol deficiency. Inositol deficiency appears to impair the ability of the cells to accumulate glycine and serine from the medium or, alternatively, to retain endogenously synthesized glycine and serine within the cells. As a consequence of lowered intracellular concentrations of one or both of these amino acids the rate of purine biosynthesis *de novo* is retarded and the intracellular concentration of purine nucleotides declines (*290*).

MAN. Increased excretion of uric acid in man following ingestion of glycine was first demonstrated in 1918 by Lewis *et al.* (*25*), and this observation has since been confirmed many times (*291–295*). Depending on the amount of glycine eaten and the period of observation uric acid excretion may almost double. Friedman (*293*) showed in 1947, however, that glycine exerted a strong uricosuric effect directly on the kidney, and others (*294, 295*) have come to the same conclusion, although there is some disagreement regarding the basis of this action. Although altered kidney function may account for all the increase in uric acid excretion noted under conditions of glycine loading, it is unfortunate that studies with labeled precursors have never been conducted to determine if there is also some stimulation of the purine biosynthetic pathway.

BIRDS. For many years it has been believed that young chickens and turkeys require glycine in the diet to achieve maximum rates of growth whereas it is not required by adult birds (*296–300*). Akrabawi and Kratzer (*301*), however, have recently observed that when chicks were fed amino acid mixtures containing 1.9% serine no supplementary glycine was required, but glycine did stimulate growth when serine was omitted. Thus the metabolic limitation that brings about a requirement for one or another of these amino acids is not at the stage of serine hydroxymethyltransferase (EC 2.1.2.1) but in the synthesis of serine from glucose. The quantitative requirements for glycine or serine also depend on the dietary content of arginine and cystine (*301, 302*).

It appears that most studies of chick and poult nutrition which have employed glycine supplementation, and with which this section is concerned, have used low-serine diets (*303*). Hence for these purposes glycine may be considered to be essential for maximum growth. The glycine requirement of turkey poults appears to be less than that of chicks (*299*), and in both cases the need for this amino acid for feather development (*304*) and for uric acid synthesis (*see below*) appears to be very important.

It has already been mentioned that the administration of glycine to hens (*1*) resulted in increased uric acid excretion. It is not surprising, therefore, that elevated blood levels of uric acid were observed when chicks were fed toxic doses of glycine (*305*); some chicks developed gout on such regimens.

However, Snetsinger and Scott (*306*) observed that glycine itself alleviated the growth-inhibitory effects in chicks of feeding excess lysine, histidine, or phenylalanine, although a combination of glycine and arginine was somewhat more effective. They postulated that glycine functioned in this way by enhancing the excretion of excess nitrogen *via* uric acid synthesis. Akrabawi and Kratzer (*301*) studied the interaction of arginine and glycine on chick growth in more detail. They found that added glycine was required for optimum growth when arginine was deficient whereas extra glycine was not required when the diet was high in arginine. Both in the case of high amino acid intake and of essential amino acid (*i.e.*, arginine) deficiency the total excretion of amino acid nitrogen increased markedly. Most of this nitrogen was excreted as uric acid, and under these conditions of accelerated purine biosynthesis *de novo* glycine appeared to become limiting; hence exogenous supplies were required (*307*).

By causing an acceleration of uric acid biosynthesis *de novo* glycine relieved the toxicity produced by ammonia, which was in turn formed from excess amino acids. Bloomfield *et al.* (*307*) demonstrated that glycine (together with glucose) protected chicks against the toxicity of ammonium acetate and markedly increased both $^{15}NH_4^+$ incorporation into uric acid and the total uric acid concentrations of liver and kidney.

It may be concluded from the variety of studies presented that glycine concentrations in cells can often be rate limiting for purine biosynthesis *de novo*. It seems likely that more exhaustive studies would show that such is more often the rule than the exception, and the variety of factors that affect the synthesis and utilization of glycine are therefore at least potentially of concern for the regulation of the purine biosynthetic pathway.

PATHWAYS OF GLYCINE SYNTHESIS AND THEIR REGULATION. The various reactions by which glycine can be synthesized are listed in Table 4-3. Of these the synthesis of glycine from serine, catalyzed by serine hydroxymethyltransferase, is the most important in most animal and microbial sys-

Table 4-3. Reactions of Glycine Biosynthesis

Substrates		Products
Serine + H_4-Folate	$\xrightarrow{\text{Pyridoxal-P}}$	Glycine + 5,10-Methylene H_4-folate
Threonine	$\xrightarrow{\text{Pyridoxal-P}}$	Glycine + Acetaldehyde
Glyoxalate + α-Amino acid	$\xrightarrow{\text{Pyridoxal-P}}$	Glycine + α-Keto acid
Sarcosine	$\longrightarrow$	Glycine + Formaldehyde
Formiminoglycine + H_4-Folate	$\longrightarrow$	Glycine + 5-Formimino H_4-folate

tems studied. The serine is in turn synthesized from glucose *via* intermediates of the glycolytic pathway.

The threonine pathway makes a small but significant contribution to the glycine used for purine biosynthesis whereas glycine synthesis from glyoxylate and sacrosine is much less important. The conversion of formiminoglycine to glycine is of importance only in certain clostridia.

GLYCINE SYNTHESIS FROM GLUCOSE *via* SERINE. It has been known for many years that glycine is not a required nutrient for mammals, and it must consequently be synthesized in amounts sufficient to supply the needs of these organisms for growth and function. This was first shown indirectly in 1906–07 when Wiechowski (*308*) and Magnus-Levy (*309*) measured the amount of glycine excreted as hippurate by animals fed benzoate over long periods of time.

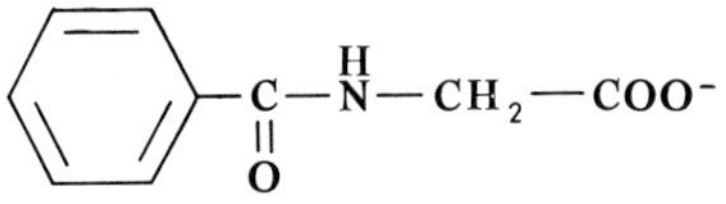

$$C_6H_5\text{—}\underset{\underset{O}{\|}}{C}\text{—}\overset{H}{N}\text{—}CH_2\text{—}COO^-$$

Hippurate

Under these conditions much more glycine was excreted than could be accounted for either by the glycine in the diets of the animals or in their body proteins. Rose and his colleagues (*310, 311*), using diets containing pure amino acids, showed much later that neither glycine nor serine were essential for the growth of mammals. Glycine is also not an essential nutrient for the growth of most animal cells in tissue culture (*312, 313, 314*). Studies too numerous to mention have shown that radioactive glucose is converted into serine and glycine in mammalian cells both *in vivo* and *in vitro*. In addition, the further incorporation of the glycine thus formed into nucleic acid purines has been demonstrated in organ and tissue cultures of animal cells (*e.g., 315, 316*).

Microorganisms that grow on glucose plus ammonium salts obviously also derive all of their glycine from these sources. Early studies of the metabolism of *Escherichia coli* by Roberts *et al.* (*317*, p. 296) showed, for example, that 32% of the radioactivity in nucleic acid guanine derived from cells grown for one hour with glucose-^{14}C was contained in C-4 plus C-5, the positions formed from glycine.

Glycine synthesis is apparently not specifically controlled by feedback inhibition or repression (*194*) but reflects the rates of serine synthesis and utilization, the activity of serine hydroxymethyltransferase, and the availability of pyridoxal phosphate and H_4-folate.

Serine may be synthesized from glycolytic intermediates derived from glucose by two alternative pathways, both of which sometimes are present in the same cells (*156*, p. 660; *281*, p. 289):

Glucose → 3-P-Glycerate ⇌ 3-P-Hydroxypyruvate ⇌ (Pyridoxal-P) 3-P-Serine → Serine

3-P-Glycerate ⇌ 2-P-Glycerate → Glycerate ⇌ Hydroxypyruvate ⇌ (Pyridoxal-P) Serine

The serine hydroxymethyltransferase (EC 2.1.2.1) reaction, through which glycine is synthesized from serine, requires H_4-folate as the second substrate and pyridoxal phosphate as cofactor.

Serine + H_4-Folate $\xrightarrow{\text{Pyridoxal-P}}$ Glycine + 5,10-Methylene H_4-folate

Serine: $^{+}H_3N{-}CH(COO^-){-}CH_2OH$

Glycine: $COO^-{-}CH_2NH_3^+$

Pyridoxal-P: ⓅOCH_2, CHO, OH, CH_3, N (pyridine ring)

Glycine synthesis by this route may thus be affected by the concentrations of serine, H_4-folate, and pyridoxal phosphate as well as by the total activity of the enzyme.

Although glycine may be formed in excess in some primary cultures of animal cells and hence may accumulate in the media (*314*), this is unusual. Even in animals which do not require dietary glycine, this amino acid does not appear to be synthesized at rates much faster than those of its utilization. Thus Arnstein and Neuberger (*318*) found that serine synthesis from glucose in growing rats exceeded glycine synthesis by only about 30% and that, although glycine was required in amounts of roughly 1.5 to 2 mmoles per day, its synthesis was only about 2.0 to 3.2 mmoles per day.

Effects of Folate Deficiency. Effects of folate deficiency on serine hydroxymethyltransferase activity have usually been studied in relation to the supply of one-carbon units; this subject will be discussed below. However, glycine synthesis and availability must be similarly affected by deficiency of this vitamin.

Sulfonamide treatment induces a state of folate deficiency in some microorganisms; one manifestation is accumulation of aminoimidazole carboxamide and its derivatives due to decreased availability of 10-formyl H_4-folate for the phosphoribosyl-aminoimidazole carboxamide formyltransferase reaction. At the same time, however, the serine hydroxymethyltransferase reaction may also be inhibited to some extent.

Thus in their early studies of aminoimidazole carboxamide accumulation in cultures of sulfonamide-inhibited *Escherichia coli* Ravel *et al.* (*209*) found that only a small amount accumulated in a glucose-salts medium, but with the addition of glycine, accumulation was proportional to glycine concentration up to 200 μg per ml. At all of the glycine concentrations used, approximately 35% was converted to aminoimidazole carboxamide. Significantly, serine could not replace glycine as a precursor of this compound (*319*).

Gots (*320*) and Greenberg (*321*) also stimulated accumulation of aminoimidazole carboxamide in sulfonamide-treated wild-type *Escherichia coli* by adding glycine, and Gots later (*210, 211*) showed that casein hydrolysate or glycine alone would increase accumulation of this compound in mutants which required *p*-aminobenzoate.

Eagle and co-workers (*312, 313, 322*) and others (*323, 324*) have observed that primary monkey kidney cells in culture required glycine for maximum growth rates, although it was not absolutely essential. Cells grown in glycine-deficient media, furthermore, usually failed to grow successfully upon subculture. Although glycine synthesis from serine and glucose could be detected in these cultures, this process was apparently limited by the availability of H_4-folate because addition of 5-formyl H_4-folate eliminated the glycine requirement. The reduction of folate to H_4-folate was concluded to be limiting.

Neuman and Tytell (*325*) observed that fortification of tissue culture media with high concentrations of folate augmented the growth of a number of cell lines, but this stimulation was usually not completely equivalent to that produced by the addition of glycine or serine themselves.

Amethopterin is an inhibitor of H_4-folate dehydrogenase and thereby indirectly inhibits all H_4-folate coenzyme reactions. Hakala (*326, 327*) showed that the growth-inhibitory effect of this antimetabolite on Sarcoma 180 cells in culture could be prevented or overcome by glycine in combination with hypoxanthine and thymidine.

Arnstein and Stankovič (*328*) showed that glycine synthesis from glucose in growing rats decreased from 2.69 to 1.65 mmoles per 100 grams of body weight per day when they were fed a folate-deficient diet. Glycine synthesis, measured by the conversion of ^{15}N-serine to urinary hippurate following a loading dose of benzoate, was reduced to one-sixth of normal in folate-deficient rats (*329*). The utilization of ^{15}N-glycine for hippurate synthesis under these conditions was actually increased, probably because of lowered glycine pools in the tissues of the folate-deficient animals.

Bridgers (*330*) has noted that the conversion of serine to glycine, and glycine concentrations themselves, declined as mouse brain developed, although serine concentrations remained approximately constant. He also found (*331*) that the total folate concentration of brain fell at about the same rate as did the rate of glycine synthesis.

The feeding of sodium benzoate to rats induced a state of glycine deficiency which could be alleviated partially by administration of folate (*332*). Apparently the rats were folate-deficient to a degree that would not support the increased demand for glycine to detoxicate the benzoate.

It is apparent from these studies that glycine synthesis from serine is decreased during folate deficiency produced in a variety of different ways. In a few systems the lowered glycine concentrations which result have been shown to limit purine biosynthesis, and it seems likely that a close study would reveal that this occurs in most cases of folate deficiency.

Effects of Pyridoxine Deficiency. Haff and Swim (*333*) have shown a reciprocal relationship between nutritional requirements for pyridoxine and for non-essential amino acids in cultures of rabbit fibroblasts. Thus addition of non-essential amino acids spared pyridoxine, and these amino acids were not required at high levels of this vitamin. In either case folate was required. In primary cultures of monkey kidney cells concentrations both of serine and glycine were reduced in cells depleted of pyridoxine (*313*).

Nonessential amino acids, and especially serine and glycine, spared pyridoxine and hence stimulated growth in pyridoxine-depleted rats (*334*). Similarly, serine and glycine could overcome the growth retardation in rats caused by the vitamin analog, deoxypyridoxine (*335*). However, pyridoxine is required for glycinc catabolism as well as for its synthesis, and Swendseid *et al.* (*336*) have shown that glycine concentrations in plasma, muscle, and liver actually increase up to threefold in pyridoxine-deficient rats. Takami *et al.* (*337*) have shown, furthermore, that the latter observation might even be due to increased synthesis of glycine. They found that although liver pyridoxal phosphate concentrations declined up to 70% in weanling rats fed a pyridoxine-deficient diet, serine hydroxymethyltransferase activity in liver extracts was actually unchanged whereas that of serine dehydratase was severely reduced. Concentrations of free serine were increased 30 to 40%.

Studies are described later which indicate that increased NAD levels in livers of animals to which large amounts of nicotinamide are administered require, or at least are associated with, increased purine biosynthesis *de novo.* Williams *et al.* (*338*) found that in pyridoxine-deficient animals pyridine nucleotides following injection of nicotinamide were 30% lower than in control animals. These results are at least consistent with lowered rates of purine synthesis in the vitamin deficiency, but in view of the results which indicate that glycine concentrations are elevated in this condition, the situation is obviously more complex than appears at first sight.

Cycloserine is an inhibitor of a number of reactions that require pyridoxal-P in microorganisms. Ishii and Sevag (*339*) studied the effect of this compound on the accumulation of aminoimidazole carboxamide in *Escherichia coli* B-96. When glucose was the sole source of substrates for purine biosynthesis, cycloserine inhibited aminoimidazole carboxamide accumulation by about 40%. The addition of serine accelerated purine biosynthesis by 25%, but cycloserine now inhibited this process by about 60%. When both

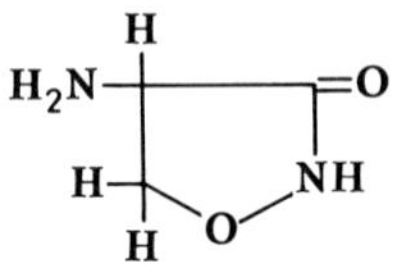

H
H_2N—C—C=O
H—C—NH
H O

D-4-Amino-3-isoxazolidone
"cycloserine"

serine and glucose were present, the rate of aminoimidazole carboxamide accumulation was almost twice that in the presence of glucose alone; cycloserine produced almost 70% inhibition. These results show clearly the importance of pyridoxal-P and of the serine hydroxymethyltransferase reaction in the provision of glycine for purine biosynthesis.

Glycine Synthesis from Threonine. Threonine can also be converted to glycine *via* the threonine aldolase (EC 4.1.2.5) reaction. In the rat 20 to 30% of dietary threonine may be cleaved to glycine (*340*), but it is still utilized for hippurate synthesis only about one-tenth as efficiently as is glycine

$$\begin{array}{c} COO^- \\ | \\ {}^+H_3N-CH \\ | \\ HC-OH \\ | \\ CH_3 \end{array} \longrightarrow \begin{array}{c} COO^- \\ | \\ CH_2NH_3^+ \end{array} + \begin{array}{c} CHO \\ | \\ CH_3 \end{array}$$

Threonine Glycine Acetaldehyde

or serine (*341*). Threonine cleavage has also been demonstrated in duck erythrocytes (*340*) and in *Bombyx mori* (*342*).

Although in most serine-glycine auxotrophs of *Escherichia coli* the conversion of threonine to glycine is too slow to support much growth (*343*), in some cases it can support at least 50% of normal growth (*344*). Wild-type *Tetrahymena geleii* requires serine or glycine plus folate for normal growth whereas several mutant strains can grow moderately well on folate alone. This suggests that threonine can serve as a source of glycine and serine to some degree (*345*).

The first demonstration of the conversion of threonine to glycine involved its use for purine biosynthesis. Ravel *et al.* (*209*) demonstrated that accumulation of aminoimidazole carboxamide in sulfonamide-inhibited cultures of *Escherichia coli* was stimulated by threonine when it was substituted for glycine. Substantial amounts of radioactive threonine were also incorporated into nucleic acid purines in this organism in place of glycine (*317*, p. 302). Krasna *et al.* (*346*) administered labeled threonine to chickens and found that it was converted to excreted uric acid one-fourth as effectively as was glycine.

Alternative Pathways of Glycine Metabolism. Table 4-4 lists a number of alternative pathways of glycine metabolism. These represent potential competitors of purine biosynthesis for the glycine which is available in cells. The significance of this competition is evaluated here for those alternative pathways about which enough information is available.

SERINE SYNTHESIS FROM GLYCINE. The rate of conversion of glycine to serine *via* serine hydroxymethyltransferase is normally quite low in the growing rat compared with the reverse reaction, but it may be increased by increasing the glycine content of the diet (*318*).

$$\text{Glycine} + \text{5,10-Methylene } H_4\text{-Folate} \xrightarrow{\text{Pyridoxal-P}} \text{Serine} + H_4\text{-Folate}$$

Table 4-4. Pathways of Glycine Metabolism

Glycine + 5,10-Methylene H_4-folate → Serine + H_4-Folate

Glycine + Succinyl-CoA → α-Amino-β-ketoadipate → CO_2 + δ-Aminolevulinate

Glycine + Arginine → Guanidoacetate + Ornithine

Glycine + Cholyl-CoA → Glycocholate + CoA

Glycine + Benzyl-CoA → Hippurate (Benzoylglycine) + CoA

Glycine + γ-Glutamylcysteine → Glutathione

Glycine → Glyoxylate + NH_3
Glycine + α-Keto acid → Glyoxylate + α-Amino acid

Glycine + Acetyl-CoA → Aminoacetone + CoA

Glycine + H_4-Folate $\xrightarrow[\text{NAD}]{}$ 5,10-Methylene H_4-folate + CO_2 + NH_3

Glycine + Phosphoribosylamine → Phosphoribosyl-glycineamide

Glycine + $tRNA^{gly}$ → Glycyl-$tRNA^{gly}$

This process is of course folate-dependent, and it is inhibited in liver homogenates from folate-deficient turkey poults (*347*). The conversion of glycine-^{14}C into proteins and phospholipids *via* serine in homogenates of folate-deficient chick liver is also retarded (*348*).

Both *Tetrahymena geleii* (*345*) and *Streptococcus faecalis* R (*349*) normally must be supplied with serine to support maximum growth rates, but in both cases this requirement may be met by adding glycine plus extra folate instead.

Williams *et al.* (*75*) have conducted a detailed study of the effect of incubation conditions on the metabolism of glycine (2 m*M*) in Ehrlich ascites tumor cells *in vitro.* They found that the conversion of glycine-^{14}C to serine increased fourfold to fivefold when cells were incubated aerobically with glucose and that the total amount of free serine present also increased threefold to fourfold in the presence of glucose. Under the same conditions, howver, the rate of glycine incorporation into acid-soluble adenine nucleotide also increased fivefold, which indicates that the increased conversion of glycine to serine did not cause any shortage of glycine for purine synthesis. Whether or not this would still be the case at low concentrations of glycine is not known.

In summary there is no indication that the conversion of glycine to serine presents any competitive threat to purine biosynthesis.

Creatine Synthesis. Although administration of moderate amounts of glycine to man did not affect the urinary excretion of creatinine, administra-

Arginine + Glycine ⟶ Guanidoacetate + Ornithine

Guanidoacetate + S-Adenosylmethionine ⟶ Creatine + S-Adenosylhomocysteine

Creatine + H_2O ⟶ Creatinine

tion of large amounts resulted in marked creatinuria as well as creatininuria (*292, 350*).

Urinary creatinine was also increased in rats given toxic doses of glycine (*351, 352, 353*) especially if arginine or arginine plus methionine were given at the same time (*354*). Muscle creatine also increased in rats (*351*) and in chicks (*304, 355*) fed high amounts of glycine.

The rate of creatine synthesis by the rat was increased only slightly when the level of dietary methionine was increased from 0.7 to 1.4% (*354, 356*). However, toxic levels of glycine increased liver fat by 50% in folic acid-deficient animals (*357*), and it has been suggested that increased creatine synthesis under these conditions induced a deficiency of *S*-adenosylmethionine which was reflected in a deficiency of choline.

The creatine content of muscle in chicks fed a low glycine (and serine) diet was found to be decreased (*355*), and addition of creatine to the diet of chicks promotes growth presumably by sparing glycine (*304, 358*). Creatine administration leads to reduced tissue activities of arginine-glycine amidinotransferase (EC 2.1.4.1) (*359, 360*), and this is thought to represent reduced synthesis of this enzyme. Ramirez *et al.* (*361*) believe, however, that the tissue creatine levels attained in such experiments are far higher than would be reached under physiological conditions.

Benzoate feeding decreased creatine excretion in man (*350*) and caused a decrease in kidney amidinotransferase activity which was greater than that caused by feeding creatine (*362*). Both the effects of benzoate and of creatine on amidinotransferase activities were reversed or prevented by supplementation of the diet with extra glycine (*362, 363*). This effect of glycine is complex and not yet completely understood (*364*).

These studies have shown that the synthesis of creatine, both in mammals and in chicks, responds both to increased and decreased dietary supplies of glycine. How well this process competes with the purine biosynthetic pathway, especially when glycine is scarce, is not known.

PORPHYRIN SYNTHESIS. Glycine is a substrate for the first step in porphyrin synthesis, and changes in the rate of this process may reduce the availability of glycine for other reactions.

Stimulation of Porphyrin Synthesis by Exogenous Glycine. Increasing the availability of glycine did not cause any increase in the urinary excretion of intermediates of the porphyrin biosynthetic pathway in normal humans

$$\underset{\text{Succinyl-CoA}}{\begin{array}{c} COO^- \\ | \\ CH_2 \\ | \\ CH_2 \\ | \\ C{=}O \\ | \\ S{-}CoA \end{array}} \quad + \quad \underset{\text{Glycine}}{\begin{array}{c} COO \\ | \\ CH_2\,NH_3^+ \end{array}} \xrightarrow{\text{Pyridoxal-P}} \underset{\alpha\text{-Amino-}\beta\text{-ketoadipate}}{\begin{array}{c} COO^- \\ | \\ {}^+H_3N{-}CH \\ | \\ C{=}O \\ | \\ CH_2 \\ | \\ CH_2 \\ | \\ COO^- \end{array}}$$

$$\alpha\text{-Amino-}\beta\text{-ketoadipate} \xrightarrow{-CO_2} \delta\text{-AMINOLEVULINATE}$$

$$\text{PORPHRINS} \longleftarrow \text{PORPHOBILINOGEN} \longleftarrow \delta\text{-AMINOLEVULINATE}$$

(*365, 366*) or those with cutaneous porphyria or various types of anemia (*367*). However, glycine loading (*i.e.*, ingestion of 25 grams of glycine) caused marked increases in the urinary excretion of δ-aminolevulinic acid and porphobilinogen (*365, 368*) in patients with acute porphyria. This effect was transient, with maximum excretion three to five hours after glycine ingestion; after six hours excretion of these intermediates declined to initial values.

Totter *et al.* (*332*) also showed that administration of glycine caused an increase in the amount of protoporphyrin excreted in the feces of rats fed a purified diet. Supplementation of the basal diet with folate also raised protoporphyrin excretion, probably by increasing glycine synthesis from serine. Because the diet used appeared to be marginal both in folate and in glycine, it is not surprising that the feeding of benzoate caused a decrease in protoporphyrin excretion, and this effect was greater than the growth inhibition caused by benzoate. Supplementation of the benzoate-containing diet either with glycine or with folate overcame the effects of benzoate both on growth and on protoporphyrin synthesis.

Experimental Porphyria in Birds. An increased rate of porphyrin synthesis in chick embryos appears to decrease the availability of glycine for purine biosynthesis. Thus induction of porphyria by injection of allylisopropyl acetylcarbamide into chick embryos, a treatment which resulted in marked increases in porphyrin biosynthesis from glycine and succinyl CoA, resulted in a lowered content of uric acid in the egg (*369*). There was no change in the conversion of adenine to uric acid, however. In a later study Talman *et al.* (*370*) showed that the total conversion of glycine-^{14}C to uric acid in 60 minutes decreased 55% following treatment with allylisopropyl acetamide. Growth was also depressed when porphyria was induced but was restored to normal by injection of adenine.

Experimental Porphyria in Mammals. In contrast to the results obtained in the studies with chicks, there is no evidence that increased use of glycine for porphyrin synthesis in rats with experimental porphyria reduces the rate of purine synthesis. Merchante *et al.* (*371*) induced hepatic porphyria with allylisopropyl acetylcarboxamide and observed that although there was no change in the liver's content of RNA or DNA, a significant decrease in total acid-soluble organic phosphorus was demonstrable. Later studies by DeMatteis *et al.* (*372*) used allylisopropyl acetamide, hexachlorobenzene, and diethoxy-carbonyl-dihydrotrimethylpyridine, and measurements were made at intervals (depending on the agent used) during 80 days of exposure to the porphyrogenic chemical. There was no change in the amount of RNA and DNA present and no consistent change in the concentrations of acid-soluble purine ribonucleotides although some apparently nonspecific changes were noted. Allantoin excretion was also measured in rats with experimental hepatic porphyria; no significant change was noted (*373*).

Human Porphyria. Taxay (*374*) reported that two of six porphyric patients had blood uric acid levels of 1–2 mg per 100 ml, compared with the normal blood uric acid range of 4–6 mg per 100 ml, with no increase in urinary excretion of uric acid. Ludwig (*375*) also observed that serum uric acid values fell to similar values during acute attacks in four patients with acute intermittent porphyria, but he believed this was caused by altered kidney function rather than by a real change in uric acid synthesis. In a later study by Dowdle *et al.* (*376*) plasma uric acid levels were observed to be normal in patients with several kinds of porphyria, and one patient with acute intermittent porphyria had decreased urinary excretion of this endproduct. The conversion of radioactivity from δ-aminolevulinate-5-^{14}C into uric acid and other products was normal (*376*). Finally, Pimstone *et al.* (*377*) found normal serum and urinary uric acid values in six patients with porphyria.

In only one study was uric acid synthesis measured in porphyric patients using ^{14}C-glycine. Both the cumulative incorporation of radioactive glycine into uric acid during a two-week period and the distribution of radioactivity within the purine ring were measured in three patients with symptomatic porphyria and in three with variegate porphyria (*377*). No major change in either parameter was observed. The investigators pointed out that they had not estimated the body pool size of uric acid or of glycine or the extent of uricolysis.

Human Polycythemias. Yü *et al.* (*378, 379*) and Laster and Muller (*380*) have studied glycine metabolism in cases of polycythemia vera and secondary polycythemia in which the amount of glycine incorporated into heme and erythrocyte proteins was more than doubled. They found that following administration of ^{15}N-glycine the time course of appearance of ^{15}N in total urinary nitrogen was normal but the time course of its appearance in urinary uric acid was slower than normal. These workers concluded that there was some diversion of glycine from uric acid synthesis to slower metabolic routes involving incorporation into nucleic acids, a redistribution consistent with the exaggerated hematopoietic requirements of these disorders.

HIPPURATE SYNTHESIS. Conjugation of glycine with benzoate to form hippurate has been observed for many years and has been used extensively as a tool to study glycine metabolism. There is a good deal of evidence that glycine may sometimes be rate limiting for hippurate synthesis in animals.

$$C_6H_5\text{–CO–CoA} + {}^{-}OOC\text{–}CH_2NH_3^{+} \longrightarrow C_6H_5\text{–}\underset{\|}{\overset{}{C}}(=O)\text{–}NH\text{–}CH_2\text{–}COO^{-}$$

Benzoyl-CoA Glycine Hippurate

Effect of Dietary Glycine on Hippurate Excretion. McCollum and Hoagland (*381, 382*) studied hippurate formation using pigs which were maintained on a practically nitrogen-free diet of starch. When hippurate was synthesized from benzoate there was little or no increase in the total urinary excretion of nitrogen whereas urinary urea nitrogen decreased to between 12 and 19% of normal. These findings were confirmed using rabbits (*383*) and men (*278*) fed low-nitrogen diets. The conclusion was drawn by these workers and others (*384, 385, 386*) that the glycine nitrogen in the excreted hippurate would normally have been converted to urea.

An increased rate of hippurate formation from benzoate was observed in pigs fed gelatin (which contains about 28% glycine) compared with that when casein, a low-glycine (*ca.* 0.5%) protein, was fed (*387, 388*); the ingestion of large amounts of gelatin is known to raise plasma levels of glycine (*280*). A similar effect on hippurate synthesis was noted when rabbits were fed enzymatic hydrolysates of gelatin and casein (*389*).

Administration of glycine alone also caused an increase in hippurate excretion in rabbits following ingestion of benozate. In one such study (*390*) the proportion of the ingested benzoate which was conjugated and excreted rose from 42 to 71%, and the investigators concluded that the rate of benzoate synthesis depended more on the availability of glycine than on the capacity of the conjugating system itself. In apparent agreement with this conclusion were observations that the rate of endogenous glycine synthesis in rats was much slower than that of hippurate (*391*). Accelerated hippurate excretion in the dog (*392*) and in man (*391, 393*) following ingestion of glycine was also demonstrated.

Administration to rabbits of sarcosine, a precursor of glycine, also caused an increased rate of hippurate excretion (*394*), and labeled hippurate has been isolated from urine following injection of ^{15}N-sarcosine into rats (*395*).

Following the recognition that benzoate and glycine affected the renal excretion of some compounds (*see below*), Quick (*396*) suggested that benzoate retarded the excretion of hippurate and that glycine prevented this effect and hence indirectly accelerated the rate of hippurate excretion.

Reversal of Benzoate Toxicity. Benzoate fed at high doses can reduce the growth rate of rats and can be lethal. Griffiths (*397*) first noted in 1929 that administration of glycine reduced this toxicity while it increased hippurate excretion. White (*398*) later attempted to alleviate benzoate toxicity by feeding a wide variety of compounds but found that only glycine or compounds which are now known to be converted to glycine (*e.g.*, sarcosine, glyoxylate) were active. He concluded that "survival and growth of young rats on diets containing benzoate occurred only when their diets furnished a supply of glycine which was adequate for the detoxication of benzoate and for the formation of new tissue proteins."

Griffith (*399*) also noted that benzoate toxicity in rats was partially relieved when the amount of yeast extract in the diet was increased; however, added glycine was still required for complete reversal of toxicity. The effect of the yeast extract was attributed to its content of pyridoxine although in view of the results of Totter *et al.* (*332*), folate might have been involved as well. The latter investigators showed that either glycine or folate could overcome the decrease in growth rate of rats fed benzoate.

Effects of Benzoate on Glycine Metabolism. Administration of benzoate to man produced a 20–30% decrease in plasma concentrations of free glycine (*400, 401*); in the guinea pig it caused a 70% reduction in the free glycine concentration of liver although there was no change in muscle concentrations of this amino acid.

Administration of benzoate to man may accelerate the endogenous biosynthesis of glycine (*402*), but benzoate appeared to have no effect on glycine biosynthesis in rats (*402*).

The interpretation of studies of the effect of hippurate synthesis on the availability of glycine for other reactions is greatly complicated by the compartmentation of glycine within the animal body. Thus as early as 1939 Rittenberg and co-workers (*403, 404*) found that only 35–45% of the glycine in excreted hippurate had originated from exogenous ^{15}N-glycine, in spite of the ingestion of large amounts of dietary labeled glycine. In later studies of humans given benzoate and glycine-^{15}N orally, the specific activity of urinary hippurate glycine was greater than that of urinary free glycine for up to six hours after a single feeding (*405, 406*). Garfinkle and Lajtha (*407*) found that the specific activity of hippurate glycine isolated from liver or kidney (the site or sites of hippurate synthesis, depending on species) following intravenous injection of benzoate and labeled glycine was under some conditions higher than that of total free glycine isolated from the same organ. They concluded that there was not only organ compartmentation of glycine with respect to hippurate synthesis but also that there must be some kind of intratissue or intracellular compartmentation of this amino acid.

These and other studies (*e.g., 283, 408, 409, 410*) indicate clearly that hippurate synthesis can lead to a shortage of glycine in one glycine pool without effect on its availability in another. Unfortunately, the appropriate studies have not been done to determine the relationship of these pools to purine biosynthesis *de novo.*

Effect of Benzoate on Uric Acid Synthesis and Excretion. Early studies of the effects of the administration of benzoate and of quinate, a precursor of benzoate, on the metabolism of uric acid have been reviewed by McCrudden (*411,* p. 171), Lewis and Karr (*412*), and Quick (*396*). Later literature has been discussed by Bröchner-Mortensen (*28*) and by Bishop and Talbott (*29*).

Most workers have found that there is a decrease of as much as 70% in urinary uric acid during the first few hours after benzoate feeding, with a smaller or no effect on 24-hour urinary uric acid excretion (*e.g., 385, 396, 412, 413*). Increased blood uric acid levels have also been observed during the period of decreased uric acid excretion (*385, 396, 412, 413*). In a detailed study of these phenomena Michael *et al.* (*413*) found that the rate of benzoate absorption from the intestine was greater than that of its conversion to hippurate and that the degree of uric acid retention was related to the amount of free benzoate present in the body. They concluded that the free benzoate was merely acting on the kidney to impede uric acid excretion; hippurate itself had no effect on uric acid excretion.

Quick (*396, 414, 415*) noted that ingestion of glycine prior to taking benzoate could completely abolish the normal inhibitory effect of benzoate on uric acid excretion. In view of the studies by Michael *et al.* (*413*) referred to above, one of the effects of added glycine was probably to decrease the concentration of free benzoate by accelerating its conversion to hippurate. However, Quick (*396*) also believed that glycine acted directly on the kidney to prevent the renal effect of benzoate on uric acid excretion. As mentioned previously it is now known that glycine has an independent uricosuric effect on the kidney. In studies with rats Friedman (*416*) observed that administration of salicylate or of salicylate plus glycine had the same effects upon uric acid excretion as did benzoate and benzoate plus glycine in man. Urinary excretion of allantoin was not affected by either treatment, however.

In view of the undeniable effects of benzoate on the renal excretion of uric acid it is generally assumed that the utilization of glycine for the conversion of this compound to hippurate has no detrimental effect on the synthesis of purines *de novo*. Although this may be the case, it is unfortunate that experiments have not been done to investigate this question directly.

OTHER PATHWAYS. There does not appear to be any indication that the conversion of glycine to nicotinuric acid, indoylacryloyl glycine, glycocholate, or glutathione might reduce the availability of this amino acid for purine biosynthesis. However, this point has not been specifically investigated.

In the dog and monkey phenylacetate is conjugated with glycine instead of with glutamine as in man and other species. The rate of phenylacetate formation is twice as great as the maximum rate of hippurate synthesis in dogs (*417*), and its excretion is elevated fourfold following simultaneous administration of phenylacetate and glycine. Again, the possible interaction of this conjugation and purine biosynthesis remains to be investigated.

H_4-Folate Coenzymes

Use of One-Carbon Units for Purine Biosynthesis *de novo*. One-carbon units at the oxidation level of formate furnish the C-2 and C-8 positions in the purine ring. The actual substrate for the insertion of the C-2 position is 10-formyl H_4-folate and that for the C-8 position is 5,10-methenyl H_4-folate.

Phosphoribosylglycineamide + 5, 10-Methenyl H_4-folate → Phosphoribosylformylglycineamide + H_4-Folate

Phosphoribosylaminoimidazole carboxamide + 10-Formyl H_4-folate → Phosphoribosylformamidoimidazole carboxamide + H_4-Folate

There is ample evidence that a deficiency in the supply of these substrates, either through limitations in the supply of appropriate one-carbon moieties themselves or through limited availability of the folate coenzyme carriers, may lead to retarded purine biosynthesis *de novo.* In contrast, it is not known whether or not a surplus of these entities can lead to acceleration of this pathway.

The factors which regulate concentrations of H_4-folate coenzymes are considered here, and the general pathways of H_4-folate coenzyme synthesis and utilization may be summarized as follows:

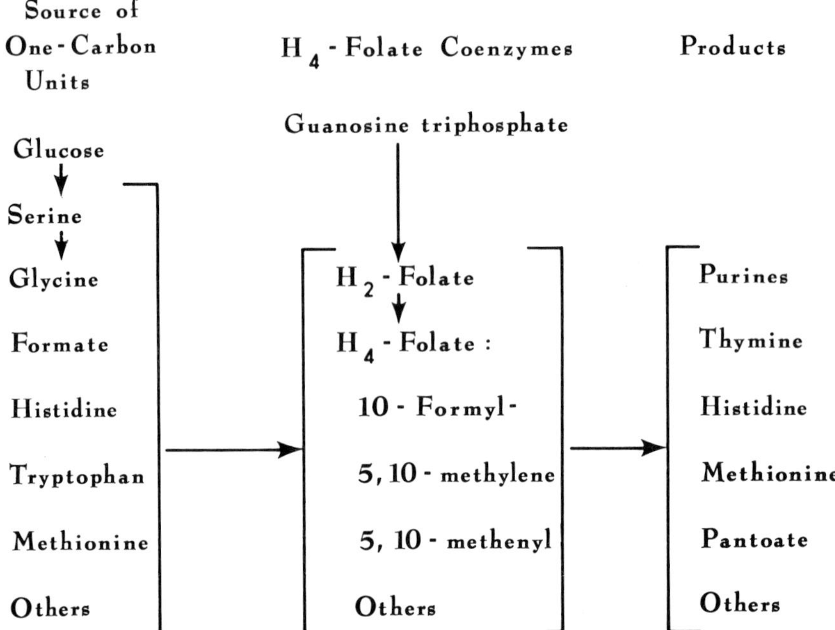

Synthesis of H_4-Folate. The major precursor of the H_4-folate molecule in nature is guanosine triphosphate. By an extensive series of interconversions 2-amino-4-hydroxy-6-hydroxymethyl-H_2-pterin-6-pyrophosphate is formed. This compound is coupled to *p*-aminobenzoate to form H_2-pteroate, and glutamate then reacts with this to form H_2-folate. The final step in H_4-folate synthesis is the reduction of H_2-folate by an enzyme usually called folate reductase or dihydrofolate reductase but which now has the official name of H_4-folate dehydrogenase (EC 1.5.1.3). Although this pathway has not yet been worked out in complete detail, the present view of it is presented in Figure 4-1.

Little is known about the regulation of the pathway of H_4-folate synthesis from guanosine triphosphate. Dalal and Gots (*418*) showed that adenylate partially inhibits one or more of the early steps of this pathway in extracts of *Salmonella typhimurium,* but the mechanism of this inhibition and its possible physiological significance have not been pursued.

Nutritional Requirements for Folate. A variety of microorganisms and all higher animals lack part or all of the pathway of H_4-folate synthesis from guanosine triphosphate and hence require exogenously supplied folate, some derivative of folate, *p*-aminobenzoate, or the endproducts of one-carbon metabolism for normal growth and function.

Microbial Cells. The role of folate in the biosynthesis of purines was established on the basis of nutritional studies with microorganisms long before the enzyme reactions involved were identified.

Stokstad (*419*) found in 1941 that purines, especially in conjunction with thymine, stimulated the growth of *Lactobacillus casei.* At this time the nutritional requirement of this organism for folate had not yet been recognized. Similar findings were also reported for *Lactobacillus arabinosus* 17-5 and *Lactobacillus pentosus* 124-2 (*420, 421*). Although purines were only stimulatory and not absolutely essential for these organisms, Snell and Mitchell (*420, 421*) demonstrated that guanine was essential for the growth of *Leuconostoc mesenteroides* P-60 in minimal medium and that adenine was essential for the growth of *Streptococcus lactis* R. In studies conducted following the recognition of folate as a growth factor and with more defined media Stokes (*422*) and Luckey *et al.* (*423*) showed that purines plus thymine were required for the optimum growth of *Streptococcus lactis* R in the absence of folate. Later studies have shown that purines can replace or spare the folate requirements of *Lactobacillus casei* (*424*), *Bacillus stearothermophilus* (*425*), and *Gaffkya homari* (*426*).

After *p*-aminobenzoate was found to be a growth factor for some microorganisms, its relationship to purines was investigated. Landy and Streightoff (*427*), for example, found that purines stimulated the growth of *Acetobacter suboxydans* when the concentration of *p*-aminobenzoate in the medium was low but had no effect when growth was optimal in the presence of high concentrations of this growth factor. Purines spared *p*-aminobenzoate requirements for growth of a strain of *Escherichia coli* (*428*) and could either spare or completely replace this compound for the growth of *Clostridium acetobutylicum* (*429*). In other studies the purine requirement for growth of *Lactobacillus arabinosus* in the presence of thymine could be partially replaced either by folate or by *p*-aminobenzoate (*430*).

These results clearly demonstrated that folate, and hence *p*-aminobenozate, was required in some way for the synthesis of purines as well as for that of thymine and several other compounds.

Animal Cells. All higher animals and all animal cells in tissue culture require exogenously supplied folate or a derivative of folate for normal growth and function. The few studies in which purines have been shown partially or completely to replace this requirement are better discussed below.

Several unsuccessful attempts have been made to increase the rate of purine biosynthesis *de novo* by administration of extra folate. Thus Bishop *et al.*

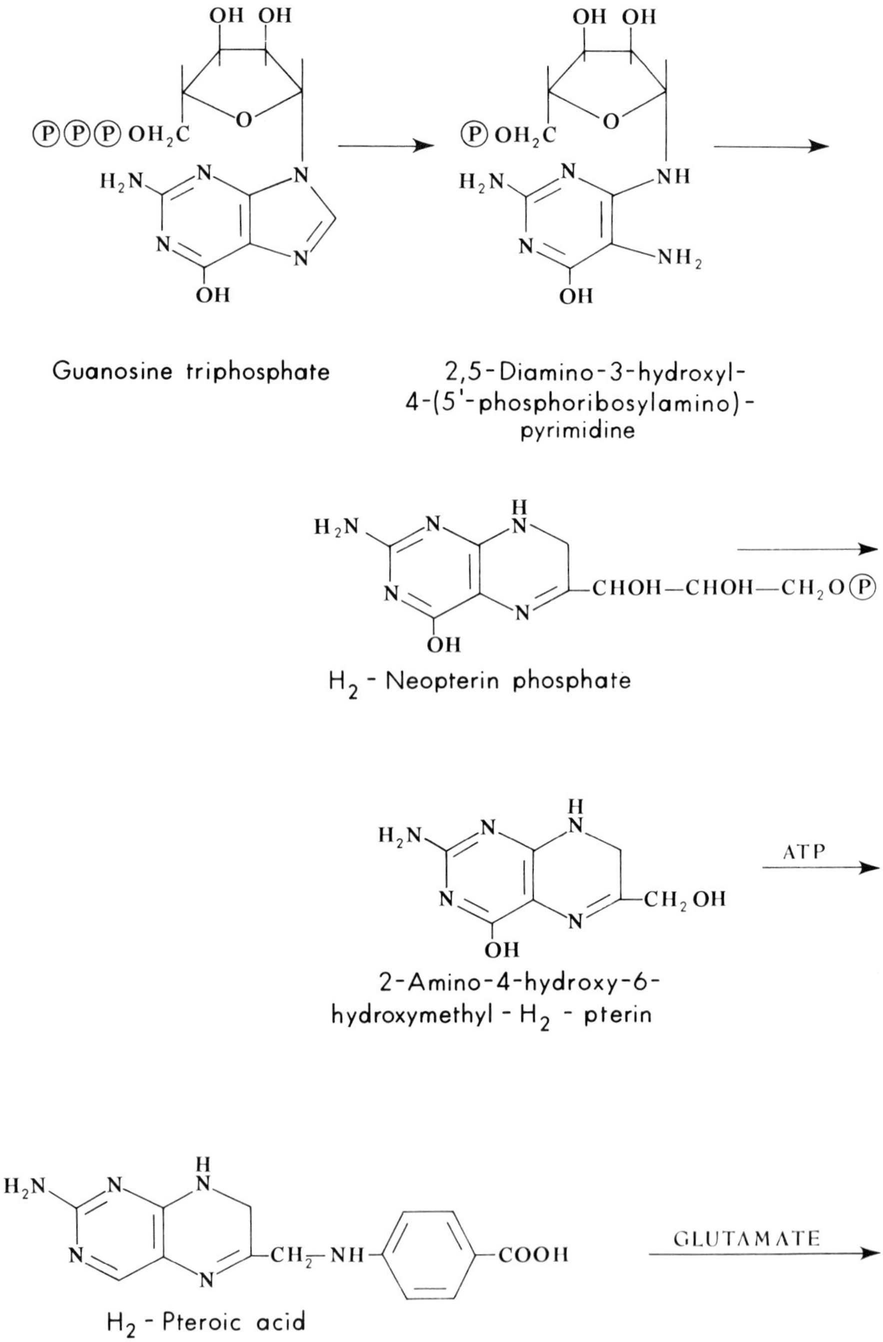

Ⓟ Ⓟ Ⓟ OH_2C — OH OH — O — H_2N — N — N — N — N — OH

→

Ⓟ OH_2C — OH OH — O — H_2N — N — NH — N — NH_2 — OH

→

Guanosine triphosphate

2,5-Diamino-3-hydroxyl-4-(5'-phosphoribosylamino)-pyrimidine

H_2N — N — H N — N — N — OH — CHOH—CHOH—CH_2OⓅ

→

H_2 - Neopterin phosphate

H_2N — N — H N — N — N — OH — CH_2OH

ATP →

2-Amino-4-hydroxy-6-hydroxymethyl - H_2 - pterin

H_2N — N — H N — N — N — CH_2—NH—(benzene ring)—COOH

GLUTAMATE →

H_2 - Pteroic acid

Figure 4-1. Folic acid

H_2N, N, H N, CH_2, C—CHOH, O, CHOH, CH_2OⓅ, N, NH_2, OH →

2,5-Diamino-3-hydroxyl-4-(5'-phospho-1'-deoxyribulosylamino)-pyrimidine

H_2N, N, H N, N, N, OH, —CHOH—CHOH—CH_3 →

H_2-Biopterin

H_2N, N, H N, N, N, OH, —CH_2OⓅⓅ →(p-AMINO-BENZOATE)

2-Amino-4-hydroxy-6-hydroxymethyl-H_2-pterin pyrophosphate

H_2N, N, H N, N, N, OH, —CH_2—NH—(benzene ring)—C(=O)—N(H)—CH(COOH)—CH_2—CH_2—COOH

H_2-Pteroylglutamic acid
(H_2-Folic acid)

biosynthesis (probable outline)

(*431*) found that administration of folate did not increase the conversion of labeled glycine into urinary urate in man, and both injection of folate into tumor-bearing mice and its inclusion in incubation media did not stimulate formate incorporation into purines in Ehrlich ascites tumor cells *in vitro* (*69, 70, 161,* and J. F. Henderson, unpublished studies). These results appear to indicate that under the conditions employed any limitation in purine biosynthesis that might involve H_4-folate coenzymes may be due to a shortage of the one-carbon unit rather than of its H_4-folate "carrier."

EFFECTS OF NUTRITIONAL DEFICIENCY. The effects of folate deficiency on purine biosynthesis in some systems have also been detected by measurements other than stimulation of growth or reversal of growth inhibition. These include inhibition of incorporation of labeled precursors into purines, accumulation or excretion of intermediates of the pathway of purine biosynthesis, decreased concentrations of purine nucleotides in cells, and altered metabolism of compounds which provide one-carbon units for purine synthesis.

Differences between Phosphoribosyl-Glycineamide Formyltransferase and Phosphoribosyl-Aminoimidazole Carboxamide Formyltransferase. There is abundant evidence, quoted here and in Chapter 2, that phosphoribosyl-aminoimidazole carboxamide formyltransferase is more sensitive to folate deficiency than is phosphoribosyl-glycineamide formyltransferase.

Numerous studies, discussed below, showed a number of years ago that folate deficiency induced in certain bacteria by sulfonamide treatment resulted in the accumulation in culture media of aminoimidazole carboxamide or its derivatives. Gots (*320, 432*) showed that the maximum accumulation of aminoimidazole carboxamide was obtained at concentrations of sulfonamides which gave 50–60% inhibition of growth. Higher drug concentrations, then, may possibly inhibit phosphoribosyl-glycineamide formyltransferase or the synthesis of glycine and 5,10-methylene H_4-folate from serine. In a study of the kinetics of aminoimidazole carboxamide accumulation Greenberg (*321*) showed that accumulation ceased after several hours and that the amount of aminoimidazole carboxamide present declined somewhat. More significantly, he observed that after 16 hours of incubation the addition of glycine was only weakly stimulatory for the accumulation process and that a new and unidentified compound was formed instead of aminoimidazole carboxamide. He concluded that the formation of aminoimidazole carboxamide was indeed inhibited by sulfonamides but that this was not demonstrable under the conditions usually used for such studies. Unfortunately, the interest of workers in this field was at that time more on the elucidation of the pathway of purine synthesis than on this discrepancy *per se*, and these observations were not followed up.

Ben-Ishai *et al.* (*433, 434*) were among the first to raise the obvious question of whether in fact the purine C-2 and C-8 positions did not have different origins, at least in sulfonamide-inhibited *Escherichia coli*, and Webb (*435*) has also discussed the same point in relation to studies with *Aerobacter aerogenes*. More recently Westby and Gots (*436*) have studied the matter in some detail using mutants of *Salmonella typhimurium* blocked in the early reactions of the purine biosynthetic pathway. They were unable to isolate a mutant lacking phosphoribosyl-glycineamide formyltransferase and were unable to procure any significant accumulation of phosphoribosyl-glycineamide under any condition of incubation of extracts or in extracts of cells grown under conditions of folate deficiency. They were able to demonstrate, however, a folate coenzyme-dependent formylation of this substrate in extracts.

Although enterobacteria have been used in most such studies, Shive (*319*) observed that other microorganisms such as *Lactobacillus arabinosus* did not accumulate aminoimidazole carboxamide during the course of sulfonamide bacteriostasis. He suggested that the earlier step in the pathway of purine synthesis might be more sensitive in these organisms. This suggestion has not been further studied.

The only direct evidence for the accumulation of phosphoribosyl-glycineamide in folate deficiency is the work of Iwai *et al.* (*437*), who used pea seedlings treated with a sulfonamide. Again this observation has not been followed up.

In mammals aminoimidazole carboxamide is a normal urinary excretory product (*438, 439*) which, as discussed below, increases during treatment with folate antimetabolites. Indirect evidence for the inhibition of phosphoribosyl-glycineamide formyltransferase was, however, obtained in Ehrlich ascites tumor cells incubated *in vitro* with aminopterin (J. F. Henderson, unpublished studies).

Hartman (*440*) has recently proposed an explanation for these phenomena based on earlier studies (*441*) of coupling of the two formyltransferase reactions. Thus the C-2 of inosinate can be nearly quantitatively transferred to phosphoribosyl-formylglycineamide *via* inosinicase, plus phosphoribosyl-aminoimidazole carboxamide formyltransferase, plus phosphoribosyl-glycineamide formyltransferase, plus 5,10-methenyl H_4-folate cyclohydrolase.

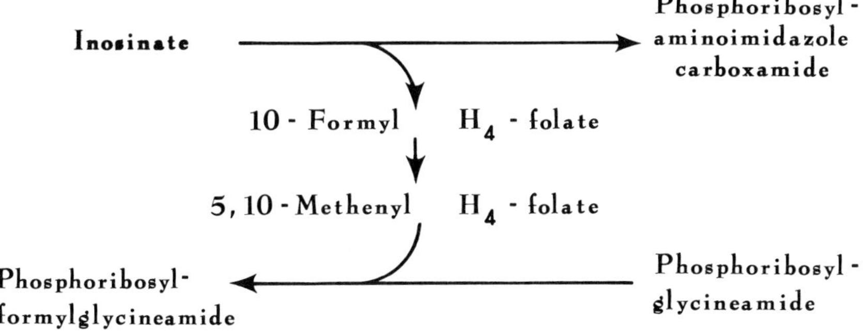

This process certainly does work in cell extracts and is often used to assay one or another of the enzymes involved because the phosphoribosyl-amino-imidazole carboxamide which is formed can be easily measured chemically.

It was suggested that if the supply of one-carbon units becomes restricted the phosphoribosyl-glycineamide formyltransferase reaction will scavenge them from available H_4-folate coenzymes and perhaps also from inosinate. Phosphoribosyl-aminoimidazole carboxamide would then accumulate. This hypothesis is attractive, but it remains to be demonstrated that such coupling can and does occur in intact cells.

Inhibition of Incorporation of Labeled Precursors. Only a few experiments have been reported which show inhibition of the incorporation of labeled precursors into purines during a nutritional deficiency of folate in animals; far more attention has been given to thymine synthesis under these conditions. Totter *et al.* (*348*) compared the extent of glycine-1-^{14}C metabolism in homogenates of liver from folate-deficient and control chicks. Glycine incorporation into nucleic acid adenine (based on specific activity measurements) was decreased about 80% and that into guanine about 50%. Glycine incorporation into serine, and into proteins and phospholipids *via* serine, was also decreased by folate deficiency. In contrast, however, the same workers (*442*) found that formate-^{14}C incorporation *in vivo* into nucleic acid purines of pooled viscera of chicks was decreased only slightly by folate deficiency. Drysdale *et al.* (*443*) similarly found that in rats which were made folate deficient by feeding succinylsulfathiazole incorporation of formate-^{14}C into nucleic acid purines *in vivo* was inhibited by 75% to 80% in liver whereas no inhibition was noted in other viscera.

Accumulation or Excretion of Aminoimidazole Carboxamide. Another measure of the effect of folate deficiency on purine biosynthesis is the accumulation (in microorganisms) or excretion (in animals) of amino-imidazole carboxamide or its ribosyl derivative as a consequence of the decreased rate of synthesis of phosphoribosyl-formamido-imidazole carboxamide. Greenberg and Spilman (*444*) found, for example, that these compounds accumulated when a *p*-aminobenzoate-requiring mutant of *Escherichia coli* was grown with limiting concentrations of this growth factor. Similarly, Dalal *et al.* (*211*) observed that aminoimidazole carboxamide accumulated during the growth of a mutant of *Salmonella typhimurium* in which the synthesis of *p*-aminobenzoate was partially blocked.

It has already been mentioned that normal human and animal urine contain small amounts of aminoimidazole carboxamide. Luhby and Cooperman (*445*) observed a slight increase in the excretion of this compound in humans with folate deficiency, although they did not consider the difference significant. Later studies, however, have clearly shown that urinary excretion of aminoimidazole carboxamide increased from 0.9 to at least 2.2 mg per day during periods of folate deficiency (*446, 447*). In rats, daily urinary excretion of this compound increased from 23 μg to 37 μg when they were placed on a folate-deficient diet (*448*).

Results of some other studies of aminoimidazole carboxamide metabolism in folate deficiency have been both difficult to interpret and in apparent contrast to conclusions based on the above-mentioned findings. Thus McGeer *et al.* (*448*) found that the recovery of radioactive aminoimidazole carboxamide in the urine of rats given a tracer dose by intraperitoneal injection was the same in control and folate-deficient groups. Herbert *et al.* (*446*) fed a loading dose of aminoimidazole carboxamide to human subjects and found a decreased recovery of this compound in the urine of folate-deficient patients, contrary to expectations. In rats, however, the same amount of an injected loading dose was recovered in the urine of control and folate-deficient animals (*448*). Further work is required to reconcile or explain these apparent discrepancies.

Concentrations of Purine Nucleotides. Surprisingly, in only a few studies have purine nucleotide concentrations been measured in folate-deficient cells. Papp and Totter (*449*) observed that concentrations of coenzyme A were reduced in livers of chicks and rats fed folate-deficient diets. While such treatment did not affect the coenzyme A levels of rat heart, those in chick heart were reduced. Folate is required for the synthesis of pantoate as well as for adenylate, and these studies consequently do not show which moiety of coenzyme A was more affected by folate deficiency. However, Totter (*450*) also reported briefly results of studies which demonstrated that adenylate and ATP concentrations were diminished in tissues of folate-deficient chicks.

INHIBITION OF H_4-FOLATE SYNTHESIS BY SULFONAMIDES. It was the study of sulfonamide action that led to the recognition that *p*-aminobenzoate was one of the precursors of folate, because these drugs act as antimetabolites to prevent the reaction of *p*-aminobenzoate with 2-amino-4-hydroxy-6-hydroxymethyl-H_2-pterin pyrophosphate to form H_2-pteroate (*see* p. 114).

Reversal of Growth Inhibition. Numerous studies were conducted in the 1940s to identify nutrients and metabolites which could prevent or reverse the growth-inhibitory actions of the sulfonamides. Thus Harris and Kohn (*451*) found that although methionine partially antagonized the effects of sulfonamides on *Escherichia coli* such antagonism could be increased by addition of xanthine or guanine. Shive and Roberts (*452*) also observed that the same purines had no effect on sulfonamide-inhibited *Escherichia coli* cultures in the absence of methionine but gave additional antagonism in the presence of this amino acid. In *Lactobacillus arabinosus* cultures, however, purines alone antagonized sulfanilamide action whereas methionine had no effect either in the presence or absence of purines (*452*). The relationship of antagonism of sulfonamide inhibition by guanine or xanthine to that produced by methionine, serine, and glycine in *Escherichia coli* was also demonstrated by Kohn (*453*).

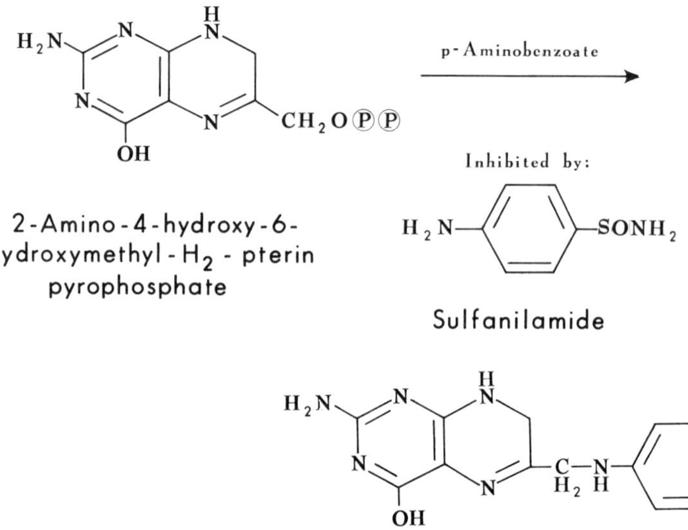

p-Aminobenzoate →

Inhibited by:

2-Amino-4-hydroxy-6-hydroxymethyl-H_2-pterin pyrophosphate

Sulfanilamide

H_2-Pteroate

Antagonism of sulfonamide inhibition by purines was later also demonstrated in studies with *Salmonella typhimurium* (*454*) and *Eremothecium ashbyii* and *Saccharomyces cerevisiae* (*455*). Snell and Mitchell (*420*) also found that purines could reverse sulfonamide action in cultures of *Lactobacillus arabinosus* and *Lactobacillus pentosus* if suboptimal amounts of *p*-aminobenzoate were also present. In an interesting application of all of these observations Martin and Fisher (*456*) showed that injection of adenine into mice would reverse the effectiveness of sulfonamides in animals infected with *Streptococcus hemolyticus*.

Accumulation of Aminoimidazole Carboxamide. It was in the early studies of sulfonamide bacteriostasis that Fox (*457*) observed that a new diazotizable but not acetylated aromatic amine accumulated under conditions of growth inhibition, and it was identified as aminoimidazole carboxamide much later by Shive *et al.* (*458*). Greenberg (*444, 459*) and Gots (*460*) subsequently demonstrated that the material which accumulated was predominately the ribosyl derivative with some free base and a small amount of the phosphoribosyl derivative; the conditions required for diazotization probably result in the formation of free aminoimidazole carboxamide. Gots (*320, 432*) observed that the maximum accumulation of aminoimidazole carboxamide in *Escherichia coli* cultures occurred at sulfonamide concentrations which produced 50 to 60% inhibition of growth. Addition of *p*-aminobenzoate to the cultures relieved the growth inhibition and stopped further accumulation of this compound, but the material already formed was not utilized.

The measurement of aminoimidazole carboxamide accumulation under a wide variety of experimental conditions has provided a great deal of information regarding the regulation of purine biosynthesis *de novo;* these studies are discussed elsewhere in this chapter.

H_4-FOLATE DEHYDROGENASE AND ITS REGULATION. The last step in the synthesis of H_4-folate *de novo* from guanosine triphosphate is H_4-folate dehydrogenase (EC 1.5.1.2; dihydrofolate reductase). It is also required for the reutilization of the H_2-folate formed as one of the products of the thymidylate synthetase reaction, and it also acts to reduce dietary folate to H_2-folate and H_4-folate.

$$\text{NADPH} + H_2\text{-Folate} \xrightarrow{H_4\text{-Folate dehydrogenase}} H_4\text{-Folate} + \text{NADP}^+$$

Variation in Enzyme Amount. The amount, or at least total activity, of H_4-folate dehydrogenase has been found to vary considerably in different cells and under different experimental conditions. Because the physiological consequences of these variations have been little explored, they will be discussed only briefly at this point.

Sirotnak (*461*) and others have studied changes in the amounts of H_4-folate dehydrogenase formed in *Diplococcus pneumoniae* as a result of mutations in the structural gene for this enzyme. Other recent studies (*e.g., 462, 463*) have shown that two forms of this enzyme exist in Leukemia L1210 cells and in *Lactobacillus casei,* that these are interconvertible, and that their relative amounts vary with the conditions of growth. The significance of these observations remains to be elucidated.

In a variety of lactic acid bacteria (*Streptococcus faecalis* R, *Streptococcus thermophilus, Lactobacillus arabinosus,* and *Lactobacillus casei*) H_4-folate dehydrogenase activity appears during the lag phase of growth and increases rapidly (up to eightfold) early in the exponential phase. Activity then declines and returns to the initial low level by the beginning of the stationary phase (*464, 465, 466*). Ohara and Silber (*464*) have also shown that the specific activity of this enzyme in *Lactobacillus casei* varies with the concentration of folate in the medium. Maximum values were obtained with a folate concentration of $1.4 \times 10^{-9}M$, with significant reduction at either higher or lower folate levels. Bloch (*467*) has observed a similar phenomenon using *Streptococcus faecalis.*

Growth of *Escherichia coli* with adenosine plus guanosine resulted in a decrease of 23% in the specific activity of H_4-folate dehydrogenase. Addition of thymidine also repressed activity, and in the presence of all three compounds the specific activity of the enzyme was reduced to 37% of the control value (*468*). When *Lactobacillus casei* was grown on a low-folate, high-purine medium, so that growth depended on thymine, the specific activity of the enzyme increased threefold to fourfold as the thymine concentration was increased (*464*). In mutant strains of *Escherichia coli* (*468*) and of *Streptococcus faecalis* (*469*) which contained elevated amounts of H_4-folate dehydrogenase growth in purine-rich media did not alter the levels of this enzyme although in the former case thymidine was still an effective repressor. The synthesis of H_4-folate dehydrogenase, therefore, seems relatively insensitive to regulation by purines.

In a variety of bacterial cells and normal and neoplastic animal and human cells exposure to folate antimetabolites leads to increased H_4-folate dehydrogenase activities, and such elevated activities are frequently associated with drug resistance. These studies have been reviewed by Nichol (*470*) and Bertino and Hillcoat (*471*), and these writers discuss the possible mechanisms by which this may occur. Such changes are not necessarily reflected in other changes in H_4-folate metabolism. Raunio and Hakala (*472*), for example, found a total lack of correlation between H_4-folate dehydrogenase activity and the activities of five other enzymes of H_4-folate metabolism in cultured Sarcoma 180 cells and two amethopterin-resistant sublines. Bertino *et al.* (*473*), with human leukocytes, and Sartorelli *et al.* (*474*), with Ehrlich ascites tumor cells, also observed no such correlation with cell populations which differed by up to 30-fold in their H_4-folate dehydrogenase activities. In contrast Sotobayashi *et al.* (*475*) measured large differences in the content of several H_4-folate coenzymes in two rat tumors that had similar dehydrogenase activities. Thus the physiological significance of excess amounts of this enzyme may well be questioned.

In contrast low or limiting amounts of H_4-folate dehydrogenase have been observed to limit the availability of H_4-folate and its coenzymes in several different situations. Lieberman and Ove (*323*), for example, have shown that primary cultures of rabbit liver, kidney, and lung required very high concentrations of folate in the medium (2×10^{-3} mM) for optimum growth compared with those required, for example, by HeLa cells (1×10^{-5} mM) (*476*). This high folate requirement could be replaced completely by adenine plus thymidine but not by either alone. The authors suggested that these primary cultures may not be able to reduce efficiently the supplied folate to the tetrahydro level.

Similar results were found in studies of primary monkey kidney cells (*322, 476*). These cultures required glycine for growth in the presence of low concentrations of folate, but use of 5-formyl H_4-folate instead of folate supported optimal growth and eliminated the requirement for glycine. Again, H_4-folate dehydrogenase activity was believed to be a limiting factor.

Finally, Walters (*477*) has reported a case of human megaloblastic anemia in which there were indications of folate deficiency but which was unaffected by treatment with normal doses of folate. However, the condition was alleviated by treatment with either very large doses of folate or by small amounts of 5-formyl H_4-folate. Assays of H_4-folate dehydrogenase in liver biopsy material indicated that its activity was reduced approximately 65% in this patient.

Inhibition by Folate Analogs. Inhibitors of H_4-folate dehydrogenase cause marked decreases in concentrations of H_4-folate coenzymes and consequent inhibition of purine biosynthesis. Studies with such drugs will be discussed at length in Chapter 8.

Synthesis of H_4-Folate Coenzymes. The preceding section has established that metabolic or nutritional alterations that result in a lowered concentration of H_4-folate, for whatever reason, usually result in diminished purine biosynthesis. The formation of the various coenzyme forms of H_4-folate must be considered next together with metabolic abnormalities that affect these reactions and their effects on the purine biosynthetic pathway.

Table 4-5. Biosynthesis of One-Carbon Units and H_4-Folate Coenzymes

Serine + H_4-Folate → 5,10-Methylene H_4-folate + Glycine

Glycine + H_4-Folate $\xrightarrow{\text{NAD}}$ 5,10-Methylene H_4-folate + CO_2 + NH_3

Formate + H_4-Folate → 10-Formyl H_4-folate

Histidine → Formiminoglutamate $\xrightarrow{H_4\text{-Folate}}$ 5-Formimino H_4-folate + Glutamate

Xanthine → Formiminoglycine $\xrightarrow{H_4\text{-Folate}}$ 5-Formimino H_4-folate + Glycine

δ-Aminolevulinate → "One-carbon"-H_4-folate

Valine → α-Keto-β-carboxyisocaproate → "One-carbon"-H_4-folate

Methionine → Formaldehyde → Formate

Methylated compounds → Formaldehyde → Formate

Glyoxylate → CO_2 + Formate

Tryptophan → Formylkynurenine → Formate

Pyruvate → Acetyl phosphate + Formate

Table 4-5 lists the reactions by which H_4-folate coenzymes are known to be formed and also several sources of one-carbon units for which reactions have not yet been worked out in detail. Reactions in which free formate is formed are also included.

Most, but not all, of these potential sources of one-carbon units for the synthesis of H_4-folate have in one system or another been shown to provide material to be incorporated into purines. The relative importance of these pathways for purine synthesis does vary considerably, however. The relative importance of the alternative pathways for purine synthesis will be discussed next.

IMPORTANCE OF SERINE. Serine is generally regarded as the major source of one-carbon units in most organisms. The early work which has led to this conclusion has been reviewed by Meister (*156*, p. 636) and Blakley (*281*, p. 267) and will not be repeated here.

Newman and Magasanik (*478*) have calculated that one gram dry weight of *Escherichia coli* has required the synthesis of 1.17 mmoles of serine just for the formation of H_4-coenzymes. This is distributed as follows: 0.92 mmole of serine C-3 for purines, 0.05 mmole for histidine, 0.18 mmole for methionine, and 0.02 mmole for thymine.

The pathways of serine biosynthesis from glucose and the intermediates of the glycolytic pathway have been discussed above. That glucose is an effective source of one-carbon units for purine synthesis has been shown both with microorganisms and animals. Thus in *Escherichia coli* grown for one hour with glucose-^{14}C, 49% of the radioactivity in nucleic acid guanine was in the C-2 plus C-8 positions (*317*, p. 296). In a study with chickens, Rieder (*479*) showed that 50% of the radioactivity in uric acid excreted following administration of glucose-1-^{14}C was in C-2 plus C-8, and the specific activity of the uric acid was at some times about the same as that of blood glucose.

Radioactivity from serine labeled in the C-3 position is naturally also readily incorporated into nucleic acid purines in *Escherichia coli* (*317*, p. 302; *480*; *481*; *482*), *Mycobacterium tuberculosis* $H_{37}R_v$ (*483*), and mouse liver and hepatoma (*484*). Elwyn and Sprinson (*286*) have also demonstrated the conversion of serine-3-^{14}C into excreted uric acid in pigeons; most of the radioactivity was in C-2 and C-8.

Cheeseman and Crosbie (*480*) have reported that when *Escherichia coli* was grown in a glucose-salts medium containing 0.03 m*M* serine-3-^{14}C the purine C-2 and C-8 positions were labeled equally. Addition of formate, however, suppressed incorporation of radioactivity, but only into the C-8 position. When 2.9 m*M* serine-^{14}C was used, 75 to 90% of the radioactivity in the purine ring was in C-2 and zero to 20% in C-8.

Pyridoxine Deficiency. As discussed above for glycine synthesis, the serine hydroxymethyltransferase reaction requires pyridoxal-phosphate. Trakatellis and Axelrad (*485*) have shown that the conversion of radioactivity from serine-3-^{14}C into whole nucleic acids of liver and spleen was considerably decreased in pyridoxine-deficient rats. Such animals also possessed fewer cells and less DNA per unit weight of spleen tissue than control animals. Takami *et al.* (*337*) have also studied the incorporation of serine-3-^{14}C into nucleic acid purines in livers of pyridoxine-deficient weaning rats under conditions in which liver pyridoxal-phosphate concentrations were reduced as much as 70%. This treatment did not alter serine hydroxymethyltransferase activity as assayed in liver extracts but caused a severe drop in that of serine dehydratase. As a consequence the serine concentrations of liver rose about 30%, and the authors attributed the apparent inhibition of incorporation of radioactivity into DNA purines more to dilution of the precursor than to inhibition of its conversion to 5,10-methylene H_4-folate.

Serine hydroxymethyltransferase is also inhibited by 5-methyl H_4-folate and by 5-formyl H_4-folate (*486*), although it is not known whether this is of any physiological significance.

IMPORTANCE OF FORMATE. Formate itself has been found to be a precursor of the C-2 and C-8 positions of purines in all animal systems tested. Detailed references would therefore not be especially useful.

Variable results have been reported with microorganisms, however. In early studies Bergmann *et al.* (*433*) found that addition of formate to sulfonamide-inhibited *Escherichia coli* cultures did not alter the accumulation of aminoimidazole carboxamide, but it was suggested (*210*) that the formate may be destroyed by the active formic hydrogenlyase of this organism. Roberts *et al.* (*317*, p. 301), however, found that formate-^{14}C was well used by *Escherichia coli* and that purine synthesis was almost its sole metabolic fate. Anomolous labeling of purines by formate in this bacterium was found by other investigators (*482*), who also studied its incorporation into thymine. In *Escherichia coli* B/1,5 formate-^{14}C was used for purine synthesis, but it did not label the serine C-3 position. Most was oxidized to CO_2, which was subsequently fixed *via* the Krebs cycle.

Formate was well used for purine synthesis by *Candida utilis* (*487*), *Pasteurella multicida* (*62*), and *Aerobacter aerogenes* (*488*), but it was not a very good precursor in *Mycobacterium tuberculosis* $H_{37}R_v$ (*483*) and *Pseudomonas fluorescens* (*488*).

Formaldehyde was utilized for purine synthesis by *Escherichia coli* somewhat less well (66%) than was formate (*317*, p. 301).

Sources of Formate. Formate (as contrasted with "formate" used as a general term for one-carbon units) has few known biological precursors, and their significance for H_4-folate coenzyme synthesis has really not been evaluated.

In microorganisms the main source of formate is thought to be the so-called phosphoroclastic cleavage of pyruvate to acetyl CoA plus formate, catalyzed by pyruvate formate-lyase.

Studies of this process have been reviewed by McCormick (*489, 490*); however the enzyme involved has so far been reported to occur only in *Esche-*

$$\underset{\text{Pyruvate}}{\begin{matrix}COO^- \\ | \\ C{=}O \\ | \\ CH_3\end{matrix}} \longrightarrow \underset{\text{Acetyl-CoA}}{H_3C{-}\overset{\overset{\displaystyle O}{\|}}{C}{-}CoA} + \underset{\text{Formate}}{HCOO^-}$$

richia coli, Streptococcus faecalis, and *Micrococcus lactilyticus.* Recent work by Nakayama *et al.* (*491*) has indicated that a multienzyme complex takes part in the reaction.

Formate has been known for many years to be excreted in animal urine in fairly significant amounts, and as early as 1913 the amount excreted was found to vary with diet (*492*).

Because availability of H_4-folate for coenzyme formation decreases in dietary folate deficiency (and as described below in cobalamin deficiency), urinary excretion of formate increases in these conditions because it cannot be utilized normally (*493, 494, 495*). Thus Stokstad *et al.* (*494*) have reported a normal formate excretion in rats of 23 μmoles per kg body weight per day; this increased to 1810 μmoles per day on a folate-deficient diet and to 730 μmoles per kg per day on a cobalamin-deficient diet.

One source of free formate in animals is methyl groups. Thus urinary formate excretion increased in rats after administration of large amounts of sarcosine, methionine, and choline (*496*). Liver microsomal oxidases convert the methyl group of a variety of compounds, including methionine (*497*) and sarcosine (*496*), to formaldehyde, which can easily be oxidized to formate. A considerable amount of the formate thus formed is further oxidized to carbon dioxide, and the relative contribution to urinary formate of this route is not known.

Another and perhaps more important source of formate in animals is tryptophan catabolism *via* formylkynurenine (shown opposite).

Rabinowitz and Tabor (*495*) showed that urinary excretion of formate rose from 1.9 to 39 μmoles after administration of 400 μmoles of tryptophan to rats receiving a normal diet and from 39 to 182 μmoles when the rats were fed a folate-deficient diet. The relative importance for purine biosynthesis of this pathway does not appear to have been studied.

Weinhouse and Friedmann (*496*), by studies of the urinary excretion of formate in the rat, estimated that the total production of free formate in these animals was 50 to 100 μmoles per hour. They point out that this is very small in proportion to the *ca.* 10,000 μmoles of CO_2 formed in the same period. Because the amount of formate actually excreted in urine is much less than this figure, most must be metabolized by conversion to 10-formyl H_4-folate and to carbon dioxide.

NH_3^+ — $CH_2—CH—COO^-$ $\xrightarrow{O_2}$ $C(=O)—CH_2—CH(NH_3^+)—COO^-$, $N(H)—CHO$ $\xrightarrow{H_2O}$

Tryptophan — Formylkynurenine

$C(=O)—CH_2—CH(NH_3^+)—COO^-$, NH_2 + $HCOO^-$

Kynurenine — Formate

Anomalous Use of Formate. Although some studies have reported that added formate-^{14}C led to equal labeling of positions C-2 and C-8 in *Saccharomyces cerevisiae* (*498*) and *Escherichia coli* (*317*, p. 301), other investigators have reported unequal labeling of these positions in the same organisms. Thus Koch and Levy (*481*) found with *Escherichia coli* B/1,5 that formate-^{14}C labeled the purine ring so that 3.5% was in C-2 and 19.7% was in C-8. The serine C-3 position was not labeled. In another study with *Escherichia coli* Nester and Spizizen (*482*) found that formate labeled adenine more than it did thymine (18,300 to 100) whereas serine-3-^{14}C gave more equal labeling (9,400 to 5,720) of these compounds. When serine-3-^{14}C was substrate, positions C-2 and C-8 were equally labeled, but when formate-^{14}C was used, the labeling ratio in these positions was 1:10. Similar results were reported by Cheeseman and Crosbie (*480*). In *Aerobacter aerogenes* formate also labeled C-8 almost exclusively (*488*).

Cheeseman and Crosbie (*480*) have concluded from studies mentioned here and previously that during normal growth of *Escherichia coli* in a glucose-salts medium serine is initially the sole source of one-carbon units and that as growth proceeds formate arising from pyruvate becomes an increasingly important source of the purine C-8. Newman (*499*) has recently also begun to study some of the anomalies of formate utilization, using serine-glycine-formate auxotrophs of *Escherichia coli.* She also found that formate was not a precursor of either serine or glycine but was incorporated well into purines. Serine in turn was the precursor of some but not all of the glycine formed. The possibility was suggested that formate might activate an otherwise nonfunctional enzyme of serine biosynthesis, although direct evidence was not obtained for this hypothesis.

Varying ratios of labeling of positions C-2 and C-8 have also been reported in animal cells *in vitro* but not *in vivo*. Thus formate labeled positions C-2 and C-8 of excreted uric acid equally in pigeons (*500, 501*), in chick visceral nucleic acid guanine (*502*), and in rat liver and pooled visceral nucleic acid purines (*443, 503*). The labeling pattern was the same in rat viscera in folate deficiency induced by sulfonamides (*443*).

The situation is much more complicated in studies with animal tissue preparations *in vitro*. Buchanan and Wilson (*504*) observed that, although the normal ratio of incorporation of formate to that of glycine in a fortified pigeon liver extract system was 2:1, under some conditions this ratio was much higher. Thus in experiments in which inosinate was present during the incubation, the incorporation ratio was 166:1, although there was very little net synthesis of inosinate. When bicarbonate was omitted, the ratio was 8:1, although again there was little net purine synthesis. Furthermore, addition of 5-formyl H_4-folate in the absence of bicarbonate stimulated labeling by formate threefold. It would appear that in the absence of net purine synthesis the reactions between added or endogenous inosinate and phosphoribosyl-aminoimidazole carboxamide shuttled back and forth with the consequent incorporation of formate-^{14}C (*via* 10-formyl H_4-folate) into the C-2 position without corresponding incorporation either of glycine-^{14}C or of formate-^{14}C into C-8. That this may occur in intact cells was suggested by observations of Thomson *et al.* (*69, 73*). These workers incubated Ehrlich ascites tumor cells *in vitro* with formate-^{14}C in the absence of glucose so that little net purine synthesis occurred; the ratio of radioactivity in C-2 to that in C-8 ranged between 2.5:1 and 10:1. In contrast, when these cells were incubated with glucose, the ratio of incorporation of formate and of glycine (which would be equivalent to that of formate into C-8) was 2:1 (*71*), as it was in bone marrow where purine biosynthesis proceeds without an exogenous supply of glucose (*73*).

The Enzyme 10-Formyl H_4-Folate Synthetase. This enzyme is required for the utilization of formate, and its immediate product is a substrate of phosphoribosyl-aminoimidazole carboxamide formyltransferase.

$$H_4\text{-Folate} + HCOO^- \xrightarrow[\text{synthetase}]{\text{10-Formyl } H_4\text{-folate}} \text{10-Formyl } H_4\text{-folate}$$

H_4-Folate   Formate   10-Formyl H_4-folate

It is widely distributed in animal cells (*505*) and appears in higher levels in immature and malignant cells than in well differentiated cells (*471*). In *Lactobacillus casei* (*464*) and *Streptococcus thermophilus* (*506*) the activity of the synthetase rose at the beginning of the lag phase, reached a peak early in the exponential phase, and then declined to reach the original level during the stationary phase. According to Nurmikko *et al.* (*506*) two peaks of activity were observed during exponential phase growth in *Streptococcus faecalis* whereas Albrecht and Hutchison (*469*) reported that it was formed as a constant fraction of the total protein synthesized during growth in this organism.

The level of activity of 10-formyl H_4-folate synthetase in bacteria was markedly dependent on the composition of the medium, even at a given stage of growth. Thus its specific activity could be increased 10-fold by addition of formate to cultures of *Micrococcus aerogenes* (*505, 507*); the enzyme from this source was also activated by ammonium ion which both stabilized it and lowered the Michaelis constant for formate 10-fold (*508*). In the presence of folate up to $1.4 \times 10^{-9}M$, enzyme activity increased as much as twofold in *Lactobacillus casei* (*464*). Nurmikko *et al.* (*506*) found that enzyme activity decreased when *Streptococcus faecalis* was grown with thymine whereas Albrecht and Hutchison (*469*) observed no effect of thymine or uracil in their strain of this organism.

Johnson and Hutchison (*509*) showed that the activity of 10-formyl H_4-folate synthetase in an amethopterin-resistant strain of *Streptococcus faecalis* was eightfold to 10-fold that of the wild type and that this increase in activity could be correlated with the drug resistance observed. In the absence of added purine this strain required for growth only 25% as much folate as did the wild type, and 8000 times as much amethopterin was required for equivalent inhibition of growth. It was concluded that this line of resistant cells was more efficient than the wild type in the use of folate for purine biosynthesis *de novo* and that the elevated synthetase activity contributed to this advantage.

This elevated enzyme activity was repressed to the level of the wild-type cells by the addition of adenine, hypoxanthine, or guanine to the culture medium before growth commenced, and the normal increase in activity during growth could be stopped at any time by the addition of purines. When low concentrations of purines were added, enzyme activity began to increase when the purine had been exhausted (*469, 510*).

Bertino and Hillcoat (*471*) were not able to inhibit the synthetase from mammalian cells by addition of high concentrations of purine nucleotides. However, Slavikova *et al.* (*511*) have reported that β-4-methoxybenzoyl-β-bromoacrylic acid was a potent inhibitor of this enzyme in a pigeon liver extract system fortified to synthesize purines; purine biosynthesis was inhibited as a consequence.

Importance of Histidine. Histidine breakdown in animal cells proceeds by the pathway shown in Figure 4-2. The 5-formimino H_4-folate formed may be converted to 5,10-methenyl H_4-folate and thence to other folate cofactors, and it may thereby be used for purine biosynthesis. Thus both urinary uric acid and allantoin were found to be labeled following administration of histidine-2-^{14}C to rats (*512, 513, 514*). All of the label in uric acid was in the C-2 and C-8 positions. Sprinson and Rittenberg (*515*) gave histidine-2-^{14}C and formate-^{13}C simultaneously to pigeons. In the excreted uric acid 84% of the ^{14}C and 91% of the ^{13}C was in the C-2 and C-8 positions. These workers also showed that histidine labeled the adenine and guanine of pooled visceral RNA in the rat; labeling of acid-soluble and nucleic acid purines of mouse liver and hepatoma has also been demonstrated by Parshin *et al.* (*484*) and by Reid *et al.* (*516*) after injection of radioactive histidine. Despite these observations histidine is generally believed to be a quantitatively minor source of one-carbon moieties in animals.

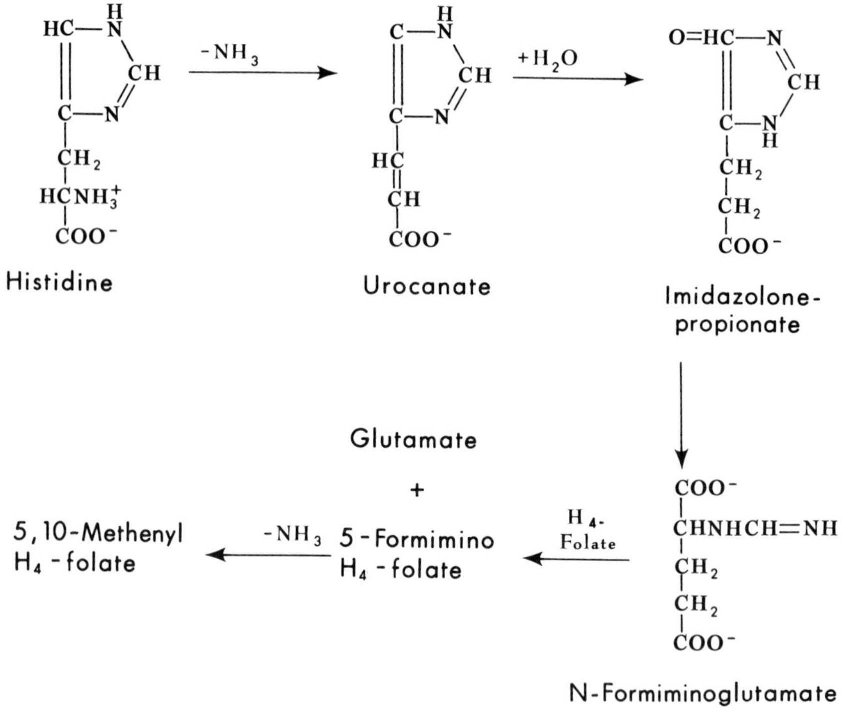

Histidine $\xrightarrow{-NH_3}$ Urocanate $\xrightarrow{+H_2O}$ Imidazolone-propionate $\rightarrow$ N-Formiminoglutamate $\xrightarrow{H_4\text{-Folate}}$ Glutamate + 5-Formimino H_4-folate $\xrightarrow{-NH_3}$ 5,10-Methenyl H_4-folate

Figure 4-2. Histidine breakdown

Groth *et al.* (*517*), however, have recently reported that the alkylating agent 1,3-bis(2-chloroethyl)-1-nitrosourea inhibited the incorporation of radioactivity from histidine-2-^{14}C into nucleic acid purines in leukemic cells, increased the excretion of formiminoglutamate, and decreased the excretion of aminoimidazole carboxamide in patients. It was suggested that this drug inhibited either formiminoglutamate formiminotransferase or 5,10-methenyl H_4-folate cyclodeaminase. The apparent rate of incorporation of formate-^{14}C into nucleic acid purines was markedly increased, probably because reduced purine nucleotide pools led to diminished dilution of specific activity.

Ravel and Magasanik (*488*) studied the conversion of catabolic products of histidine metabolism in several microorganisms that metabolize histidine differently. *Aerobacter aerogenes* 1033 and *Salmonella typhimurium* 10136 form formamide as one endproduct, and no radioactivity from histidine was found in purines in these cells. In contrast, *Pseudomonas fluorescens* 6 and *Pseudomonas aeruginosa* convert histidine in part to formate, and in these organisms histidine was used almost without dilution for purine synthesis. In *Pseudomonas fluorescens,* histidine-2-^{14}C gave preferential labeling to C-8 (*488*).

Formiminotransferase (EC 2.1.2.5) Deficiency. In this disease the conversion of formiminoglutamate, derived from the breakdown of histidine, to 5-formimino H_4-folate is retarded. Arakawa *et al.* (*518, 519, 520*) have studied four such patients in whom this enzyme activity, when measured in liver biopsy material, was decreased approximately 50% but was in no case completely absent. Other reactions of H_4-folate metabolism were unchanged. Urinary excretion of aminoimidazole carboxamide was noted to be elevated approximately fivefold to 10-fold in such patients, and the amount excreted following administration of a loading dose of this compound was increased about threefold to fivefold (*520, 521, 522*). Further study (*523*) showed that the activity of phosphoribosyl-aminoimidazole carboxamide formyltransferase in erythrocytes of patients with formiminotransferase deficiency was normal. The conclusion was drawn that purine biosynthesis *de novo* was inhibited due to a shortage of 10-formyl H_4-folate.

IMPORTANCE OF GLYCINE. Glycine may not only be incorporated intact into the C-4, C-5, and N-7 positions of the purine ring but may also be converted to H_4-folate coenzymes which are used for the C-2 and C-8 positions.

Conversion to One-Carbon Units. The most important reaction by which glycine can be converted to one-carbon units is the following:

$$\text{Glycine} + H_4\text{-Folate} + \text{NAD} \underset{}{\overset{\text{Pyridoxal-P}}{\rightleftharpoons}} \text{5,10-Methylene } H_4\text{-folate} + \text{NADH} + CO_2 + NH_4^+$$

Because this reaction is reversible, it may also serve as a route of glycine biosynthesis, and in such a case the 5,10-methylene H_4-folate may be derived from serine *via* the serine hydroxymethyltransferase reaction (*524*). The 5,10-methylene H_4-folate produced from glycine may of course also react with another molecule of glycine to form serine, also *via* the serine hydroxymethyltransferase reaction (*343*). This reaction is found both in animals and microorganisms; it is discussed further by Blakley (*281*, p. 283) and Meister (*156*, p. 636).

Another pathway is also believed to occur at least in animal liver but is probably of little significance:

$$\text{Glycine} \longrightarrow \text{Glyoxylate} \longrightarrow \text{Formate} + CO_2$$

The formate so formed may be utilized as described previously. A number of studies with *Escherichia coli* (*e.g., 343, 525*) have indicated that glyoxylate is not a good source of one-carbon units in this organism.

Early evidence for the relationship of one or both of these pathways to purine metabolism was provided by the observation that following the administration of glycine-2-^{14}C to pigeons the C-2 plus C-8 positions of excreted uric acid contained almost half as much radioactivity as did C-5 (*526*). Twenty-five percent of the radioactivity in urinary uric acid excreted by human subjects following administration of glycine-2-^{14}C was also in the C-2 plus C-8 positions (*377*). Labeling of hypoxanthine *via* the glycine decarboxylase system has also been observed in avian liver extracts (*527*).

In subsequent studies Edmonds *et al.* (*528*) showed that the use of the same precursor led to considerable labeling of C-2 of nucleic acid purines in *Saccharomyces cerevisiae* (the C-8 was not isolated). Roberts *et al.* (*317*, p. 303) found that growth of *Escherichia coli* with glycine-2-^{14}C led to almost equal labeling of C-4 plus C-5 and C-2 plus C-8. Labeling of purine C-2 plus C-8 positions from glycine-2-^{14}C was also demonstrated with *Pseudomonas fluorescens* and *Aerobacter aerogenes* (*488*). Finally, Malathi and Ramakrishnan (*483*) found that growth of *Mycobacterium tuberculosis* $H_{37}R_v$ with serine-3-^{14}C led to labeling of the purine C-2 plus C-8 positions that was fivefold greater than when an equal concentration and specific activity of glycine was used.

Anomalous Labeling. Growth with glycine-2-^{14}C led to equal labeling of positions C-2 and C-8 in *Aerobacter aerogenes* and *Pseudomonas fluorescens* (*488*), *Mycobacterium tuberculosis* $H_{37}R_v$ (*483*), and *Escherichia coli* (*484*). Further studies with wild-type *Escherichia coli* showed, however, that at low concentrations of glycine-^{14}C the C-2 position was preferentially labeled whereas C-2 and C-8 were equally labeled when high glycine concentrations were used (*529*). This is in contrast to the results obtained when a serine-glycine auxotroph, *Escherichia coli* PA 15, was grown with 6.7 m*M* glycine-2-^{14}C (*480, 530*); in this case 51% of the purine radioactivity was in C-2 with less than 2% in C-8. The interpretation of these results is discussed below.

Regulation of the Conversion of Glycine to One-Carbon Units. The use of glycine as a one-carbon source in microorganisms varies with growth conditions. As just mentioned, Koch (*529*) found that in *Escherichia coli* B/1,5 the purine C-8 was labeled (in addition to C-5) at low concentrations of glycine-2-^{14}C, but at high glycine concentrations the labeling of C-2, C-8, and C-5 was equal and of the same specific activity as the precursor. Tracer amounts of glycine-2-^{14}C labeled C-5 only. Bull and Woods (*531*) observed that the utilization of the glycine C-2 as a one-carbon source (in this case for the methyl group of methionine) was repressed in the presence of serine in the serine-glycine auxotroph *Escherichia coli* PA 15. Similarly other serine-glycine auxotrophs required adaptation when transferred from media containing either serine plus formate or formate alone to media containing glycine (*478*). This suggests that the glycine-cleaving system was repressed by formate or some derivative of serine. In another study of serine-glycine auxotrophs of *Escherichia coli* Pizer (*343*) found that in the absence of serine, the preferred source of one-carbon units, most of the one-carbon units came from sources other than the C-2 of glycine.

Arnstein and Neuberger (*318*) noted that the conversion of the C-2 of glycine to the C-3 of serine was greatly increased in the rat when the dietary level of glycine was increased, and the C-2 of glycine was an important source of serine only when fed at abnormally high levels. It therefore seemed that endogenously synthesized glycine was not extensively converted to H_4-folate coenzymes. This conclusion is supported by the observation that the conversion of glycine C-2 to urinary formate was considerably less than that of other one-carbon unit precursors (*496*).

Inherited Abnormalities. The inherited human disease called non-ketogenic hyperglycinemia appears to involve a deficiency in the enzyme which converts glycine to 5,10-methylene H_4-folate, carbon dioxide, and ammonia. This defect has been demonstrated by studies of the metabolism of radioactive glycine in the whole patient and in homogenates of liver biopsies (*532–536*). Both serine dehydratase and serine hydroxymethyltransferase activities were normal. These results certainly indicate that the glycine decarboxylase reaction is quantitatively a very important pathway of glycine catabolism in man as well as an important source of one-carbon units. De Groot *et al.* (*535*) treated several patients with this disease with a diet free of serine and glycine but supplemented with methionine as an alternative one-carbon source. Blood glycine levels declined only when extra methionine was fed, and the workers suggested that this was the result of less demand on the serine-glycine pathways as sources of one-carbon units. However, direct demonstration of this point still is lacking.

Relief of Glycine Toxicity. Consumption of large amounts of glycine is toxic to animals, and there is suggestive evidence that its conversion to one-carbon units may be an important route of its detoxification. Studies of glycine toxicity have also shown that the extent of detoxification, if this is what is happening, is strongly influenced by the availability of the vitamin substrates and cofactors of the glycine decarboxylase reaction. Thus in mammals administration of folate counteracts most of the toxic effects of excess glycine in that it restores the growth rate of rats, lowers blood amino nitrogen and urinary creatinine to normal, and restores liver fat to normal (*351, 352, 353, 357, 537*). Preventive treatment with folate prevents the normal rise in muscle creatine concentrations (*351*).

Machlin *et al.* (*305*) observed that blood uric acid concentrations of chicks rose from 4 to 8.6 mg per 100 ml when the diet was supplemented with 6% glycine. Administration of extra folate reduced this value to 6.1 mg per 100 ml.

Supplementation of diets with cobalamin (*538, 539*), pyridoxine (*540*), riboflavin (*541*), and niacin (*542*) also helped to relieve glycine toxicity. Richert *et al.* (*543*) have observed that the decarboxylation of glycine-1-^{14}C in homogenates of pigeon liver was impaired when birds were fed diets deficient in folate, pyridoxine, or niacin.

IMPORTANCE OF δ-AMINOLEVULINATE. The δ carbon of δ-aminolevulinate, an intermediate in porphyrin biosynthesis, is derived from the α-carbon of glycine. Nemeth *et al.* (*544*) showed that this carbon of δ-aminolevulinate was converted to one-carbon units in duck erythrocytes and in pigeons, and thence it was incorporated into purines. Thus the specific activity of the C-2 of nucleic acid guanine of the erythrocytes labeled from δ-aminolevulinate-5-^{14}C was half that labeled from glycine-2-^{14}C. In uric acid formed by pigeons most of the radioactivity was in positions C-2 plus C-8. The conversion of this compound to the C-2 plus C-8 positions of urinary uric acid has also been demonstrated with human subjects (*376*).

Braunshtein *et al.* (*545*) also demonstrated the conversion of C-5 of δ-aminolevulinate to nucleic acid purines of liver and excreted uric acid in pigeons. In homogenates of pigeon liver in which δ-aminolevulinate-5-^{14}C replaced formate in a purine biosynthetic system both inosinate and the product of its catabolism, hypoxanthine, were labeled. These workers also

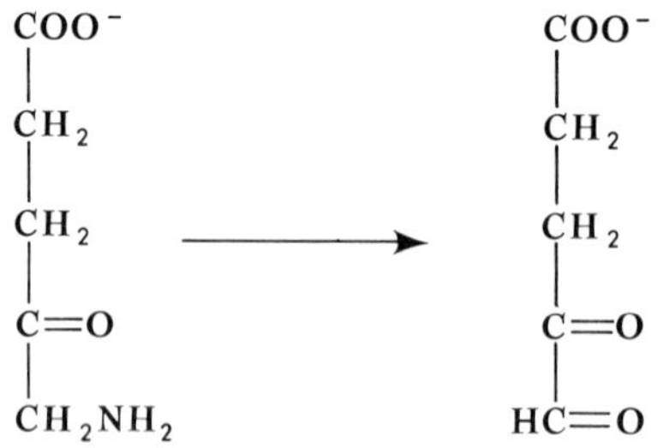

COO^- — CH_2 — CH_2 — $C{=}O$ — CH_2NH_2 ⟶ COO^- — CH_2 — CH_2 — $C{=}O$ — $HC{=}O$

δ-Aminolevulinate 4,5-Dioxyvalerate

showed that cycloserine and isonicotinic hydrazide, inhibitors of transamination (*546*), abolished conversion of labeled precursor into nucleic acid purines *in vivo* and reduced radioactivity in excreted uric acid to 40 to 50% of control values. These compounds were also inhibitory in homogenates. These results were taken to indicate that δ-aminolevulinate was deaminated before the C-5 was removed. This point was subsequently demonstrated directly by Spryshkova and Poznaskaya (*547*), who showed not only that radioactivity from the product of deamination, 4-5-dioxyvaleric acid-5-^{14}C, was incorporated into purines more efficiently than was δ-aminolevulinate but also that cycloserine and isonicotinic hydrazide had no effect on this process. However, further details of this metabolic pathway are not known.

Importance of Methionine. Malathi and Ramakrishnan (*483*) showed that growth of *Mycobacterium tuberculosis* $H_{37}R_v$ with methionine-methyl-^{14}C led to very little labeling of nucleotide adenine and guanine. It was a much poorer precursor than was formate.

Sime and Johnson (*548*) studied the conversion of methionine-methyl-^{14}C to uric acid in the chick. About 9% of the injected methionine radioactivity was found in the uric acid, which had a specific activity 0.1% that of the precursor. Almost all (92.6%) of the uric acid radioactivity was in positions C-2 plus C-8; 56% was in C-2, and 36% in C-8. The methionine methyl group presumably is converted to formaldehyde and then to formate.

Importance of Other Pathways. Webb (*435*) has demonstrated that valine-1-^{14}C was converted into one-carbon units in *Aerobacter aerogenes* and that nucleic acid adenine, guanine, and thymine were labeled; the specific activities of the purines were about twice that of thymine. The following is believed to be the general pathway followed; the physiological significance of this route is probably small.

$$\underset{\text{Valine}}{{}^{-}OOC{-}CH(NH_3^+){-}CH(CH_3){-}CH_3} \longrightarrow \underset{\alpha\text{-Keto-}\beta\text{-carboxy-isocaproate}}{{}^{-}OOC{-}C({=}O){-}CH(COO^-){-}CH(CH_3)_2} \longrightarrow C_1\text{-UNIT} + \underset{\alpha\text{-Keto-isocaproate}}{{}^{-}OOC{-}C({=}O){-}CH_2{-}CH(CH_3)_2}$$

Finally, Decker *et al.* (*549*) have shown that *Clostridium kluyveri* converted $^{14}CO_2$ into the methyl group of methionine and into the C-2 and C-8 positions of the purine ring. The process furnished 70% of the carbon used for these two positions, acetate providing the remainder. These workers postulated that CO_2 was reduced to formate which then proceeded through the one-carbon pool in the usual manner.

LIMITATION OF PURINE SYNTHESIS BY AVAILABILITY OF ONE-CARBON SOURCES. That not only H_4-folate but also one-carbon moieties may be limiting for purine biosynthesis in bacteria was again suggested by early studies. Thus Williams *et al.* (*550,* p. 202) reported that for some bacteria (unnamed) the addition of formate could enhance the ability of aminoimidazole carboxamide to serve as a purine substitute. They later reported that the ability of cell suspensions of *Lactobacillus arabinosus* to utilize aminoimidazole carboxamide depended not only on glucose and phosphate but also on formate (*319*). Simliarly under certain conditions formate seemed to be more rate limiting for utilization of aminoimidazole carboxamide in *Saccharomyces cerevisiae* than was the concentration of this base (*498*). Formate limitation for purine biosynthesis may also explain the finding of Bergmann *et al.* (*551*) that 4-formamido-imidazole 5-carboxamide was twice as effective as aminoimidazole carboxamide for supporting growth of purineless mutants of *Escherichia coli.* Because there is reason (from other studies) to believe that the formamido derivative is not utilized as such, it was probably hydrolyzed to formate plus aminoimidazole carboxamide.

Similar but less extensive observations on the limited availability of one-carbon moieties have been made in a few animal systems. Thus 72% of the ureide carbon of newly formed uric acid in pigeons was derived from administered formate-^{13}C (*500, 501*). That serine may not ordinarily supply enough one-carbon units for maximum rates of purine biosynthesis in Ehrlich ascites tumor cells *in vitro* is suggested by the observed stimulation of this pathway when formate was added to the medium (*106,* and J. F. Henderson and L. J. Fontenelle, unpublished studies).

Interconversion of H_4-Folate Coenzymes. One of the H_4-folate coenzymes used for purine biosynthesis *de novo,* 5,10-methenyl H_4-folate, is not formed directly from any of the above-mentioned sources of one-carbon units and must be synthesized from the 5-formimino H_4-folate, 5,10-methylene H_4-folate, and 10-formyl H_4-folate coenzymes formed in other reactions. Similarly the 10-formyl H_4-folate required for purine synthesis can be derived not only directly from formate but also secondarily from other one-carbon sources *via* 5,10-methenyl H_4-folate and 5,10-methylene H_4-folate. These interconversions of the H_4-folate coenzymes will be discussed next.

PATHWAY OF INTERCONVERSION. Figure 4-3 shows the interrelationships among the H_4-folate coenzymes and the pathways by which they are at least potentially interconverted.

REGULATION OF THE PRINCIPAL ENZYMES OF INTERCONVERSION. The two main enzymes to be considered are 5,10-methylene H_4-folate dehydrogenase (EC 1.5.1.5) and 5,10-methenyl H_4-folate cyclohydrolase (EC 3.5.4.9). The 5,10-methylene H_4-folate reductase is irreversible and acts only in

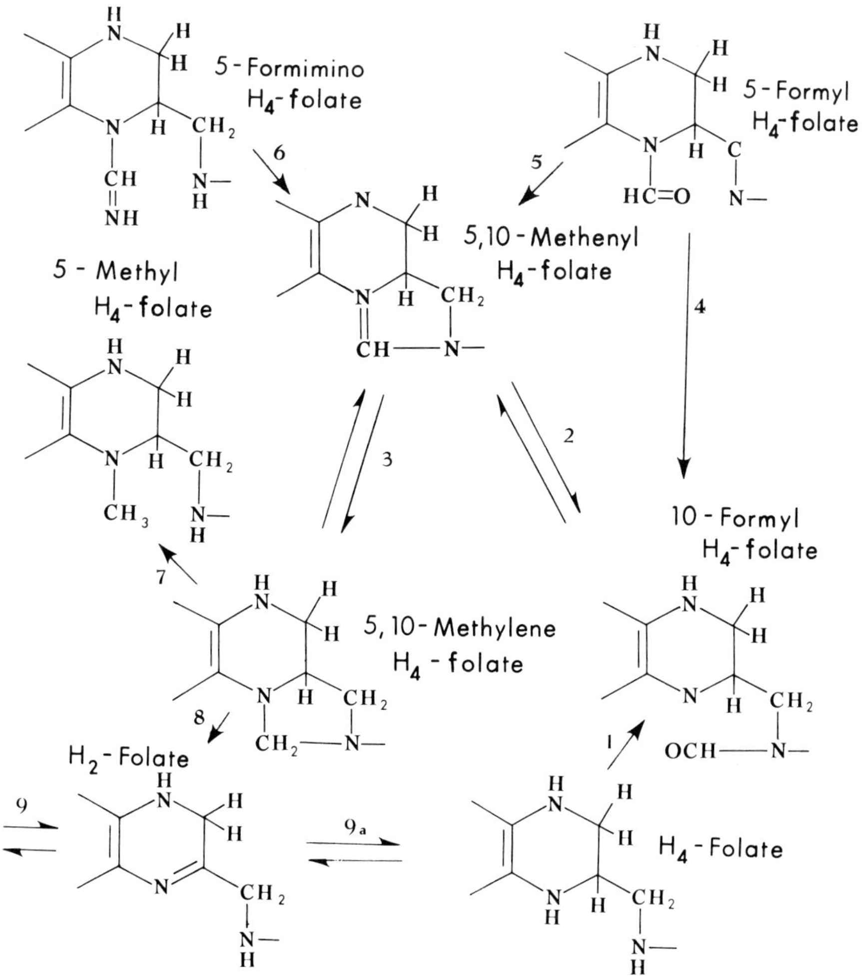

Figure 4-3. Interconversions of folate coenzymes

1.	*Formyl tetrahydrofolate synthetase*	6.3.4.3
2.	*Methenyl tetrahydrofolate cyclohydrolase*	3.5.4.9
3.	*Methylene tetrahydrofolate dehydrogenase*	1.5.1.5
4.	*5-Formyl tetrahydrofolate isomerase*	
5.	*5-Formyl tetrahydrofolate isomerase (cyclodehydrase)*	
6.	*Formimino tetrahydrofolate cyclodeaminase*	4.3.1.4
7.	*5,10-Methylene tetrahydrofolate reductase*	1.1.1.68
8.	*Thymidylate synthetase*	
9.	*Dihydrofolate dehydrogenase*	1.5.1.4
9a.	*Tetrahydrofolate dehydrogenase*	1.5.1.3

methionine biosynthesis. Its regulation is considered below, with the discussion of the effects of methionine and cobalamin on H_4-folate coenzyme availability.

5,10-Methylene H_4-Folate Dehydrogenase. The substrate in one direction of this reversible reaction, 5,10-methylene H_4-folate, is required for the serine-glycine interconversion and for thymidylate synthesis whereas the substrate in the other direction, 5,10-methenyl H_4-folate, is required for the synthesis of phosphoribosyl-formylglycineamide in the pathway of purine biosynthesis *de novo*.

5,10-Methylene H_4-folate + NAD^+ ($NADP^+$) $\rightleftharpoons$ (5,10-Methylene H_4-folate dehydrogenase) 5,10-Methenyl H_4-folate + NADH (NADPH)

The equilibrium of the enzyme from calf thymus favors the synthesis of 5,10-methenyl H_4-folate (*552*), although care must be taken in attempting to extrapolate this observation to the operation of the enzyme in intact cells. The dehydrogenase is widely distributed (*471*) and has greater activity in immature mammalian cells than in those which are well differentiated.

Ohara and Silber (*464*) have observed that the specific activity of the dehydrogenase in *Lactobacillus casei* appeared to have peaks early and late in the period of growth and that the time course of enzyme activity varied greatly with the folate concentration of the medium. Although the interpretation of these results is obscure, in these respects this enzyme differs markedly from H_4-folate dehydrogenase (EC 1.5.1.3) and 10-formyl H_4-folate synthetase (EC 6.3.4.3); in addition the latter enzymes were inhibited by high levels of folate in the medium whereas activity of 5,10-methylene H_4-folate dehydrogenase was stimulated at high folate levels.

Dalal and Gots (*553, 554*) have shown that the 5,10-methylene H_4-folate dehydrogenase from *Salmonella typhimurium* was inhibited by purine ribonucleoside triphosphates, and Taylor *et al.* (*555*) showed that this was also true of the enzyme from a methionine-cobalamin auxotroph of *Escherichia coli.* The *Salmonella* enzyme was inhibited 50% (at high substrate concentrations) by about 0.4 m*M* ATP or GTP but was only one-tenth as sensitive to purine ribonucleoside monophosphates. The enzyme from *Escherichia coli* was much less sensitive, and 1 m*M* ATP or GTP produced only 30 to 35% inhibition under the conditions of the assay. In both cases 20 to 30% of the original activity remained even at high concentrations of purine ribonucleoside triphosphates. In contrast to these results Albrecht *et al.* (*556*) have observed that the dehydrogenase from *Streptococcus faecium* var. *durans* was not inhibited by purine ribonucleotides.

Dalal and Gots (*553*) have speculated that the observed inhibition of 5,10-methylene H_4-folate dehydrogenase by purine ribonucleotides, if this does have physiological significance, may be a means of preventing unnecessary conversion of 5,10-methylene H_4-folate to 5,10-methenyl H_4-folate and 10-formyl H_4-folate, the substrates for purine biosynthesis *de novo.* The retention of some activity even at very high concentrations of purine ribonucleotide inhibitors may be required to provide H_4-folate coenzymes for reactions other than purine biosynthesis.

In *Lactobacillus casei* 5,10-methylene H_4-folate dehydrogenase was repressed when cells were grown in the presence of high (1 m*M*) concentrations of thymine (*464*), and the enzyme from a methionine-cobalamin auxotroph of *Escherichia coli* was repressed 35–45% when inosine or guanosine was added to growth media (*555*); thymidine had no effect. No repression of dehydrogenase activity was observed when wild-type *Salmonella typhimurium* was grown with adenine, and inhibitors of purine biosynthesis *de novo* did not alter this response. In contrast enzyme activity rose twofold to threefold when purine auxotrophs were grown with limiting concentrations of purines (*553*).

Albrecht *et al.* (*556*) have shown that the rate of synthesis of the dehydrogenase was repressed 67% in *Streptococcus faecium* var. *durans* when serine was added to the basal medium which contained glycine, adenine, and folate. Adenine itself had no effect on the synthesis of the enzyme. These authors speculated that when 5,10-methylene H_4-folate is synthesized from serine, less 10-formyl H_4-folate need be converted to it; hence the enzymes required for this interconversion need not be made.

The physiological significance for purine biosynthesis *de novo* of repression of 5,10-methylene H_4-dehydrogenase in a methionine-cobalamin auxotroph of *Escherichia coli* has been suggested by Taylor *et al.* (*555*). In cells grown in the presence of guanosine to give a 45% decrease in dehydrogenase activity there was a 47% decrease in the conversion of radioactivity from serine-3-^{14}C

into total nucleic acids; these results were assumed to reflect an effect on purine biosynthesis and not to be caused by any direct effect of guanosine or its metabolites on the purine biosynthetic pathway itself. These assumptions remain to be verified.

5,10-Methenyl H_4-Folate Cyclohydrolase. Little is known about the regulation of 5,10-methylene H_4-folate cyclohydrolase activity.

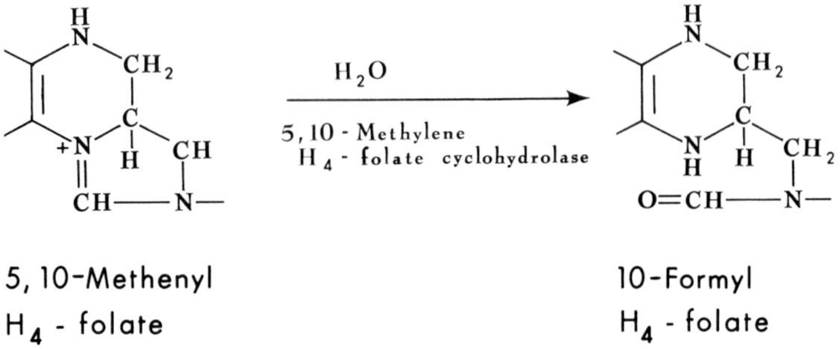

H_2O

5,10 - Methylene H_4 - folate cyclohydrolase

5,10-Methenyl H_4 - folate → 10-Formyl H_4 - folate

This enzyme may serve to furnish 10-formyl H_4-folate from serine, glycine, histidine, or other sources in the absence either of formate or 10-formyl H_4-folate synthetase. Alternatively, it may serve to furnish 5,10-methenyl H_4-folate and other coenzymes in cells which make sufficient 10-formyl H_4-folate.

Albrecht *et al.* (*556*) have reported that addition of serine to culture media leads to repression of the cyclohydrolase in *Streptococcus faecium* var. *durans;* serine hydroxymethyltransferase is also repressed but to a much smaller extent.

PERTURBATION OF COENZYME INTERCONVERSIONS. The interconversion of H_4-folate coenzyme is altered in certain mutant animal, human, and microbial cells, and these reactions may also be involved in some cases of adenine toxicity.

Altered Enzyme Amounts in Ade3 *Mutants of* Saccharomyces Cerevisiae. *Ade3* mutants of *Saccharomyces cerevisiae* require both adenine and histidine for growth (*e.g., 557, 558*), and at limiting concentrations of these nutrients there is an accumulation of phosphoribosyl-aminoimidazole carboxamide (*e.g., 559, 560*); early genetic studies (*561*) led to the conclusion that this locus has a regulatory rather than a structural function.

Although it was first reported (*560*) that phosphoribosyl-aminoimidazole carboxamide formyltransferase was missing in *ade3* mutants, Jones and Magasanik (*562, 563*) later showed by more refined assay procedures that this enzyme activity was present in normal amounts. Instead they found 10-formyl H_4-folate synthetase and 5,10-methenyl H_4-folate cyclohydrolase to be missing and the activity of 5,10-methylene H_4-folate dehydrogenase to be reduced.

These results were confirmed by Nagy *et al.* (*564*), who also found similar changes in enzyme activities in *ade9* mutants of *Schizosaccharomyces pombe.*

Still more recent studies (*565, 566*) using enzyme assays that apparently are more sensitive than those used previously have come to somewhat different conclusions. Lazowski and Luzzati have found, for example, that 10-formyl H_4-folate synthetase activity was reduced from 70.0 to 4.5–10.0 units in different *Saccharomyces cerevisiae ade3* mutants, that cyclohydrolase activity was reduced from 40.8 to 5.2–6.3 units, and the dehydrogenase from 8.2 to 2.5–2.9 units. These investigators also showed that yeast contained two forms of 5,10-methylene H_4-folate dehydrogenase, only one of which was present in *ade3* mutants. Lomax *et al.* (*567*) have suggested that the primary biochemical lesion in these mutants is the loss of this particular dehydrogenase isozyme and that the other changes are secondary to this. Further study is required on this point, however.

Lomax *et al.* (*567*) have also isolated a number of variant *ade3* mutants. Several require only adenine and are designated *ade3(his$^+$)* to distinguish them from the adenine- and histidine-requiring mutants described above, which are designated *ade3(his$^-$)*. Other strains required histidine but not adenine. Supplementation of any of these mutants with adenine plus histidine or adenine plus methionine inhibited growth whereas growth was stimulated if all three compounds were added. The only detectable biochemical difference between *ade3(his$^+$)* and *ade3(his$^-$)* mutants was that the 10-formyl H_4-folate synthetase activity of the former was between 36 and 106% of normal whereas that of the latter was about 10% of normal. These changes in enzyme amounts and their relationship to adenine and histidine synthesis are outlined in Figure 4-4.

Why *ade3* mutants require both adenine and histidine for growth remains to be explained, as well as why, in the absence of these compounds, they accumulate phosphoribosyl-aminoimidazole carboxamide derived from the histidine biosynthetic pathway. Because of decreased levels of 10-formyl H_4-folate synthetase and 5,10-methenyl H_4-folate cyclohydrolase activities in *ade3(his$^-$)* mutants, phosphoribosyl-aminoimidazole carboxamide cannot be converted back to purine nucleotides, and there is consequently a loss of ATP. This process is stopped by the addition of histidine, which exerts feedback inhibition of ATP phosphoribosyltransferase. The requirement for adenine presumably results from lack of H_4-folate coenzymes for the early steps of the purine biosynthetic pathway and from the above-mentioned loss of ATP.

Apparently *ade3(his$^+$)* mutants can synthesize enough 10-formyl H_4-folate to convert phosphoribosyl-aminoimidazole carboxamide back to purine ribonucleotides and hence do not require addition of histidine to shut off the synthesis of this intermediate. Mutants that can grow in histidine alone may have enough 5,10-methylene H_4-folate dehydrogenase and 10-formyl H_4-folate

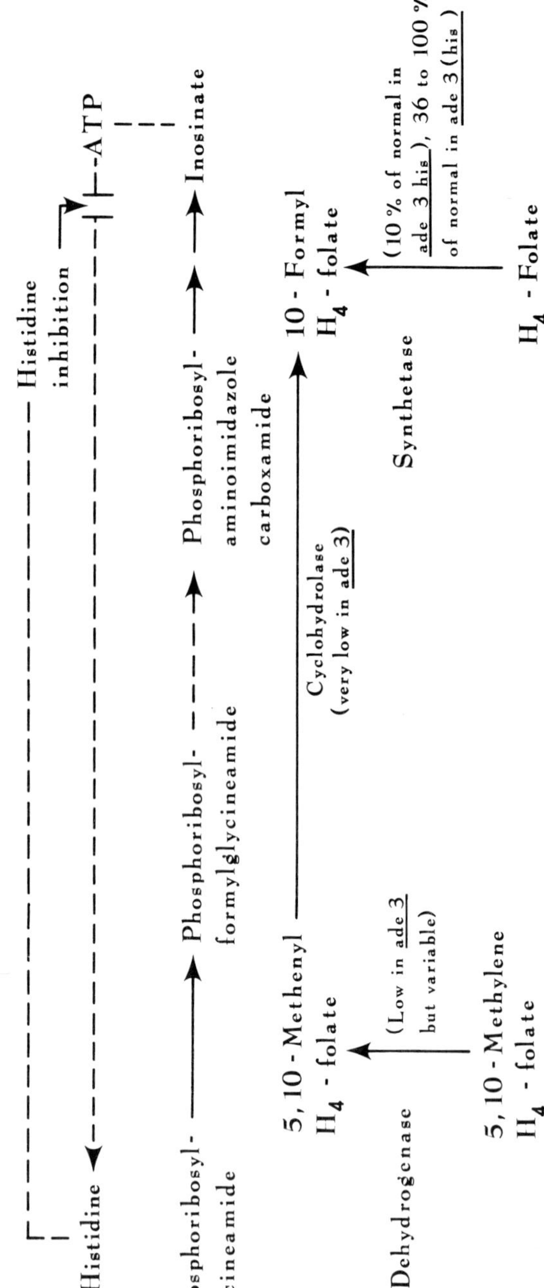

Figure 4-4. Altered amounts of enzymes of H_4-folate interconversion in ade3 *mutants of* Saccharomyces cerevisiae

synthetase activities to permit sufficient purine synthesis for growth when ATP is not being diverted to the histidine biosynthetic pathway. The basis of inhibition of growth by histidine remains unclear.

Altered Enzyme Amounts in Amethopterin-Resistant Cells. It has already been mentioned that numerous lines of cells are known that are resistant to folate analogs such as amethopterin and that contain elevated concentrations of H_4-folate dehydrogenase. Hakala *et al.* (*568*) selected two such lines, one developed in media supplemented with glycine plus hypoxanthine (H), and the other in media to which glycine plus thymidine had been added (T). In later studies (*472*) the activities of other enzymes of one-carbon metabolism were measured in these lines and compared with those in the parent lines; these results are presented in Table 4-6.

Table 4-6. Enzymes of H_4-Folate Coenzyme Metabolism[a]

In wild-type Sarcoma 180 cells and amethopterin-resistant sublines developed in the presence of hypoxanthine (H) or thymidine (T)

	Enzyme Activity		
Enzyme	*Wild Type, Units*	*H, Units*	*T, Units*
Serine hydroxymethyltransferase	40	39	39
5,10-Methylene H_4-folate dehydrogenase	117	40	261
5-10-Methenyl H_4-folate cyclohydrolase	24	24	78
10-Formyl H_4-folate synthetase	40	20	56
Thymidylate synthetase	7.7	10	0.28
H_4-Folate dehydrogenase	0.38	17	26

[a] From Raunio and Hakala (*472*)

Although some of the changes in enzyme activities observed may be fortuitous, it should be noted that cells that have to synthesize purines (T) require about 30 times as much one-carbon units as do those that must synthesize thymine (H). It may at least be asked, therefore, whether the changes observed are compatible with greater or lesser requirements for H_4-folate coenzymes. The cells (H) which do not have to synthesize purines have no particular need for the dehydrogenase and cyclohydrolase, and the former is present in lower than normal amounts. It should be recalled that the dehydrogenase is repressed in the presence of adenine in certain bacteria; hypoxanthine may possibly have a similar effect. In (T) cells, which require 10-formyl H_4-folate and 5,10-methenyl H_4-folate for purine synthesis, dehydrogenase and cyclohydrolase activities are markedly elevated.

Studies by Johnson and Hutchison (*509*) on elevated 10-formyl H_4-folate synthetase activity in certain amethopterin-resistant bacteria have been discussed above.

Altered Enzyme Amounts in Inherited Human Diseases. In 1966 Arakawa *et al.* (*569*) reported studies of three children with mental retardation, microcephaly, and other neurological problems, but who were not anemic; they had hyperfolicacidemia and did not excrete increased amounts of formiminoglutamate following a loading dose of histidine. The only enzymatic abnormality found was a reduction in erythrocyte 5,10-methenyl H_4-folate cyclohydrolase from about 0.7 unit to about 0.3 unit and a drop in the activity of this enzyme in liver biopsy material from about 0.3 to 0.1 unit. Unfortunately the urinary excretion of aminoimidazole carboxamide was not measued although the investigators suggested that these patients might have a deficiency in 10-formyl H_4-folate. More recently, Arakawa (*570*) has remarked that these cases are being reinvestigated to confirm the identity of the enzyme that is deficient.

Purine Toxicity. Many early studies of the reversal of sulfonamide inhibition in bacteria indicated that purines (usually adenine) were often themselves toxic. Thus Harris and Kohn (*451, 453*) found that xanthine or guanine increased the effect of sulfonamides on *Escherichia coli* in the absence of methionine whereas hypoxanthine or adenine increased their effect in the presence and absence of methionine. The presence of methionine, guanine, and xanthine reversed sulfonamide inhibition. In a sulfonamide-resistant strain hypoxanthine or adenine inhibited growth whereas xanthine or guanine had no effect. Shive and Roberts (*452*) also observed adenine toxicity in *Escherichia coli;* in this case however adenosine, inosine, xanthine, and guanine all reversed sulfonamide inhibition (*571*). Adenine was not toxic for *Lactobacillus arabinosus* 17-5 (*452*). A mixture of adenine, guanine, and xanthine (of which adenine may have been the only active ingredient) inhibited the growth of a *p*-aminobenzoate-dependent strain of *Escherichia coli* when the organism was grown with this growth factor but without amino acid supplementation (*428*). In a later study of the same organism Lampen *et al.* (*572*) observed that *p*-aminobenzoate was spared by purines plus a mixture of amino acids. Kalle and Gots (*573*) found that addition of histidine helped reverse adenine toxicity in sensitive strains of *Salmonella typhimurium.*

When *Lactobacillus arabinosus* R-26 was grown on folate-free media, addition of low concentrations of adenine stimulated growth whereas growth was inhibited by high concentrations of this purine. Adenine toxicity was reversed by folate or by thymidine (*574*).

The interpretation of these almost miscellaneous observations was greatly aided by the studies of adenine-sensitive mutants of *Salmonella typhimurium* made by Dalal *et al.* (*575*). They found that in addition to a thiamine requirement induced by adenine (*see* Chapter 7) the addition of pantothenic acid or its pantoyl moiety and of methionine would prevent or reverse adenine toxicity. The effect of methionine was enhanced in the presence of lysine; in the presence of lysine, homocysteine partly replaced methionine. In two strains sulfadiazine treatment greatly increased sensitivity to adenine. A third strain was a leaky mutant for *p*-aminobenzoate.

The common factor of all of these results of adenine toxicity is folate and H_4-folate metabolism. Coenzymes of H_4-folate are required for the synthesis of methionine from homocysteine and of pantoate from α-ketoisovalerate (*156*, p. 753). A shortage of coenzyme A due to retarded pantoate synthesis might account for the effect of lysine in relieving adenine toxicity, because succinyl CoA is involved in its synthesis. It would thus appear that adenine can in some way reduce intracellular concentrations of H_4-folate coenzymes. Wild-type organisms grown under optimum conditions would appear to have a sufficient excess of these compounds so that adenine would not reduce their concentration to a critical point except when very high amounts were added to growth media.

Adenine toxicity is most commonly observed when intracellular concentrations of H_4-folate and its coenzyme forms are already decreased by one means or another (*e.g.*, reduced nutritional supply of folate, decreased synthesis of *p*-aminobenzoate, sulfonamide treatment, and so forth). Under these conditions H_4-folate concentrations may be reduced to a level just sufficient to permit growth, and any further diminution induced by adenine would then produce noticeable inhibition of growth.

It has at least implicitly been assumed that these inhibitory effects of purines are the result of the above-mentioned inhibition and repression of 5,10-methylene H_4-folate dehydrogenase by purine nucleotides. The possible toxic effects of such inhibition would depend first on the identity of the major source of one-carbon units for H_4-folate coenzyme synthesis in the organisms studied. Thus serine and perhaps glycine could be converted to 5,10-methylene H_4-folate without hindrance even if dehydrogenase activity were inhibited. A deficiency in the effective activity of this enzyme would be harmful in this regard only if formate or even histidine were the major one-carbon sources; this seems unlikely.

A second possibly deleterious effect of reduction in 5,10-methylene H_4-folate dehydrogenase activity might be caused by the use of the products of this reaction for processes other than purine synthesis. Under conditions of purine toxicity cells presumably do not synthesize purines or require 5,10-methenyl H_4-folate and 10-formyl H_4-folate, and the former coenzyme is involved in no other known reaction. The only other known reaction of 10-formyl H_4-folate is in the initiation of protein synthesis in some but not all microorganisms. It must be concluded that the precise enzymatic bases of purine toxicity in the cases described above require further investigation.

A somewhat different type of purine toxicity, but one which was also related to an effect on one-carbon metabolism, was observed by Newman and Magasanik (*478*) in serine-glycine auxotrophs of *Escherichia coli.* (Formate would replace these amino acids.) These cells ordinarily grew promptly when transferred from a serine-containing medium to one containing glycine, and vice-versa. If, however, they were grown first in a medium containing serine plus a purine (adenine, guanine, or xanthine), there was a two to four hour lag before growth resumed when they were put into a glycine-containing medium; under similar circumstances they grew immediately if the second medium was supplemented either with formate alone or with glycine plus formate. In similar experiments the same results were obtained when the first growth medium contained serine plus formate or formate alone. It appears that the production of one-carbon units from glycine was repressed both by purines and by formate, but the details of these effects remain obscure.

Use of H_4-Folate Coenzymes by Alternative Pathways. Aside from purine biosynthesis the most important uses of H_4-folate coenzymes are in the synthesis of thymidylate, methionine, and formylmethionyl-tRNA; they are also required for the synthesis of serine from glycine, and in the synthesis of the pantoyl moiety of coenzyme A. These reactions are listed in Table 4-7. The process of serine synthesis has already been discussed, and little is known about the reaction involved in pantoate synthesis. There is some reason to believe, however, that purine biosynthesis, methionine synthesis, thymidylate synthesis, and formylmethionyl-tRNA synthesis may under some conditions compete for limited supplies of H_4-folate coenzymes. These studies are reviewed in this section.

Table 4-7. Alternative Pathways of H_4-Folate Coenzyme Metabolism

Deoxyuridylate + 5,10-Methylene H_4-folate → Thymidylate + H_2-Folate

Homocysteine + 5-Methyl H_4-folate → Methionine + H_4-Folate

Methionyl-tRNA + 10-Formyl H_4-folate → Formylmethionyl-tRNA + H_4-Folate

Glycine + 5,10-Methylene H_4-folate → Serine + H_4-Folate

α-Ketoisovalerate + H_4-Folate coenzyme → Ketopantoate + H_4-Folate

FORMYLMETHIONYL-tRNA SYNTHESIS. Some bacteria, such as *Escherichia coli* and *Salmonella typhimurium,* require formylmethionyl-tRNA in the initiation of protein synthesis and cannot synthesize proteins when rendered deficient in folate (*576*). Other organisms including animal cells, *Streptococcus faecalis* R (*577*), and *Streptococcus faecium* (*578*) do not require formylmethionyl-tRNA for initiation of protein synthesis even though they require exogenous folate for growth.

$$\text{10-Formyl H}_4\text{-folate} + \text{Methionyl-tRNA} \longrightarrow \text{Formylmethionyl-tRNA} + \text{H}_4\text{-Folate}$$

One case has been reported of probable competition for 10-formyl H_4-folate between formylmethionyl-tRNA synthesis and the phosphoribosyl-aminoimidazole carboxamide formyltransferase reaction of the pathway of purine biosynthesis. Goldberger and Berberich and their colleagues (*579, 580, 581*) found that the genetic loci for the enzymes of the histidine biosynthetic pathway (which comprise a single operon) can be transcribed either simultaneously or sequentially in *Salmonella typhimurium*. The simultaneous mode presumably results from the formation of a separate messenger RNA and initiation of protein synthesis for each individual enzyme. In the sequential mode there presumably is a single polycistronic messenger RNA for the whole group of enzymes, and protein synthesis is initiated only once.

Leaky histidine mutants that were partially blocked after the formation of phosphoribosyl-aminoimidazole carboxamide exhibited sequential derepression of the histidine biosynthetic enzymes upon exhaustion of exogenous histidine; those blocked before this step were derepressed simultaneously. Derepression in the latter mutants could be shifted to a sequential mode by addition of ribosyl-aminoimidazole carboxamide to the medium; derepression in the former class of mutants could be shifted to the simultaneous mode upon addition of adenine.

It has been suggested that the simultaneous mode of derepression requires the synthesis of a great deal more formylmethionyl-tRNA than does the sequential mode. If this be assumed, then it is further hypothesized that the conversion of phosphoribosyl-aminoimidazole carboxamide (whether produced endogenously or from exogenously-supplied nucleoside) to purine ribonucleotides produces a drain on 10-formyl H_4-folate so that it is more economical to transcribe the histidine operon sequentially. Alternatively, when compounds were added to the medium which spared 10-formyl H_4-folate (*i.e.*, adenine) or which supplied H_4-folate coenzyme (*i.e.*, serine), the mode of transcription changed from sequential to simultaneous. This proposal seems quite logical, but in view of the great complexity of the system it must remain only a hypothesis at this time.

Thymidylate Synthesis. In animal cells that receive adequate dietary supplies of coenzyme A, methionine, serine, and glycine the most important reactions of H_4-folate coenzymes are in the synthesis of purines and of thymidylate. Because the latter compounds are required for nucleic acid synthesis and cell division, it may be expected that there would be increased requirements for H_4-folate and its coenzymes in growing and rapidly dividing tissues. Indeed, Herbert (*582*) remarks that the daily adult requirement for folate can be increased as much as sixfold above the usual intake of 50 μg per day by any rise in metabolic rate or rate of cell turnover.

Felix and DeMars (*583*) attempted to grow in tissue culture skin fibroblasts taken from patients with hypoxanthine-guanine phosphoribosyltransferase (EC 2.4.2.8) deficiency (the Lesch-Nyhan syndrome, described in Chapter 9). These cells have accelerated rates of purine biosynthesis and hence require increased amounts of H_4-folate coenzymes for this purpose. These authors found that such cells would grow only slowly or not at all in media that supported good growth of normal fibroblasts. Further study revealed that supplementation with extra folate (*i.e.*, increasing its concentration from $4.5 \times 10^{-8}M$ to $2.5 \times 10^{-6}M$) allowed the enzyme-deficient fibroblasts to grow as rapidly as did normal cells. Previous work with fibroblasts from Lesch-Nyhan patients (*584*) had used tissue culture media that already contained high folate concentrations. It has been assumed that growth retardation under these conditions is a result of a lowered rate of synthesis of thymidylate.

Such a functional deficiency of folate probably also occurs in at least some patients with the Lesch-Nyhan syndrome. Such patients grow, for example, at retarded rates. One of the original patients reported by Nyhan subsequently developed a severe megaloblastic anemia (*585*), and this type of anemia has also been noted in several other patients with this disease (*e.g.*, *586–589*) or with severe gout (*590*). This anemia is reported to be unresponsive to folate or cobalamin (*585, 586, 587*), but Van der Zee *et al.* (*586, 587*) observed that improvement followed administration of adenine. This purine base would inhibit purine biosynthesis (*see* Chapter 5) and hence relieve the drain on the pool of H_4-folate coenzymes caused by accelerated rates of purine formation. The inability of folate itself to relieve the observed megaloblastic anemia might indicate that the formation of one-carbon units for H_4-folate coenzyme synthesis might be more limiting for this process than is the availability of H_4-folate itself. However, this possibility remains to be investigated.

The Lesch-Nyhan syndrome also involves a variety of central nervous system abnormalities, and the possibility that they might result from decreased availability of H_4-folate coenzymes resulting from accelerated purine biosynthesis has been considered by several investigators (*e.g.*, *591, 592*). A large number of experimental (*593–599*) and clinical (*600–603*) studies, for example, link folate metabolism to brain development and function. Benke and Anderson (*592*) have attempted to treat Lesch-Nyhan patients with folate alone or with folate plus adenine; under the conditions employed no therapeutic benefit appeared to be derived by the patients. The possible role of folate deficiency in this disease cannot yet be ruled out, however, and this subject requires further study.

METHIONINE SYNTHESIS. Early studies of microbial nutrition under various conditions demonstrated quite clearly that deficiencies of, or supplementation with, methionine and cobalamin could under some circumstances markedly affect the rate of purine biosynthesis *de novo*. Some of these results were at first interpreted as indicating that methionine served as an important one-carbon source for purine synthesis. It now seems likely, however, that methionine and cobalamin influence purine synthesis by their effects on the enzymes of methionine biosynthesis, which in turn influence the availability of H_4-folate for other reactions. Similar, though not identical, phenomena have been observed in animals.

Pathways of Methionine Biosynthesis. At least three routes of methionine biosynthesis are known (*281*, p. 322; *604; 605*).

Betaine + Homocysteine ⟶ Methionine + Dimethylglycine

5 - Methyl H_4- folate + Homocysteine ⟶ Methionine + H_4 - Folate

5 - Methyl H_4- folate + Homocysteine ⟶ (Cobalamin / S-Adenosylmethionine) Methionine + H_4 - Folate

The first pathway occurs in animals but is not the major route unless fairly large amounts of choline or betaine are fed. The second is the major pathway of methionine synthesis in green plants, yeast, and in some microorganisms when they are grown in the absence of cobalamin. The third pathway is the more important reaction in animals, in enterobacteria, and some other microorganisms when they are grown in the presence of cobalamin. In this case the methyl group is transferred from 5-methyl H_4-folate to enzyme-bound cobalamin and thence to homocysteine; *S*-adenosylmethionine plays a rather complicated catalytic role.

In addition to the methyltransferase reactions just described 5,10-methylene H_4-folate reductase must also be considered because it furnishes the methyl donor for the second and third pathways of methionine biosynthesis.

5,10 Methylene H_4 - folate ⟶ (5,10 - Methylene H_4 - folate reductase) 5-Methyl H_4 - folate

Regulation of Methionine Synthesis. A major site of control of methionine synthesis both in microorganisms and in animals is through regulation of the amount or activity (or both) of 5,10-methylene H_4-folate reductase. Thus in mutants of *Escherichia coli* that are auxotrophic for methionine and cobalamin, reductase formation is repressed both at high methionine concentrations in the absence of cobalamin and at high cobalamin concentrations in the absence of methionine (*555, 606, 607*). In the latter case it may be presumed that methionine is being synthesized *via* the cobalamin-dependent methyltransferase and hence methionine or a derivative is probably the real co-repressor. Dickerman and Weissbach (*608*) have demonstrated derepression of 5,10-methylene H_4-folate reductase synthesis at low methionine concentrations in a methionine and cobalamin auxotroph, *Escherichia coli* K_{12} 2276, as well as repression at high methionine concentrations. Greene *et al.* (*609*) have presented evidence which suggests that *S*-adenosylmethionine (which is readily formed by microorganisms when methionine is supplied) is the active regulatory metabolite.

Activity of 5-methyl H_4-folate reductase in rat liver was not affected by feeding low-methionine or high-methionine diets (*610*), but it was inhibited by *S*-adenosylmethionine when assayed in liver extracts (*611*). Kutzbach and Stokstad (*611*) have proposed that this might be a physiologically significant control mechanism because the concentrations of *S*-adenosylmethionine reflect those of methionine.

The activity of cobalamin-dependent 5-methyl H_4-folate homocysteine methyltransferase in both chick (*612*) and rat (*610, 613*) liver not unexpectedly declines when animals are fed diets deficient in cobalamin, and this activity appears to be repressed in both species when high-methionine diets are fed. Conversely dietary methionine deficiency leads to increased methyltransferase activity in liver.

Effects of Methionine and Cobalamin on Purine Biosynthesis. Synthesis of 5-methyl H_4-folate without subsequent transfer of the methyl group to form methionine could lead to a progressive accumulation of this H_4-folate coenzyme and a consequent drop in the concentrations of free H_4-folate and its other coenzyme derivatives. The "methyl trap" hypothesis suggests not only that this happens under certain conditions but that it leads to an effective deficiency of H_4-folate coenzymes for thymidylate and purine synthesis and perhaps for other processes as well. In particular, it is suggested that the decline in methyltransferase activity which accompanies cobalamin deficiency leads to an excess of 5-methyl H_4-folate synthesis at the expense of other coenzymes while an increased supply of exogenous methionine would relieve or prevent this condition by inhibiting the reductase. The validity of the methyl trap hypothesis has been debated recently (*e.g., 281*, p. 453; *614*), and the question cannot yet be considered settled. However, the evidence presented below indicates that the observed effects of variation in dietary cobalamin and methionine levels on purine biosynthesis are for the most part consistent with this idea.

The previously mentioned studies demonstrating elevated urinary excretion of aminoimidazole carboxamide in folate-deficient human patients showed that cobalamin deficiency also led to abnormal metabolism of this compound. Two- to sevenfold increases in daily urinary excretion of aminoimidazole carboxamide were observed in different studies of cobalamin-deficient patients (*445, 446, 447, 615*), while the recovery of an aminoimidazole carboxamide load was decreased from control values of 9–13% to 3–6%; urinary excretion of aminoimidazole carboxamide was increased threefold in cobalamin-deficient rats (*448*). These results are obviously consistent with the view that cobalamin deficiency, leading to decreased methionine synthesis, produces also a state of effective folate deficiency.

In bacteria the addition of cobalamin to culture media has been shown to relieve partial folate deficiencies. Thus cobalamin depressed the accumulation of aminoimidazole carboxamide in sulfonamide-inhibited *Escherichia coli* cultures (*320, 423, 433*), but Gots and Chu (*210*) observed that it was somewhat less effective than methionine in this regard in a *p*-aminobenzoate-requiring strain of the same organism. The utilization of aminoimidazole carboxamide, a process which requires 10-formyl H_4-folate, was accelerated by the addition of cobalamin in certain purineless mutants of *Escherichia coli* (*432*). These results are also consistent with the methyl trap hypothesis.

It has been mentioned previously that feeding of high levels of glycine (4 to 9% of the diet) to chicks results in growth inhibition. Hsu and Combs (*538*) and Machlin *et al.* (*305*) have reported that administration not only of folate but also of cobalamin relieved the growth inhibition so produced and reduced blood levels of glucose, non-protein nitrogen, and amino nitrogen, and of urinary urea nitrogen and creatinine. However, although supplementation with folate lowered the elevated blood uric acid levels, administration of cobalamin led to further increases in blood uric acid concentrations. For example, feeding 6% glycine led to an increase of blood uric acid from 4 to 8.6 mg per 100 ml, and further supplementation with folate and cobalamin produced values of 6.1 and 10.2 mg per 100 ml, respectively (*305*). When both cobalamin and 9% glycine were fed, urate deposits in the feet were noted.

It has been suggested that folate relieves glycine toxicity by increasing its conversion to 5,10-methylene H_4-folate *via* the glycine decarboxylase reaction, and it might be expected that cobalamin would do the same. It is unclear, therefore, why this vitamin should apparently increase uric acid synthesis under these conditions.

An early study (*448*) indicated that the administration of methionine to cobalamin-deficient rats had no effect on the elevated urinary excretion of aminoimidazole carboxamide. However, Oace *et al.* (*616*), using a basal diet that was more deficient in methionine, showed that addition either of cobalamin or of methionine led to a reduction in daily excretion of aminoimidazole carboxamide from 42–56 μg to the control level of 15–25 μg. This is what one would expect if methionine inhibited the synthesis of 5-methyl H_4-folate and hence relieved the folate deficiency induced by cobalamin deficiency.

Numerous studies have shown effects of methionine on purine biosynthesis in microorganisms. Thus when adenine-requiring mutants of *Saccharomyces cerevisiae* which produced aminoimidazole ("purple" mutants) were also made methionine-dependent, the accumulation of the pink pigment derived from aminoimidazole depended on methionine. Adenine-dependent white cultures could be converted to pink cultures by addition of methionine or by endogenous synthesis of methionine in strains without a methionine requirement (*616*). Similarly, studies of aminoimidazole accumulation in biotin-deficient yeast and bacteria also employed methionine supplementation to achieve maximum yields (*265–268*). It must be assumed that these organisms were in effect partially folate deficient, and the addition of methionine relieved this condition through repression of 5,10-methylene H_4-folate reductase.

In *Escherichia coli,* in contrast to these results with *Saccharomyces cerevisiae,* addition of methionine seemed to inhibit the accumulation of aminoimidazole carboxamide. These results at first led to the belief that the methyl group of methionine was being used as a one-carbon source for the purine C-2 and C-8 positions. Ben-Ishai and co-workers (*433, 434*), for example, found that the addition of methionine slightly decreased accumulation of aminoimidazole carboxamide under these conditions whereas methionine plus *p*-aminobenzoate caused marked reduction. Ethionine did the same, and it was suggested that the methyl group of methionine (or that derived from the ethyl group of ethionine) provided the C-2 of the purine ring and hence that the diminution of aminoimidazole carboxamide was due to its conversion to purines. Gots and Chu (*210*) also found that methionine depressed aminoimidazole carboxamide accumulation in a *p*-aminobenzoate-requiring mutant of *Escherichia coli.* Although it was presumed that the methyl group of methionine was a source of C-2, formate had no effect on the accumulation. In another study, however, Gots (*432*) found that in *Escherichia coli* cultures whose growth was inhibited 50 to 60% by sulfadiazine addition of methionine released the growth inhibition without stopping accumulation of aminoimidazole carboxamide.

Finally, however, Gots and Love (*60*) showed that methionine still inhibited accumulation of aminoimidazole carboxamide in *Escherichia coli* B-96, a mutant that cannot convert phosphoribosyl-aminoimidazole carboxamide to inosinate. Thus this effect of methionine must have been exerted prior to the synthesis of this intermediate of purine biosynthesis, not by increasing its utilization by supplying one-carbon units.

These observations are difficult to account for, but they might be explained by recent studies of Dickerman and Weissbach (who used the methionine and cobalamin auxotroph *Escherichia coli* K_{12} 2276). Addition of low concentrations of methionine caused a derepression of 5,10-methylene H_4-folate reductase, and growth was inhibited as a consequence. Because the latter effect was relieved by addition of guanosine, it was assumed that increased synthesis of 5-methyl H_4-folate led to depletion of H_4-folate coenzymes for purine biosynthesis (*608*).

Inherited Abnormalities. Arakawa (*618*) and Mudd (*619, 620*) and their collaborators have reported two human cases of apparent cobalamin-dependent 5-methyl H_4-folate homocysteine methyltransferase deficiency. The first such patient was described in 1967 (*618*) and had megaloblastic anemia as well as mental retardation and other neurological abnormalities. Methyltransferase activity in liver biopsy material was reduced to about 30% of normal. Urinary excretion of aminoimidazole carboxamide, both before and after a loading oral dose, was considered to be somewhat elevated.

The second case (*619, 620*) was an infant with diffuse neuropathology who also had obvious abnormalities of sulfur amino acid metabolism. Liver methyltransferase activity was about 20% of normal while that of kidney was about 4% of control values. It was noted, however, that this patient also exhibited methylmelonicaciduria, which is known to be the result of cobalamin deficiency. It was suggested, therefore, that the basic defect was in the synthesis of the methyl-cobalamin cofactor for the methyltransferase rather than in the apoenzyme. It is not certain now which was the case in the patient reported by Arakawa *et al.* (*618*).

Conclusions

This rather extensive review has clearly demonstrated that the rate of purine biosynthesis *de novo* is far more responsive to the concentrations of the substrates of this pathway than has usually been thought, and that the concentrations of these substrates may be affected by a variety of experimental or pathological conditions. The fact that each of the six substrates may control the rate of purine synthesis in one or another system examined indicates: a) that almost any of the reactions of the purine biosynthetic pathway may be rate limiting, depending on conditions; b) that the amounts of the enzymes of the pathway are present in excess; and c) that endproduct inhibition is not necessarily the most important mechanism for the regulation of purine biosynthesis.

The concentration of almost every substrate of the purine biosynthetic pathway is apparently affected by a number of factors that alter the rate of its synthesis or of its utilization by alternative pathways of metabolism, and purine biosynthesis is thus quite responsive to changes in rates of broad areas of intermediary metabolism. Although the significance of this sensitivity to other aspects of metabolism can be appreciated in the case of uricotelic animals, the physiological advantage of this for ureotelic animals and microorganisms is far less clear.

There are a number of experimental or pathological conditions in which the concentration of one or another substrate of purine biosynthesis is known to be increased or decreased but in which the rate of purine biosynthesis *de novo* has not been accurately assessed. Thus the increases in glutamine concentrations of some tissues which accompany elevated blood ammonia concentrations, and which in turn are caused by exercise, liver disease, and the like, would be expected to increase the rate of purine biosynthesis. Changes in the rate of this pathway would also be expected upon feeding benzoate or phenylacetate or by dietary and hormonal conditions that affect tissue amino acid concentrations. In many of these cases measurements of urinary excretion of uric acid have merely proved ambiguous or controversial, and more sensitive measurements of the rate of biosynthesis are needed.

Factors affecting intracellular concentrations of PP-ribose-P have hardly been explored. It may be suspected, however, that the synthesis of this substrate, and also the rate of purine biosynthesis, will be affected by the variety of dietary and hormonal conditions that are known to affect rates of the glycolytic and pentose phosphate pathways and the concentrations of their intermediates. The effects of variation in carbon dioxide concentrations on purine biosynthesis in animal cells also has not been examined. Both areas invite further investigation.

In conclusion, it is suspected that the observations presented in this chapter represent merely the top of an iceberg and that further investigation would reveal a far greater degree of plasticity of purine biosynthesis to environmental conditions and rates of other areas of metabolism than has generally been thought.

References

1. Von Knierem, W., *Z. Biol (Munich)* (1877) **13,** 36.
2. Cech, C. O., *Ber. Deut. Chem. Ges.* (1877) **10,** 1461.
3. Meyer, H., Jaffe, W., *Ber. Deut. Chem. Ges.* (1877) **10,** 1930.
4. Von Schröder, W., *Z. Physiol. Chem.* (1878) **2,** 228.
5. Fisher, R. B., *Biochem. J.* (1935) **29,** 2192.
6. Tasaki, I., Okumura, J. I., *J. Nutr.* (1964) **83,** 34.
7. Teekell, R. A., Richardson, C. E., Watts, A. B., *Poultry Sci.* (1968) **47,** 1260.
8. O'Dell, B. L., Woods, W. D., Laerdal, O. A., Jeffay, A. M., Savage, J. E., *Poultry Sci.* (1960) **39,** 426.
9. Okumura, J. I., Tasaki, I., *J. Nutr.* (1969) **97,** 316.
10. Rostagno, H. S., Featherston, W. R., *Poultry Sci.* (1970) **49,** 1719.
11. Featherston, W. R., *Poultry Sci.* (1969) **48,** 646.
12. Krakoff, I. H., Karnofsky, D. A., *Amer. J. Physiol.* (1958) **195,** 244.

13. Tournut, J., Montlaur-Ferradou, P., *C. R. Soc. Biol.* (1962) **156**, 2136.
14. Lloyd, M. D., Reed, C. A., Fritz, J. C., *Poultry Sci.* (1949) **28,** 69.
15. Peterson, D. W., Hamilton, W. H., Lilyblade, A. L., *J. Nutr.* (1971) **101,** 347.
16. Burian, R., Schur, H., *Arch. Ges. Physiol.* (1901) **87,** 239.
17. Siven, V. O., *Skand. Arch. Physiol.* (1900) **11,** 123.
18. Rose, W. C., *Physiol. Rev.* (1923) **3,** 544.
19. Hopkins, F. G., Hope, W. B., *J. Physiol. (London)* (1898) **23,** 271.
20. Folin, O., *Amer. J. Physiol.* (1905) **13,** 66.
21. Leathes, J. B., *J. Physiol. (London)* (1906) **35,** 125.
22. Mendel, L. B., Brown, E. W., *J. Amer. Med. Ass.* (1907) **49,** 896.
23. Smetanka, F., *Arch. Ges. Physiol.* (1911) **138,** 217.
24. Mendel, L. B., Stehle, R. L., *J. Biol. Chem.* (1915) **22,** 215.
25. Lewis, H. B., Dunn, M. S., Doisy, E. A., *J. Biol. Chem.* (1918) **36,** 9.
26. Borsook, H., Keighley, G. L., *Proc. Roy. Soc. Ser. B* (1935) **118,** 488.
27. Folin, O., Berglund, H., Derick, C., *J. Biol. Chem.* (1924) **60,** 361.
28. Bröchner-Mortensen, K., *Medicine (Baltimore)* (1940) **19,** 161.
29. Bishop, C., Talbott, J. H., *Pharmacol. Rev.* (1953) **5,** 231.
30. Taylor, A. E., Rose, W. C., *J. Biol. Chem.* (1914) **18,** 519.
31. Raiziss, G. W., Dubin, H., Ringer, A. I., *J. Biol. Chem.* (1914) **19,** 473.
32. Rose, W. C., *J. Biol. Chem.* (1921) **48,** 575.
33. Leopold, J. S., Bernhard, A., Jacobi, H. G., *Amer. J. Dis. Child.* (1924) **27,** 243.
34. Leopold, J. S., Bernhard, A., Jacobi, H. G., *Amer. J. Dis. Child.* (1925) **29,** 191.
35. Moraczewski, W. v., Grzycki, S., Janowski, H., Sliwenski, R., *Klin. Wochenschr.* (1933) **12,** 738.
36. Benedict, S. R., *J. Lab. Clin. Med.* (1916) **2,** 1.
37. Young, E. G., Conway, C. F., Crandall, W. A., *Biochem. J.* (1938) **32,** 1138.
38. Crandall, W. A., Young, E. G., *Biochem. J.* (1938) **32,** 1133.
39. Calloway, D. H., Margen, S., *Fed. Proc., Fed. Amer. Soc. Exp. Biol.* (1968) **27,** 725.
40. Bowering, J., Calloway, D. H., Margen, S., Kaufmann, N. A., *J. Nutr.* (1970) **100,** 249.
41. Bien, E. J., Yü, T. F., Benedict, J. D., Gutman, A. B., Stetten, D., Jr., *J. Clin. Invest.* (1953) **32,** 778.
42. Cathcart, E. P., *J. Physiol. (London)* (1909) **39,** 311.
43. Smetanka, F., *Arch. Ges. Physiol.* (1911) **138,** 217.
44. Umeda, N., *Biochem. J.* (1915) **9,** 421.
45. Höst, H. F., J. *Biol. Chem.* (1919) **38,** 17.
46. Graham, G., Poulton, E. P., *Quart. J. Med.* (1913) **7,** 13.
47. Lewis, H. B., Corley, R. C., *J. Biol. Chem.* (1923) **55,** 373.
48. Höst, H. F., *J. Biol. Chem.* (1919) **38,** 17.
49. Gibson, H. V., Doisy, E. A., *J. Biol. Chem.* (1923) **55,** 605.
50. Lennox, W. G., *J. Biol. Chem.* (1925) **66,** 521.
51. Roman, H., *C. R. Trav. Lab. Carlsberg Ser. Physiol.* (1956) **26,** 299.
52. Lindegren, C. C., "The Yeast Cell," p. 15–1, Educational Publ., St. Louis, 1949.
53. Leupold, U., Hottinguer, H., *Heredity* (1954) **8,** 243.
54. Ephrussi, B., Hottinguer, H., Tavlitzki, J., *Ann. Inst. Pasteur Paris* (1949) **76,** 419.
55. Reaume, S. E., Tatum, E. L., *Arch. Biochem.* (1949) **22,** 331.
56. Tavlitzki, J., *Rev. Can. Biol.* (1951) **10,** 48.
57. Love, S. H., Gots, J. S., *J. Biol. Chem.* (1955) **212,** 647.
58. Stewart, R. C., Sevag, M. G., *Arch. Biochem. Biophys.* (1952) **41,** 9.
59. Sevag, M. G., Stewart, R. C., *Arch. Biochem. Biophys.* (1952) **41,** 14.
60. Gots, J. S., Love, S. H., *J. Biol. Chem.* (1954) **210,** 395.
61. Slotnick, I. J., Sevag, M. G., *Arch. Biochem. Biophys.* (1955) **57,** 491.

62. Issaly, A. S., Stoppani, A. O. M., *Proc. Soc. Exp. Biol. Med.* (1963) **113,** 970.
63. Abrams, R., Goldinger, J. M., *Arch. Biochem. Biophys.* (1952) **35,** 243.
64. Totter, J. R., *J. Amer. Chem. Soc.* (1954) **76,** 2196.
65. Totter, J. R., Best, A. N., *Arch. Biochem. Biophys.* (1955) **54,** 318.
66. Paterson, A. R. P., Zbarsky, S. H., *Biochim. Biophys. Acta* (1955) **18,** 441.
67. LePage, G. A., *Cancer Res.* (1953) **13,** 178.
68. Edmonds, M., LePage, G. A., *Cancer Res.* (1955) **15,** 93.
69. Thomson, R. Y., Smellie, R. M. S., Davidson, J. N., *Biochim. Biophys. Acta* (1958) **29,** 308.
70. Thomson, R. Y., Smellie, R. M. S., Goutier, R., Davidson, J. N., *Biochim. Biophys. Acta* (1956) **22,** 585.
71. Henderson, J. F., LePage, G. A., *J. Biol. Chem.* (1959) **234,** 2364.
72. Harrington, H., *J. Biol. Chem.* (1958) **233,** 1190.
73. Thomson, R. Y., Ricceri, G., Perretta, M., *Biochim. Biophys. Acta* (1960) **45,** 87.
74. Bernstein, H., *J. Gen. Microbiol.* (1961) **25,** 41.
75. Williams, A. M., Finlayson, J. S., Tews, J. K., *Biochim. Biophys. Acta* (1963) **74,** 24.
76. Herscovics, A., Johnstone, R. M., *Biochim. Biophys. Acta* (1964) **91,** 365.
77. Henderson, J. F., Khoo, M. K. Y., *J. Biol. Chem.* (1965) **240,** 2349.
78. Ellis, D. P., Scholefield, P. G., *Can. J. Biochem. Physiol.* (1962) **40,** 343.
79. Uppin, B. I., Scholefield, P. G., *Can. J. Biochem.* (1965) **43,** 209.
80. McKerns, K. W., *Can. J. Biochem.* (1965) **43,** 923.
81. McKerns, K. W., "The Gonads," p. 137, Appleton, New York, 1969.
82. McKerns, K. W., "Functions of the Adrenal Cortex," Vol. 1, p. 479, Appleton, New York, 1968.
83. Hall, R., *J. Biol. Chem.* (1963) **238,** 306.
84. Hall, R., Tubmen, J., *J. Biol. Chem.* (1965) **240,** 3132.
85. Lindsay, R. H., Cash, A. G., Hall, J. B., *Biochem. Biophys. Res. Commun.* (1967) **29,** 850.
86. Lindsay, R. H., Cash, A. G., Hall, J. B., *Endocrinology* (1969) **84,** 534.
87. McKerns, K. W., *Biochim. Biophys. Acta* (1969) **192,** 318.
88. Henderson, J. F., Khoo, M. K. Y., *J. Biol. Chem.* (1965) **240,** 2358.
89. Wong, P. C. L., Ph.D. Thesis, Flinders University of South Australia, 1970.
90. Kelley, W. N., Fox, I. H., Wyngaarden, J. B., *Clin. Res.* (1970) **18,** 457.
91. Fox, I. H., Kelley, W. N., *Ann. Intern. Med.* (1971) **74,** 424.
92. Hershko, A., Razin, A., Mager, J., *Biochim. Biophys. Acta* (1969) **184,** 64.
93. Hershko, A., Razin, A., Shoshani, T., Mager, J., *Biochim. Biophys. Acta* (1967) **149,** 59.
94. Bondy, P. K., "Duncan's Diseases of Metabolism," Bondy, P. K., Rosenberg, L. E., Eds., 6th ed., p. 279, Saunders, Philadelphia, 1969.
95. Beaconsfield, P., Ginsburg, J., Jeacock, M. K., *Develop. Med. Child. Neurol.* (1964) **6,** 469.
96. Gudbjarnason, S., Cowan, C., Bing, R. J., *Life Sci.* (1967) **6,** 1093.
97. Beaconsfield, P., Ginsburg, J., Kosinski, Z., *Nature (London)* (1965) **205,** 50.
98. Gudbjarnason, S., DeSchryver, C., Chiba, C., Yamonaka, J., Bing, R. J., *Circ. Res.* (1964) **15,** 320.
99. Benjamin, W., Gellhorn, A., *J. Lipid Res.* (1966) **7,** 285.
100. Gumaa, K. A., McLean, P., *Biochem. J.* (1969) **115,** 1009.
101. De la Garza, S. A., Tepperman, H. M., Tepperman, J., *J. Nutr.* (1970) **100,** 1027.
102. Marks, P. A., Feigelson, P., *J. Biol. Chem.* (1957) **226,** 1001.
103. Hiatt, H. H., *J. Biol. Chem.* (1957) **229,** 725.
104. Hollmann, S., "Non-Glycolytic Pathways of Metabolism of Glucose," p. 115, Academic, New York, 1964.
105. Henderson, J. F., Khoo, M. K. Y., *J. Biol. Chem.* (1965) **240,** 2363.

106. Fontenelle, L. J., Henderson, J. F., *Can. J. Biochem.* (1969) **47**, 419.
107. Dische, Z., Ingals, D., *Arch. Biochem. Biophys.* (1963) **101**, 489.
108. Brin, M., Shohet, S. S., Davidson, C. S., *J. Biol. Chem.* (1958) **230**, 319.
109. Brin, M., *Isr. J. Med. Sci.* (1967) **3**, 792.
110. Sie, H.-G., Nigam, V. N., Fishman, W. H., *Biochim. Biophys. Acta* (1961) **50**, 277.
111. Brin, M., "Thiamine Deficiency: Biochemical Lesions and Their Clinical Significance," *Ciba Found. Study Group Pap.* (1967) **28**, 87.
112. Holowach, J., Kauffman, F., Ikossi, M. G., Thomas, C., McDougal, D. B., Jr., *J. Neurochem.* (1968) **15**, 621.
113. Perretta, M., Pieber-Perretta, M., Minguell, J., *Arch. Biochem. Biophys.* (1964) **105**, 449.
114. Gerber, G. B., Altman, K. I., *Nature (London)* (1958) **182**, 1513.
115. McNutt, W. S., Jr., *J. Biol. Chem.* (1958) **233**, 189.
116. Harbers, E., Heidelberger, C., *J. Biol. Chem.* (1959) **234**, 1249.
117. Harrington, H., *Biochim. Biophys. Acta* (1963) **68**, 509.
118. Hurlbert, R. B., Kammen, H. O., *J. Biol. Chem.* (1960) **235**, 443.
119. Switzer, R. L., *J. Biol. Chem.* (1969) **244**, 2854.
120. Fox, I. H., Kelley, W. N., *J. Biol. Chem.* (1971) **246**, 5739.
121. Switzer, R. L., *Biochem. Biophys. Res. Commun.* (1968) **32**, 320.
122. Switzer, R. L., *J. Biol. Chem.* (1970) **245**, 483.
123. Wong, P. C. L., Murray, A. W., *Biochemistry* (1969) **8**, 1608.
124. Preiss, J., Handler, P., *J. Biol. Chem.* (1957) **225**, 759.
125. Flaks, J. G., "Methods in Enzymology," Colowick, S. P., Kaplan, N. O., Eds., Vol. VI, p. 158, Academic, New York, 1963.
126. Murray, A. W., Wong, P. C. L., *Biochem. Biophys. Res. Commun.* (1967) **29**, 582.
127. Switzer, R. L., *Fed. Proc., Fed. Amer. Soc. Exp. Biol.* (1968) **27**, 290.
128. Kornberg, A., Lieberman, I., Simms, E. S., *J. Biol. Chem.* (1955) **215**, 389.
129. Remy, C. N., Remy, W. T., Buchanan, J. M., *J. Biol. Chem.* (1955) **217**, 885.
130. Tarr, H. L. A., *Can. J. Biochem. Physiol.* (1960) **38**, 683.
131. Crabtree, G. W., Henderson, J. F., *Cancer Res.* (1971) **31**, 985.
132. Switzer, R. L., *Fed. Proc., Fed. Amer. Soc. Exp. Biol.* (1967) **26**, 560.
133. Atkinson, D. E., Fall, L., *J. Biol. Chem.* (1967) **242**, 3241.
134. Klungsöyr, L., Hagemen, J. H., Fall, L., Atkinson, D. E., *Biochemistry* (1968) **7**, 4035.
135. David, J., Wiesmeyer, H., *Biochim. Biophys. Acta* (1970) **208**, 68.
136. Standerfer, S. B., Handler, P., *Proc. Soc. Exp. Biol. Med.* (1955) **90**, 270.
137. Handschumacher, R. E., Creasey, W. A., Jaffe, J. J., Pasternak, C. A., Hankin, L., *Proc. Nat. Acad. Sci.* (1960) **46**, 178.
138. Creasey, W. A., Hankin, L., Handschumacher, R. E., *J. Biol. Chem.* (1961) **236**, 2064.
139. Von Euler, L. H., Rubin, R. J., Handschumacher, R. E., *J. Biol. Chem.* (1963) **238**, 2464.
140. Marchetti, M., Puddu, P., Caldarera, C. M., *Biochim. Biophys. Acta* (1962) **61**, 826.
141. Windmueller, H. G., *J. Nutr.* (1965) **85**, 221.
142. Bloomfield, R. A., Letter, A. A., Wilson, R. P., *Biochim. Biophys. Acta* (1969) **187**, 266.
143. Letter, A. A., Ph.D. Thesis, University of Missouri, 1970.
144. Rajalakshmi, S., Handschumacher, R. E., *Biochim. Biophys. Acta* (1968) **155**, 317.
145. Kelley, W. N., Fox, I. H., Wyngaarden, J. B., *Biochim. Biophys. Acta* (1970) **215**, 512.
146. Kelley, W. N., Greene, M. L., Fox, I. H., Rosenbloom, F. M., Levy, R. I., Seegmiller, J. E., *Metab. Clin. Exp.* (1970) **19**, 1025.
147. Smith, R. C., Salmon, W. D., *Arch. Biochem. Biophys.* (1969) **129**, 554.

148. Shull, K. H., McConomy, J., Vogt, M., Castillo, A., Farber, E., *J. Biol. Chem.* (1966) **241,** 5060.
149. Shull, K. H., Kisilevsky, R., *Biochem. Pharmacol.* (1971) **20,** 2781.
150. Rapp, W. G., Sacks, J., *Arch. Biochem. Biophys.* (1965) **111,** 142.
151. Abrams, R., *Arch. Biochem. Biophys.* (1952) **37,** 270.
152. Abrams, R., *J. Amer. Chem. Soc.* (1951) **73,** 1888.
153. Takahashi, T., Inai, Y., Okamura, S., Takahashi, H., *Agr. Biol. Chem.* (1969) **33,** 377.
154. Meister, A., *Harvey Lect.* (1969) **63**, 139.
155. Meister, A., *Physiol. Rev.* (1956) **36,** 103.
156. Meister, A., "Biochemistry of the Amino Acids," 2nd ed., Academic, New York, 1965.
157. Sonne, J. C., Lin, I., Buchanan, J. M., *J. Biol. Chem.* (1956) **220,** 389.
158. Levenberg, B., Hartman, S. C., Buchanan, J. M., *J. Biol. Chem.* (1956) **220,** 379.
159. Salzman, N. P., Eagle, H., Sebring, E. D., *J. Biol. Chem.* (1958) **230**, 1001.
160. Greenlees, J., LePage, G. A., *Cancer Res.* (1956) **16,** 808.
161. Smellie, R. M. S., Thomson, R. Y., Davidson, J. N., *Biochim. Biophys. Acta* (1958) **29,** 59.
162. Henderson, J. F., LePage, G. A., McIver, F. A., *Cancer Res.* (1957) **17,** 609.
163. Henderson, J. F., *J. Biol. Chem.* (1962) **237,** 2631.
164. Fontenelle, L. J., Henderson, J. F., *Biochim. Biophys. Acta* (1969) **177,** 88.
165. Henderson, J. F., Khoo, M. K. Y., *J. Biol. Chem.* (1965) **240,** 3104.
166. Henderson, J. F., Paterson, A. R. P., Caldwell, I. C., Hori, M., *Cancer Res.* (1967) **27,** 715.
167. Belkhode, M. L., Gotto, A. M., Touster, O., *Cancer Res.* (1967) **27,** 1073.
168. Feigelson, P., Feigelson, M., *J. Biol. Chem.* (1963) **238,** 1073.
169. Feigelson, M., Feigelson, P., *J. Biol. Chem.* (1966) **241**, 5819.
170. Nishiitsutsujii-Uwo, J. M., Ross, B. D., Krebs, H. A., *Biochem. J.* (1967) **103,** 852.
171. Wu, C., Bauer, J. M., *Cancer Res.* (1960) **20,** 848.
172. Dunn, M. S., Camien, M. N., Rockland, L. B., Shankman, S., Goldberg, S. C., *J. Biol. Chem.* (1944) **155,** 591.
173. Pitts, R. F., *N. Engl. J. Med.* (1971) **284**, 32.
174. Bessman, S. P., *Advan. Clin. Chem.* (1959) **2,** 136.
175. Lund, P., *Biochem. J.* (1970) **118,** 35.
176. Tigerman, H., MacVicar, R., *J. Biol. Chem.* (1951) **189,** 793.
177. Du Ruisseau, J. P., Greenstein, J. P., Winitz, M., Birnbaum, S. M., *Arch. Biochem. Biophys.* (1957) **68,** 161.
178. Duda, G. D., Handler, P., *J. Biol. Chem.* (1958) **232,** 303.
179. Bessman, S. P., Bessman, A. N., *J. Clin. Invest.* (1955) **34,** 622.
180. Flock, E. V., Block, M. A., Grindlay, J. H., Mann, F. C., Bollman, J. L., *J. Biol. Chem.* (1957) **200,** 529.
181. Krebs, H. A., *Biochem. J.* (1935) **29,** 1951.
182. Marliss, E. B., Aoki, T. T., Pozefsky, T., Most, A. S., Cahill, G. F., *J. Clin. Invest.* (1971) **50,** 814.
183. Lund, P., *Biochem. J.* (1971) **124**, 653.
184. Walshe, J. M., *Lancet* (1953) **i,** 1075.
185. Hourani, B. T., Hamlin, E. M., Reynolds, T. B., *Arch. Intern. Med.* (1971) **127,** 1033.
186. Steigmann, F., Kazemi, F., Dubin, A., Kissane, J., *Amer. J. Gastroenterol.* (1963) **40,** 378.
187. Steigmann, F., Condon, R. E., Silverman, D. A., Bombeck, C. T., Alavi, I., Dubin, A., *Amer. J. Gastroenterol.* (1970) **54**, 355.
188. Seegmiller, J. E., Schwartz, R., Davidson, C. S., *J. Clin. Invest.* (1954) **33,** 984.
189. Brandstaetter, S., Barzelai, D., *Amer. J. Dig. Dis.* (1960) **5,** 945.

190. Moser, H. W., Efron, M. L., Brown, H., Diamond, R., Neumann, C. G., *Amer. J. Med.* (1967) **42,** 9.
191. Russell, A., Levin, B., Oberholzer, V. G., Sinclair, L., *Lancet* (1962) **ii,** 699.
192. Henderson, J. F., Biochim. Biophys. Acta (1963) **76,** 173.
193. Frieden, C., *J. Biol. Chem.* (1965) **240,** 2028.
194. Umbarger, H. E., *Annu. Rev. Biochem.* (1969) **38,** 323.
195. Frieden, C., *J. Biol. Chem.* (1963) **238,** 3286.
196. Erwin, V. G., *Mol. Pharmacol.* (1969) **5,** 615.
197. Christensen, H. N., Streicher, J. A., Elbinger, R. L., *J. Biol. Chem.* (1948) **172**, 515.
198. Scherwin, P., Bessman, S. P., Waelsch, H., *J. Biol. Chem.* (1950) **184,** 37.
199. Bessman, S. P., Magnes, J., Scherwin, P., Waelsch, H., *J. Biol. Chem.* (1948) **175,** 817.
200. Peraino, C., Harper, A. E., *Arch. Biochem. Biophys.* (1962) **97,** 442.
201. Sapirstein, M. R., *Proc. Soc. Exp. Biol. Med.* (1943) **52**, 334.
202. Najarian, J. S., Harper, H. A., *Proc. Soc. Exp. Biol. Med.* (1956) **92,** 560.
203. Winitz, M., du Ruisseau, J. P., Otey, M. C., Birnbaum, S. M., Greenstein, J. P., *Arch. Biochem. Biophys.* (1956) **64,** 368.
204. Barak, A. J., Humoller, F. L., Mahler, D. J., Holthaus, J. M., *Gastroenterology* (1962) **43,** 35.
205. McDermott, W. V., Wareham, J., Riddell, A. G., *N. Engl. J. Med.* (1955) **253,** 1093.
206. Singh, I. D., Barclay, J. A., Cooke, W. T., *Lancet* (1954) **i,** 1004.
207. McDermott, W. V., Jr., Henneman, D. H., Laumont, C., *J. Clin. Invest.* (1957) **36,** 913.
208. Najarian, J. S., Harper, H. A., McCorkle, H. J., *Surgery* (1958) **44,** 11.
209. Ravel, J. M., Eakin, R. E., Shive, W. J., *J. Biol. Chem.* (1948) **172,** 67.
210. Gots, J. S., Chu, E. C., *J. Bacteriol.* (1952) **64,** 537.
211. Dalal, F. R., Gots, R. E., Gots, J. S., *J. Bacteriol.* (1966) **91**, 507.
212. Moat, A. G., Wilkins, C. A., Jr., Friedman, H., *J. Biol. Chem.* (1956) **223,** 985.
213. Betheil, J. J., Feigelson, M., Feigelson, P., *Biochim. Biophys. Acta* (1965) **104,** 92.
214. Feigelson, M., Gross, P. R., Feigelson, P., *Biochim. Biophys. Acta* (1962) **55,** 495.
215. Goodlad, G. H. J., Munro, M. W., *Biochem. J.* (1959) **73**, 343.
216. Hellman, L., *Science* (1949) **109,** 280.
217. Thorn, G. W., Prunty, F. T. G., Forsham, P. H., *Science* (1947) **105,** 528.
218. Thorn, G. W., Forsham, P. H., Prunty, F. T. G., Hills, A. G., *J. Amer. Med. Ass.* (1948) **137,** 1005.
219. Conn, J. W., Louis, L. H., Wheeler, C. E., *J. Lab. Clin. Med.* (1948) **33,** 651.
220. Conn, J. W., Louis, L. H., Johnston, M. W., *J. Lab. Clin. Med.* (1949) **34,** 255.
221. Bishop, C., Garner, W., Talbott, J. H., *J. Clin. Invest.* (1951) **30,** 879.
222. Benedict, J. D., Roche, M., Soloway, S., Stetten, D., Jr., *J. Clin. Invest.* (1950) **29,** 1104.
223. Iqbal, K., Ottaway, J. H., *Biochem. J.* (1970) **119,** 145.
224. DeMars, R., *Biochim. Biophys. Acta*' (1958) **27,** 435.
225. Eagle, H., Washington, C. L., Levy, M., Cohen, L., *J. Biol. Chem.* (1966) **241**, 4994.
226. Paul, J., Fottrell, P. F., *Biochim. Biophys. Acta* (1963) **67,** 334.
227. Rijven, A. H. G. C., *Biochim. Biophys. Acta* (1961) **52,** 213.
228. Holzer, H., Meche, D., Wulff, K., Liess, K., Heilmeyer, L., Jr., *Advan. Enzyme Regul.* (1967) **5,** 211.
229. Truffa-Bachi, P., Cohen, G. N., *Annu. Rev. Biochem.* (1968) **37**, 79.
230. Shapiro, B. M., Stadtman, E. R., *Annu. Rev. Microbiol.* (1970) **24,** 501.
231. Stadtman, E. R., Ginsburg, A., Ciardi, J. E., Yeh, J., Hennig, S. B., Shapiro, B. M., *Advan. Enzyme Regul.* (1970) **8,** 99.

232. Ravel, J. M., Humphreys, J. S., Shive, W., *Arch. Biochem. Biophys.* (1965) **111,** 721.
233. Rebello, J. L., Strauss, N., *J. Bacteriol.* (1969) **98,** 683.
234. Pateman, J. A., *Biochem. J.* (1969) **115,** 769.
235. Katunuma, N., Matsuda, Y., Kuroda, Y., *Advan. Enzyme Regul.* (1970) **8,** 73.
236. Wu, C., *Comp. Biochem. Physiol.* (1963) **8,** 335.
237. Richterich-Van Baerle, R., Goldstein, L., Dearborn, E. H., *Enzymologia* (1957) **18,** 327.
238. Pamiljans, V., Krishnaswamy, P. R., Dumville, G., Meister, A., *Biochemistry* (1962) **1,** 153.
239. Speck, J. F., *J. Biol. Chem.* (1949) **179,** 1405.
240. Elliott, W. H., *Biochem. J.* (1951) **49,** 106.
241. Kapoor, M., Bray, D. F., *Biochemistry* (1968) **7,** 3583.
242. Charles, H. P., *Nature (London)* (1962) **195,** 359.
243. Charles, H. P., Broadbent, J. A., *Nature (London)* (1964) **201,** 1004.
244. De Serres, F. J., *Mutat. Res.* (1966) **3,** 420.
245. Woods, R. A., *Mol. Gen. Genet.* (1969) **105,** 314.
246. Vivian, A., Charles, H. P., *J. Gen. Microbiol.* (1970) **61,** 263.
247. Charles, H. P., Roberts, G. A., *J. Gen. Microbiol.* (1968) **51,** 211.
248. Katz, D., Rosenberger, R. F., *Biochim. Biophys. Acta* (1970) **224,** 279.
249. Pappenheimer, A. M., Jr., Hottle, G. A., *Proc. Soc. Exp. Biol. Med.* (1940) **44,** 645.
250. Mistry, S. P., Dakshinamurti, K., *Vitam. Horm. (New York)* (1964) **22,** 1.
251. Koser, S. A., Wright, M. H., Dorfman, A., *Proc. Soc. Exp. Biol. Med.* (1942) **51,** 204.
252. Stokes, J. L., Larsen, A., Gunness, M., *J. Bacteriol.* (1947) **54,** 219.
253. Stokes, J. L., Larsen, A., Gunness, M., *J. Biol. Chem.* (1947) **167,** 613.
254. Lardy, H. A., Potter, R. L., Elvehjem, C. A., *J. Biol. Chem.* (1947) **169,** 451.
255. Shive, W., Rodgers, L. L., *J. Biol. Chem.* (1947) **169,** 453.
256. Potter, R. L., Elvehjem, C. A., *J. Biol. Chem.* (1948) **172,** 531.
257. Moat, A. G., Emmons, E. K., *J. Bacteriol.* (1954) **68,** 687.
258. Perlman, D., *Amer. J. Bot.* (1948) **35,** 36.
259. Wessman, G. E., Allen, L. P., Werkman, C. H., *J. Bacteriol.* (1954) **67,** 554.
260. MacLeod, P. R., Lardy, H. A., *J. Biol. Chem.* (1949) **179,** 733.
261. Wahba, A. J., Ravel, J. M., Shive, W., *Biochim. Biophys. Acta* (1954) **14,** 569.
262. Wahba, A. J., Shive, W., *J. Biol. Chem.* (1954) **211,** 155.
263. Ahmad, F., Rose, A. H., *J. Gen. Microbiol.* (1962) **28,** 147.
264. Chamberlain, N., Cutts, N. S., Rainbow, C., *J. Gen. Microbiol.* (1952) **7,** 54.
265. Cutts, N. S., Rainbow, C., *J. Gen. Microbiol.* (1950) **4,** 150.
266. Chamberlain, N., Rainbow, C., *J. Gen. Microbiol.* (1954) **11,** 180.
267. Friedman, H., Moat, A. G., *Arch. Biochem. Biophys.* (1958) **78,** 146.
268. Whitaker, J. A. M., Umbreit, W. W., *Arch. Biochem. Biophys.* (1962) **96,** 541.
269. Lones, D. P., Rainbow, C., Woodward, J. D., *J. Gen. Microbiol.* (1958) **19,** 146.
270. Woodward, J. D., Rainbow, C., *J. Gen. Microbiol.* (1961) **25,** 141.
271. Moat, A. G., Nasuti, F., *Fed. Proc., Fed. Amer. Soc. Exp. Biol.* (1960) **19,** 313.
272. Katsuki, H., *J. Biochem. (Tokyo)* (1959) **46,** 979.
273. Katsuki, H., *J. Biochem. (Tokyo)* (1959) **46,** 621.
274. Ahmad, F., Rose, A. H., Garg, N. K., *J. Gen. Microbiol.* (1961) **24,** 69.
275. Rose, A. H., *J. Gen. Microbiol.* (1960) **23,** 143.
276. Rose, A. H., Nickerson, W. J., *J. Bacteriol.* (1956) **72,** 324.
277. Rose, A. H., *Nature (London)* (1960) **186,** 139.
278. Mitchell, H. H., Hamilton, T. S., "The Biochemistry of the Amino Acids," Chemical Catalog Co., New York, 1929.

279. Bach, S. J., "The Metabolism of Protein Constituents in the Mammalian Body," p. 6, Clarendon Press, Oxford, 1952.
280. Arnstein, H. R. V., *Advan. Protein Chem.* (1954) **9,** 1.
281. Blakley, R. L., "The Biochemistry of Folic Acid and Related Pteridines," Elsevier, New York, 1969.
282. Greenberg, D. M., "Metabolic Pathways," 3rd ed., Vol. 3, Academic, New York, 1969.
283. Howell, R. R., Speas, M., Wyngaarden, J. B., *J. Clin. Invest.* (1961) **40,** 2076.
284. Shemin, D., Rittenberg, D., *J. Biol. Chem.* (1947) **167,** 875.
285. Gutman, A. B., Yü, T.-F., Black, H., Yalow, R. S., Berson, S. A., *Amer. J. Med.* (1958) **25**, 917.
286. Elwyn, D., Sprinson, D. B., *J. Biol. Chem.* (1950) **184,** 465.
287. Reichard, P., *Acta Chem. Scand.* (1949) **3,** 422.
288. Anderson, E. P., Åkvist, S., *Acta Chem. Scand.* (1956) **10,** 1576.
289. Lembach, K., Charalampous, F. C., *J. Biol. Chem.* (1967) **242,** 2599.
290. Charalampous, F., Wahl, M., Ferguson, L., *J. Biol. Chem.* (1961) **236,** 2552.
291. Christman, A. A., Mosier, E. C., *J. Biol. Chem.* (1929) **83,** 11.
292. Adams, M., Power, M. H., Boothby, W. M., *Amer. J. Physiol.* (1937) **118,** 562.
293. Friedman, M., *J. Clin. Invest.* (1947) **26,** 815.
294. Kaplan, D., Diamond, H., Wallace, S. L., Halberstam, D., *Ann. Rheum. Dis.* (1969) **28,** 180.
295. Yü, T.-F., Kaung, C., Gutman, A. B., *Amer. J. Med.* (1970) **49,** 352.
296. Almquist, H. J., "Proteins and Amino Acids in Nutrition," Sahyun, M., Ed., p. 221, Reinhold, New York, 1948.
297. Almquist, H. J., Stokstad, E. L. R., Mecchi, E., Manning, P. D. V., *J. Biol. Chem.* (1940) **134,** 213.
298. Almquist, H. J., Grau, C. R., *J. Nutr.* (1944) **28,** 325.
299. Kratzer, F. H., Williams, D., *J. Nutr.* (1948) **35,** 315.
300. Jukes, T. H., Stokstad, E. L. R., Belt, M., *J. Nutr.* (1947) **33**, 1.
301. Akrabawi, S. S., Kratzer, F. H., *J. Nutr.* (1968) **95,** 41.
302. Akrabawi, S. S., Kratzer, F. H., *Proc. Soc. Exp. Biol. Med.* (1969) **130,** 1270.
303. *Nutr. Rev.* (1968) **26,** 279.
304. Hegsted, D. M., Briggs, G. M., Elvehjem, C. A., Hart, E. B., *J. Biol. Chem.* (1941) **140**, 191.
305. Machlin, L. J., Lankenau, A. H., Denton, C. A., Bird, H. R., *J. Nutr.* (1952) **46,** 389.
306. Snetsinger, D. C., Scott, H. M., *Poultry Sci.* (1961) **40,** 1675.
307. Bloomfield, R. A., Letter, A. A., Wilson, R. P., *Arch. Biochem. Biophys.* (1969) **129,** 196.
308. Wiechowski, W., *Beitr. Chem. Physiol. Pathol.* (1906) **7,** 204.
309. Magnus-Levy, A., *Biochem. Z.* (1907) **6,** 523.
310. McCoy, R. H., Rose, W. C., *J. Biol. Chem.* (1937) **117,** 581.
311. Rose, W. C., Burr, W. W., Sallach, H. J., *J. Biol. Chem.* (1952) **194,** 321.
312. Eagle, H., Levinton, L., "Cells and Tissues in Culture; Methods, Biology and Physiology," Willmer, E. N., Ed., Vol. 1, p. 277, Academic, New York, 1965.
313. Eagle, H., *Science* (1959) **130,** 432.
314. Lucy, J. A., "Cells and Tissues in Culture; Methods, Biology, and Physiology," Willmer, E. N., Ed., Vol. 1, p. 297, Academic, New York, 1965.
315. Salzman, N. P., Sebring, E. D., *Arch. Biochem. Biophys.* (1959) **84,** 143.
316. Webb, W., Biggers, J. D., *Biochim. Biophys. Acta* (1961) **54**, 249.
317. Roberts, R. B., Abelson, P. H., Cowie, D. B., Bolton, E. T., Britten, R. J., *Carnegie Inst. Wash. Publ.* (1955) No. 607.
318. Arnstein, H. R. V., Neuberger, A., *Biochem. J.* (1953) **55,** 271.
319. Shive, W., *Fed. Proc., Fed. Amer. Soc. Exp. Biol.* (1953) **12,** 639.
320. Gots, J. S., *Arch. Biochem.* (1950) **29,** 222.

321. Greenberg, G. R., *Fed. Proc., Fed. Amer. Soc. Exp. Biol.* (1953) **12**, 651.
322. Eagle, H., Freeman, A. E., Levy, M., *J. Exp. Med.* (1958) **107,** 643.
323. Lieberman, I., Ove, P., *J. Biol. Chem.* (1960) **235,** 1119.
324. Rappaport, C., Melnick, J. L., *Fed. Proc., Fed. Amer. Soc. Exp. Biol.* (1957) **16,** 429.
325. Neuman, R. E., Tytell, A. A., *Proc. Soc. Exp. Biol. Med.* (1960) **103,** 763.
326. Hakala, M. T., *Science* (1957) **126,** 255.
327. Hakala, M. T., Taylor, E., *J. Biol. Chem.* (1959) **234,** 126.
328. Arnstein, H. R. V., Stantovic, V., *Biochem. J.* (1956) **62,** 190.
329. Elwyn, D., Sprinson, D. B., *J. Biol. Chem.* (1956) **184,** 474.
330. Bridgers, W. F., *J. Neurochem.* (1968) **15,** 1325.
331. McClain, L. D., Bridgers, W. F., *J. Neurochem.* (1970) **17**, 763.
332. Totter, J. R., Amos, E. S., Keith, C. K., *J. Biol. Chem.* (1949) **178,** 847.
333. Haff, R. F., Swim, H. E., *Proc. Soc. Exp. Biol. Med.* (1957) **94,** 779.
334. Williams, M. A., *J. Nutr.* (1962) **76,** 35.
335. Gershoff, S. N., Faragalla, F. F., *J. Biol. Chem.* (1959) **234**, 2391.
336. Swendseid, M. E., Villalobos, J., Friedrich, B., *J. Nutr.* (1964) **82,** 206.
337. Takami, M., Fujioka, M., Wada, H., Taguchi, T., *Proc. Soc. Exp. Biol. Med.* (1968) **129,** 110.
338. Williams, M. A., Gunning, B., Pertel, R., *Proc. Soc. Exp. Biol. Med.* (1962) **109,** 442.
339. Ishii, K., Sevag, M. G., *Antibiot. Chemother. (Washington, D. C.)* (1956) **6,** 500.
340. Meltzer, H. L., Sprinson, D. B., *J. Biol. Chem.* (1952) **197,** 461.
341. Chao, F.-C., Delwiche, C. C., Greenberg, D. M., *Biochim. Biophys. Acta* (1953) **10,** 103.
342. Bricteux-Gregoire, S., Dewandre, A., Florkin, M., *Arch. Int. Physiol.* (1960) **68,** 281.
343. Pizer, L. I., *J. Bacteriol.* (1965) **89,** 1145.
344. Van Lenten, E. J., Simmonds, S., *J. Biol. Chem.* (1965) **240,** 3361.
345. Dewey, V. C., Kidder, G. W., *J. Gen. Microbiol.* (1960) **22**, 72.
346. Krasna, A. I., Peyser, P., Sprinson, D. B., *J. Biol. Chem.* (1952) **198,** 421.
347. Vohra, P., Lantz, F. H., Kratzer, F. H., *J. Biol. Chem.* (1956) **221,** 501.
348. Totter, J. R., Kelley, B., Day, P. L., Edwards, R. R., *J. Biol. Chem.* (1950) **186,** 145.
349. Holland, B. R., Meinke, W. W., *J. Biol. Chem.* (1949) **178**, 7.
350. Brand, E., Harris, M. M., Sandberg, M., Ringer, A. I., *Amer. J. Physiol.* (1929) **90,** 296.
351. Pagé, E., Martel, F., Gingras, R., *Rev. Can. Biol.* (1949) **8,** 298.
352. Martel, F., Pagé, E., Gingras, R., *Rev. Can. Biol.* (1947) **6,** 802.
353. Martel, F., *Laval Med.* (1950) **15,** 966.
354. Roth, J. S., Allison, J. B., *Proc. Soc. Exp. Biol. Med.* (1949) **70,** 327.
355. Almquist, H. J., Mecchi, E., Kratzer, F. H., *J. Biol. Chem.* (1941) **141,** 365.
356. Cohn, M., Simmonds, S., Chandler, J. P., du Vigneaud, V., *J. Biol. Chem.* (1946) **162,** 343.
357. Kelley, B., Totter, J. R., *Fed. Proc., Fed. Amer. Soc. Exp. Biol.* (1950) **9,** 189.
358. Jukes, T. H., *J Nutr.* (1941) **22,** 315.
359. Walker, J. B., *Biochim. Biophys. Acta* (1959) **36**, 574.
360. Fitch, C. D., Hsu, C., Dinning, J. S., *J. Biol. Chem.* (1960) **235,** 2362.
361. Ramirez, E., Calva, E., Trejo, A., *Biochem. J.* (1970) **119,** 757.
362. Fitch, C. D., Hsu, C., Dinning, J. S., *Biochim. Biophys. Acta* (1961) **52,** 194.
363. Coleman, D. L., *Arch. Biochem. Biophys.* (1961) **94,** 183.
364. *Nutr. Rev.* (1964) **22,** 182.
365. Richards, F. F., Scott, J. J., *Clin. Sci.* (1961) **20,** 387.
366. Prato, V., Massaro, A. L., Mazza, U., Bianco, G., Accatino, G., *Boll. Soc. Ital. Biol. Sper.* (1965) **41,** 1074.

367. Massaro, A. L., Mazza, U., Bianco, G., Accatino, G., Prato, V., *Boll. Soc. Ital. Biol. Sper.* (1965) **41,** 1078.
368. Massaro, A. L., Bianco, G., Accatino, G., *Boll. Soc. Ital. Biol. Sper.* (1965) **41,** 1076.
369. Labbe, R. F., Talman, E. L., Aldrich, R. A., *Biochim. Biophys. Acta* (1954) **15,** 590.
370. Talman, E. L., Labbe, R. F., Aldrich, R. A., Sears, D., *Arch. Biochem. Biophys.* (1959) **80,** 446.
371. Merchante, A., Wajchenberg, B. L., Schwartz, S., *Proc. Soc. Exp. Biol. Med.* (1957) **95,** 221.
372. De Matteis, F., Slater, T. F., Wang, D. Y., *Biochim. Biophys. Acta* (1963) **68,** 100.
373. De Matteis, F., Prior, B. E., *Biochem. J.* (1962) **83,** 1.
374. Taxay, E. P., *Lancet* (1961) **ii,** 936.
375. Ludwig, G. D., *J. Clin. Invest.* (1963) **42,** 953.
376. Dowdle, E., Mustard, P., Spong, N., Eales, L., *Clin. Sci.* (1968) **34,** 233.
377. Pimstone, N. R., Dowdle, E. B., Eales, L., *S. Afr. Med. J.* (1969) **43,** 961.
378. Yü, T.-F., Weissmann, B., Sharney, L., Kupfer, S., Gutman, A. B., *Amer. J. Med.* (1956) **21,** 901.
379. Yü, T.-F., Wasserman, L. R., Benedict, J. D., Bien, E. J., Gutman, A. B., Stetten, D., Jr., *Amer. J. Med.* (1953) **15,** 845.
380. Laster, L., Müller, A. F., *Amer. J. Med.* (1953) **15,** 857.
381. McCollum, E. V., Hoagland, D. R., *J. Biol. Chem.* (1913) **16,** 299.
382. McCollum, E. V., Hoagland, D. R., *J. Biol. Chem.* (1913) **16,** 321.
383. Lewis, H. B., *J. Biol. Chem.* (1914) **17,** 503.
384. Terroine, E. F., Bay, G., *Arch. Int. Pharmacodyn. Ther.* (1939) **63,** 300.
385. Swanson, W. W., *J. Biol. Chem.* (1925) **62,** 565.
386. Stekol, J. A., *Annu. Rev. Biochem.* (1941) **10,** 273.
387. Abderhalden, E., Strauss, H., *Z. Physiol. Chem.* (1914) **91,** 81.
388. Csonka, F. A., *J. Biol. Chem.* (1924) **60,** 545.
389. Griffith, W. H., Lewis, H. B., *J. Biol. Chem.* (1923) **57,** 697.
390. Griffith, W. H., Lewis, H. B., *J. Biol. Chem.* (1923) **57,** 1.
391. Arnstein, H. R. V., Neuberger, A., *Biochem. J.* (1951) **50,** 154.
392. Quick, A. J., *J. Biol. Chem.* (1926) **67,** 477.
393. Kingsbury, F. B., *Proc. Soc. Exp. Biol. Med.* (1922) **20,** 405.
394. Abbott, L. D., Jr., Lewis, H. B., *J. Biol. Chem.* (1939) **131,** 479.
395. Bloch, K., Schoenheimer, R., *J. Biol. Chem.* (1940) **135,** 99.
396. Quick, A. J., *J. Biol. Chem.* (1931) **92,** 65.
397. Griffith, W. H., *J. Biol. Chem.* (1929) **82,** 415.
398. White, A., *Yale J. Biol. Med.* (1941) **13,** 759.
399. Griffith, W. H., *J. Biol. Chem.* (1929) **85,** 751.
400. Christensen, H. N., Cooper, P. F., Jr., Johnson, R. D., Lynch, E. L., *J. Biol. Chem.* (1947) **168,** 191.
401. De Vries, A., Alexander, B., *J. Clin. Invest.* (1948) **27,** 665.
402. Gray, C. H., Neuberger, A., *Biochem. J.* (1950) **47,** 81.
403. Waelsch, H., Rittenberg, D., *Science* (1939) **90,** 423.
404. Rittenberg, D., Schoenheimer, R., *J. Biol. Chem.* (1939) **127,** 329.
405. Watts, R. W. E., Crawhall, J. C., *Biochem. J.* (1959) **73,** 277.
406. Crane, C. W., Neuberger, A., *Biochem. J.* (1960) **74,** 313.
407. Garfinkle, D., Lajtha, A., *J. Biol. Chem.* (1963) **238,** 2429.
408. Garfinkle, D., *J. Biol. Chem.* (1963) **238,** 2435.
409. Yamanaka, M., Ishii, K., Oda, T., *Clin. Chim. Acta* (1959) **4,** 549.
410. Amsel, L. P., Levy, G., *J. Pharm. Sci.* (1969) **58,** 321.
411. McCrudden, F. H., "Uric Acid. The Chemistry, Physiology, and Pathology of Uric Acid and Physiologically Important Purine Bodies with a Discussion of the Metabolism of Gout," Fort Hill Press, Boston, 1905.

412. Lewis, H. B., Karr, W. G., *J. Biol. Chem.* (1916) **25,** 13.
413. Michael, S. T., Looney, J. M., Borkovic, E. J., *Amer. J. Physiol.* (1944) **140,** 548.
414. Quick, A. J., *J. Biol. Chem.* (1932) **98,** 157.
415. Quick, A. J., *J. Biol. Chem.* (1933) **101,** 475.
416. Friedman, M., *Amer. J. Physiol.* (1948) **152,** 302.
417. Quick, A. J., Cooper, M. A., *J. Biol. Chem.* (1932) **99,** 119.
418. Dalal, F. R., Gots, J. S., *Biochem. Biophys. Res. Commun.* (1965) **20,** 509.
419. Stokstad, E. L. R., *J. Biol. Chem.* (1941) **139,** 475.
420. Snell, E. E., Mitchell, H. K., *Arch. Biochem.* (1942) **1,** 93.
421. Snell, E. E., Mitchell, H. K., *Proc. Nat. Acad. Sci.* (1941) **27,** 1.
422. Stokes, J., *J. Bacteriol.* (1944) **48,** 201.
423. Luckey, T. D., Briggs, G. M., Jr., Elvehjem, C. A., *J. Biol. Chem.* (1944) **152,** 157.
424. Elion, G. B., Hitchings, G. H., *J. Biol. Chem.* (1950) **185,** 651.
425. Baker, H., Hutner, S. H., Sobotka, H., *Ann. N. Y. Acad. Sci.* (1955) **62,** 349.
426. Aaronson, S., Rodriguez, E., *J. Bacteriol.* (1958) **75,** 660.
427. Landy, M., Streightoff, F., *Proc. Soc. Exp. Biol. Med.* (1943) **52,** 127.
428. Lampen, J. O., Roepke, R. R., Jones, M. J., *J. Biol. Chem.* (1946) **164,** 789.
429. Housewright, R. D., Koser, S. A., *J. Infec. Dis.* (1944) **75,** 113.
430. Lampen, J. O., Jones, M. J., *J. Biol. Chem.* (1947) **170,** 133.
431. Bishop, C., Rand, R., Talbott, J. H., *Metab. Clin. Exp.* (1955) **4,** 174.
432. Gots, J. S., *Fed. Proc., Fed. Amer. Soc. Exp. Biol.* (1950) **9,** 178.
433. Bergmann, E. D., Volcani, B. E., Ben-Ishai, R., *J. Biol. Chem.* (1952) **194,** 521.
434. Ben-Ishai, R., Volcani, B., Bergmann, E. D., *Experientia* (1951) **7,** 63.
435. Webb, M., *Biochem. J.* (1958) **70,** 472.
436. Westby, C. A., Gots, J. S., *J. Biol. Chem.* (1969) **244,** 2095.
437. Iwai, K., Nakagawa, S., Okinaka, O., *Biochim. Biophys. Acta* (1963) **68,** 152.
438. Braunshtein, A. E., Vinkelman, G. I., *Biokhimiya* (1958) **23,** 887.
439. McGeer, P. L., McGeer, E. G., Griffin, M. C., *Can. J. Biochem. Physiol.* (1961) **39,** 591.
440. Hartman, S. C., "Metabolic Pathways," Greenberg, D. M., Ed., 3rd ed., Vol. 4, p. 1, Academic, New York, 1970.
441. Warren, L., Flaks, J. G., Buchanan, J. M., *J. Biol. Chem.* (1957) **229,** 627.
442. Totter, J. R., Volkin, E., Carter, C. E., *J. Amer. Chem. Soc.* (1951) **73,** 1521.
443. Drysdale, G. R., Plant, G. W. E., Lardy, H. A., *J. Biol. Chem.* (1951) **193,** 533.
444. Greenberg, G. R., Spilman, E., *J. Biol. Chem.* (1956) **219,** 411.
445. Luhby, A. L., Cooperman, J. M., *Lancet* (1962) **ii,** 1381.
446. Herbert, V., Streiff, R. R., Sullivan, L. W., McGeer, P. L., *Lancet* (1964) **ii,** 45.
447. Middleton, J. E., Coward, R. F., Smith, P., *Lancet* (1964) **ii,** 258.
448. McGeer, P. L., Sen, N. P., Grant, D. A., *Can. J. Biochem.* (1965) **43,** 1367.
449. Papp, E. M., Totter, J. R., *J. Biol. Chem.* (1952) **199,** 547.
450. Totter, J. R., *J. Cell. Comp. Physiol.* (1953) **41** Suppl., 241.
451. Harris, J. S., Kohn, H. I., *J. Biol. Chem.* (1941) **141,** 989.
452. Shive, W., Roberts, E. C., *J. Biol. Chem.* (1946) **162,** 463.
453. Kohn, H. I., *Ann. N. Y. Acad. Sci.* (1943) **44,** 503.
454. Winkler, K. C., de Haan, P. G., *Arch. Biochem. Biophys.* (1948) **18,** 97.
455. Schapfer, W. H., *Experientia* (1946) **2,** 188.
456. Martin, G. J., Fisher, C. V., *J. Biol. Chem.* (1942) **144,** 289.
457. Fox, C. L., Jr., *Proc. Soc. Exp. Biol. Med.* (1942) **51,** 102.
458. Shive, W., Ackerman, W. W., Gordon, M., Getzendander, M. E., Eaken, R. E., *J. Amer. Chem. Soc.* (1947) **69,** 725.

459. Greenberg, G. R., *J. Amer. Chem. Soc.* (1952) **74**, 6307.
460. Gots, J. S., *Nature (London)* (1953) **172**, 256.
461. Sirotnak, F. M., *Genetics* (1970) **65**, 391.
462. Dunlap, R. B., Gundersen, L. E., Huennekens, F. M., *Biochem. Biophys. Res. Commun.* (1971) **42**, 772.
463. Harding, N. G. L., Martelli, M. F., Huennekens, F. M., *Arch. Biochem. Biophys.* (1970) **137**, 295.
464. Ohara, O., Silber, R., *J. Biol. Chem.* (1969) **244**, 1988.
465. Soini, J., Nurmikko, V., *Acta Chem. Scand.* (1963) **17**, 947.
466. Nurmikko, V., Soini, J., Äärimaa, O., *Acta Chem. Scand.* (1965) **19**, 129.
467. Bloch, A., *Biochim. Biophys. Acta* (1970) **201**, 323.
468. Burchall, J. J., Hitchings, G. H., *Advan. Enzyme Regul.* (1968) **6**, 323.
469. Albrecht, A., Hutchinson, D. J., *J. Bacteriol.* (1964) **87**, 792.
470. Nichol, C. A., *Advan. Enzyme Regul.* (1968) **6**, 305.
471. Bertino, J. R., Hillcoat, B. L., *Advan. Enzyme Regul.* (1968) **6**, 335.
472. Raunio, R., Hakala, M. T., *Biochem. Pharamacol.* (1968) **17**, 1744.
473. Bertino, J. R., Silber, R., Freeman, M., Alenty, A., Albrecht, M., Gabrio, B. W., Huennekens, F. M., *J. Clin. Invest.* (1963) **42**, 1899.
474. Sartorelli, A. C., Booth, B. A., Bertino, J. R., *Arch. Biochem. Biophys.* (1964) **108**, 53.
475. Sotobayashi, H., Rosen, F., Nichol, C. A., *Biochemistry* (1966) **5**, 3878.
476. Eagle, H., *Science* (1955) **122**, 501.
477. Walters, T. R., *J. Pediat.* (1967) **70**, 686.
478. Newman, E. B., Magasanik, B., *Biochim. Biophys. Acta* (1963) **78**, 437.
479. Rieder, S. V., *Arch. Biochem. Biophys.* (1960) **86**, 318.
480. Cheeseman, P., Crosbie, G. W., *Biochem. J.* (1966) **99**, 24P.
481. Koch, A. L., Levy, H. R., *J. Biol. Chem.* (1955) **217**, 947.
482. Nester, E. W., Spizizen, J., *J. Bacteriol.* (1961) **82**, 867.
483. Malathi, V. G., Ramakrishnan, T., *Biochem. J.* (1966) **98**, 594.
484. Parshin, A. N., Ostroumova, M. N., Goryukhina, T. A., *Biokhimiya* (1967) **32**, 746.
485. Trakatellis, A. C., Axelrod, A. E., *Biochem. J.* (1965) **95**, 344.
486. Schirch, L., Ropp, M., *Biochemistry* (1967) **6**, 253.
487. Kerr, S., Chernigoy, F., *J. Biol. Chem.* (1953) **200**, 887.
488. Revel, H. R. B., Magasanik, B., *J. Biol. Chem.* (1958) **233**, 439.
489. McCormick, N. G., Ordal, E. J., Whiteley, H. R., *J. Bacteriol.* (1962) **83**, 887.
490. McCormick, N. G., Ordal, E. J., Whiteley, H. R., *J. Bacteriol.* (1962) **83**, 899.
491. Nakayama, H., Midwinter, G. G., Krampitz, L. P., *Arch. Biochem. Biophys.* (1971) **143**, 526.
492. Dakin, H. D., Janney, N. W., Wakeman, A. J., *J. Biol. Chem.* (1913) **14**, 341.
493. Friedmann, B., Nakada, H. I., Weinhouse, S., *J. Biol. Chem.* (1954) **210**, 413.
494. Stokstad, E. L. R., Webb, R. E., Shah, E., *J. Nutr.* (1966) **88**, 225.
495. Rabinowitz, J. C., Tabor, H., *J. Biol. Chem.* (1958) **233**, 252.
496. Weinhouse, S., Friedmann, B., *J. Biol. Chem.* (1952) **197**, 733.
497. MacKenzie, C. G., Chandler, J. P., Keller, E. B., Rachele, J. R., Cross, N., du Vigneaud, V., *J. Biol. Chem.* (1949) **180**, 99.
498. Williams, W. J., Buchanan, J. M., *J. Biol. Chem.* (1953) **202**, 253.
499. Newman, E. B., *Can. J. Microbiol.* (1970) **16**, 933.
500. Sonne, J. C., Buchanan, J. M., Delluva, A. M., *J. Biol. Chem.* (1948) **173**, 69.
501. Buchanan, J. M., Sonne, J. C., *J. Biol. Chem.* (1946) **166**, 781.
502. Marsh, J. H., *J. Biol. Chem.* (1951) **190**, 633.
503. Heinrich, M. R., Wilson, D. W., *J. Biol. Chem.* (1950) **186**, 447.

504. Buchanan, J. M., Wilson, D. W., *Fed. Proc., Fed. Amer. Soc. Exp. Biol.* (1953) **12**, 646.
505. Whiteley, H. R., *Comp. Biochem. Physiol.* (1960) **1**, 227.
506. Nurmikko, V., Soini, J., Taiminen, S., Kyyhkynen, H., *Acta Chem. Scand.* (1965) **19**, 135.
507. Whiteley, H. R., Osborn, M. J., Huennekens, F. M., *J. Biol. Chem.* (1959) **234**, 1538.
508. Welch, W. H., Irwin, C. L., Himes, R. H., *Fed. Proc., Fed. Amer. Soc. Exp. Biol.* (1968) **27**, 793.
509. Johnson, A. H., Hutchison, D. J., *J. Bacteriol.* (1964) **87**, 786.
510. Albrecht, A. M., Hutchison, D. J., *Fed. Proc., Fed. Amer. Soc. Exp. Biol.* (1963) **22**, 205.
511. Slavikova, V., Semonsky, M., Slavik, K., Volejnikova, J., *Biochem. Pharmacol.* (1966) **15**, 763.
512. Brown, D. D., Silva, O. L., McDonald, P. B., Snyder, S. H., Kies, M. W., *J. Biol. Chem.* (1960) **235**, 154.
513. Reid, J. C., Landefeld, M. O., Simpson, J. L., *J. Nat. Cancer Inst.* (1952) **12**, 929.
514. Reid, J. C., Landefeld, M. O., *Arch. Biochem. Biophys.* (1951) **34**, 219.
515. Sprinson, D. S., Rittenberg, D., *J. Biol. Chem.* (1952) **198**, 655.
516. Reid, J. C., Temmer, O. S., Bacon, M. O., *J. Nat. Cancer Inst.* (1956) **17**, 189.
517. Groth, D. P., D'Angelo, J. M., Vogler, W. R., Mingioli, E. S., Betz, B., *Cancer Res.* (1971) **31**, 332.
518. Arakawa, T., *Amer. J. Med.* (1970) **48**, 594.
519. Arakawa, T., Ohara, K., Kudo, Z., Tada, K., Hayashi, T., Mizuno, T., *Tohoku J. Exp. Med.* (1963) **80**, 370.
520. Arakawa, T., Ohara, K., Takahashi, Y., Ogasawara, J., Hayashi, T., Chiba, R., Wada, Y., Tada, K., Mizuno, T., Okamura, T., Yoshida, T., *Ann. Paediat.* (1965) **205**, 1.
521. Arakawa, T., Wada, Y., *Tohoku J. Exp. Med.* (1966) **88**, 99.
522. Arakawa, T., Tamura, T., Higashi, O., Ohara, K., Tanno, K., Honda, Y., Narisawa, K., Konno, T., Wada, Y., Soto, Y., Mizuno, T., *Tohoku J. Exp. Med.* (1968) **94**, 3.
523. Arakawa, T., Hirono, H., *Tohoku J. Exp. Med.* (1966) **88**, 161.
524. Motokawa, Y., Kikuchi, G., *J. Biochem. (Tokyo)* (1969) **65**, 71.
525. Pitts, J. D., Stewart, J. A., Crosbie, G. W., *Biochim. Biophys. Acta* (1961) **50**, 361.
526. Karlsson, J. L., Barker, H. A., *J. Biol. Chem.* (1949) **177**, 597.
527. Yoshida, T., Kikuchi, G., *Arch. Biochem. Biophys.* (1971) **145**, 658.
528. Edmonds, M., Delluva, A. M., Wilson, D. W., *J. Biol. Chem.* (1952) **197**, 251.
529. Koch, A. L., *J. Biol. Chem.* (1955) **217**, 931.
530. Crosbie, G. W., *Biochem. J.* (1966) **99**, 21P.
531. Bull, F. G., Woods, D. D., *J. Gen. Microbiol.* (1963) **31**, xxiv.
532. Ando, T., Nyhan, W. L., Gerritson, T., Gang, L., Heiner, D. C., Bray, P. F., *Pediat. Res.* (1968) **2**, 254.
533. Yoshida, T., Kikuchi, G., Tada, K., Narisawa, K., Arakawa, T., *Biochem. Biophys. Res. Commun.* (1969) **35**, 577.
534. Tada, K., Narisawa, K., Yoshida, T., Konno, T., Yokoyama, Y., Nakagawa, H., Tanno, K., Mochizuki, K., Arakawa, T., Yoshida, T., Kikuchi, G., *Tohoku J. Exp. Med.* (1969) **98**, 289.
535. De Groot, C. J., Troelstra, J. A., Hommes, F. A., *Pediat. Res.* (1970) **4**, 238.
536. Yoshida, T., Kikuchi, G., *Biochem. Biophys. Res. Commun.* (1969) **35**, 577.
537. Dinning, J. S., Keith, C. K., Day, P. L., Totter, J. R., *Proc. Soc. Exp. Biol. Med.* (1949) **72**, 262.
538. Hsu, P.-T., Combs, G. F., *J. Nutr.* (1952) **47**, 73.

539. Stern, J. R., McGinnis, J., *Proc. Soc. Exp. Biol. Med.* (1951) **76,** 233.
540. Pagé, E., Gingras, R., *Trans. Roy. Soc. Can. Sect. 5* (1946) **40,** 119.
541. Martin, G. J., *Proc. Soc. Exp. Biol. Med.* (1946) **63,** 528.
542. Groschke, A. C., Briggs, G. M., *J. Biol. Chem.* (1946) **165,** 739.
543. Richert, D. A., Amberg, R., Wilson, M., *J. Biol. Chem.* (1962) **237,** 99.
544. Nemeth, A. M., Russell, C. S., Shemin, D., *J. Biol. Chem.* (1957) **229,** 415.
545. Braunshtein, A. E., Poznanskaya, A. A., Spryshkova, R. A., Gnuchev, N. V., *Dokl. Biochem.* (1964) **154–9,** 283.
546. Sauberlich, H. A., "The Vitamins," Sebrell, W. H., Jr., Harris, R. S., Eds., 2nd ed., Vol. 2, p. 33, Academic, New York, 1968.
547. Spryshkova, R. A., Poznaskaya, A. A., *Dokl. Biochem.* (1966) **168,** 216.
548. Sime, J. T., Johnson, B. C., *J. Biol. Chem.* (1955) **215,** 41.
549. Decker, K., Jungermann, K., Thauer, R. K., Hunt, S. V., *Biochim. Biophys. Acta* (1967) **141,** 202.
550. Williams, R. J., Eakin, R. E., Beerstecher, E., Jr., Shive, W., "The Biochemistry of the B Vitamins," Reinhold, New York, 1950.
551. Bergmann, E. D., Volcani, B. E., Ben-Ishai, R., *J. Biol. Chem.* (1952) **194,** 531.
552. Yeh, Y. C., Greenberg, D. M., *Biochim. Biophys. Acta* (1965) **105,** 279.
553. Dalal, F. R., Gots, J. S., *Biochem. Biophys. Res. Commun.* (1966) **22,** 340.
554. Dalal, F. R., Gots, J. S., *J. Biol. Chem.* (1967) **242,** 3636.
555. Taylor, R. T., Dickerman, H., Weissbach, H., *Arch. Biochem. Biophys.* (1966) **117,** 405.
556. Albrecht, A. M., Pearce, F. K., Hutchison, D. J., *J. Bacteriol.* (1968) **95,** 1779.
557. Roman, H., *Cold Spring Harbor Symp. Quant. Biol.* (1956) **21,** 157.
558. Levinthal, M., Fogel, S., Hurst, D. D., *Genetics* (1962) **47,** 967.
559. Dorfman, B. Z., *Genetics* (1963) **48,** 887.
560. Mazlen, A. S., Eaton, N. R., *Biochem. Biophys. Res. Commun.* (1967) **26,** 590.
561. Clavillier, L., Luzzati, M., Slonimski, P. P., *C.R. Soc. Biol.* (1960) **154,** 1970.
562. Jones, E. W., Magasanik, B., *Biochem. Biophys. Res. Commun.* (1967) **29,** 600.
563. Jones, E. W., Magasanik, B., *Bacteriol. Proc.* (1967) 127.
564. Nagy, M., Heslot, H., Poirier, L., *C.R. Acad. Sci. Ser. D* (1969) **269,** 1268.
565. Lazowska, J., Luzzati, M., *Biochem. Biophys. Res. Commun.* (1970) **39,** 40.
566. Lazowska, J., Luzzati, M., *Biochem. Biophys. Res. Commun.* (1970) **39,** 34.
567. Lomax, C. A., Gross, T. S., Woods, R. A., *J. Bacteriol.* (1971) **107,** 1.
568. Hakala, M. T., Zakrzewski, S. F., Nichol, C. A., *J. Biol. Chem.* (1961) **236,** 952.
569. Arakawa, T., Fujii, M., Ohara, K., Watanabe, S., Karashashi, M., Kobayashi, M., Hirono, H., *Tohoku J. Exp. Med.* (1966) **88,** 341.
570. Arakawa, T., *Amer. J. Med.* (1970) **48,** 594.
571. Shive, W., *Ann. N.Y. Acad. Sci.* (1950) **52,** 1212.
572. Lampen, J. O., Jones, M. J., Roepke, R. R., *J. Biol. Chem.* (1949) **180,** 423.
573. Kalle, G. P., Gots, J. S., *Proc. Soc. Exp. Biol. Med.* (1962) **109,** 277.
574. Soška, J., *J. Bacteriol.* (1966) **91,** 1840.
575. Dalal, F. R., Gots, R. E., Gots, J. S., *J. Bacteriol.* (1966) **91,** 507.
576. Eisenstadt, J., Lengyel, P., *Science* (1966) **154,** 524.
577. Samuel, C. E., D'Ari, L., Rabinowitz, J. C., *J. Biol. Chem.* (1970) **245,** 5115.
578. Pine, M. J., Gordon, B., Sarimo, S. S., *Biochim. Biophys. Acta* (1969) **179,** 439.
579. Goldberger, R. F., Berberich, M. A., *Proc. Nat. Acad. Sci.* (1965) **54,** 279.
580. Marver, D., Berberich, M. A., Goldberger, R. F., *Science* (1966) **153,** 1655.
581. Berberich, M. A., Kovach, J. S., Goldberger, R. F., *Proc. Nat. Acad. Sci.* (1967) **57,** 1857.

582. Herbert, V., *Vitam. Horm. (New York)* (1968) **26,** 525.
583. Felix, J. S., DeMars, R., *Proc. Nat. Acad. Sci.* (1969) **62,** 536.
584. Rosenbloom, F. M., Henderson, J. F., Caldwell, I. C., Kelley, W. N., Seegmiller, J. E., *J. Biol. Chem.* (1968) **243,** 1166.
585. Nyhan, W. L., *Fed. Proc., Fed. Amer. Soc. Exp. Biol.* (1968) **27,** 1034.
586. Van der Zee, S. P. M., Schretlen, E. D. A. M., Monnens, L. A. H., *Lancet* (1968) **i,** 1427.
587. Van der Zee, S. P. M., Lommen, E. J. P., Trijbels, J. M. F., Schretlin, E. D. A. M., *Acta Paediat. Scand.* (1970) **59**, 259.
588. Manzke, H., *Helv. Paediat. Acta* (1967) **22,** 258.
589. Marie, J., Royer, P., Rappaport, R., *Arch. Fr. Pediat.* (1967) **24,** 501.
590. Hawkins, C. F., Ellis, H. A., Rawson, A., *Ann. Rheum. Dis.* (1965) **24**, 224.
591. Milunsky, A., Graef, J. W., Gaynor, M. F., *J. Pediat.* (1968) **72**, 790.
592. Benke, P. J., Anderson, J., *Pediat. Res.* (1969) **3,** 356.
593. Arakawa, T., Mizuno, T., Sakai, K., Chida, K., Watanabe, A., Ohara, K., Coursin, D. B., *Tohoku J. Exp. Med.* (1969) **97,** 385.
594. Arakawa, T., Mizuno, T., Honda, Y., Tamura, T., Sakai, K., Tatsumi, S., Chiba, F., Coursin, D. B., *Tohoku J. Exp. Med.* (1969) **97,** 391.
595. O'Dell, B. L., Whitley, J. R., Hogan, A. G., *Proc. Soc. Exp. Biol. Med.* (1948) **69,** 272.
596. Wada, Y., Arakawa, T., *Tohoku J. Exp. Med.* (1968) **96,** 313.
597. Murphy, M. L., Dagg, C. P., Karnofsky, D. A., *Pediatrics* (1957) **19,** 701.
598. Arakawa, T., Fujii, M., Hayashi, T., *Tohoku J. Exp. Med.* (1967) **91,** 143.
599. Zumin, C., Borrone, C., *Minerva Pediat.* (1955) **7,** 66.
600. Grant, H. C., Hoffbrand, A. V., Wells, D. G., *Lancet* (1965) **ii,** 763.
601. Luhby, A. L., Eagle, F. J., Roth, E., Cooperman, J. M., *Amer. J. Dis. Child.* (1961) **102**, 482.
602. Strachan, R. W., Henderson, J. G., *Quart. J. Med.* (1967) **36,** 189.
603. Herbert, V., *Ann. Intern. Med.* (1968) **68,** 956.
604. Jaenicke, L., Rüdiger, H., *Fed. Proc., Fed. Amer. Soc. Exp. Biol.* (1971) **30,** 160.
605. Jukes, T. H., *Fed. Proc., Fed. Amer. Soc. Exp. Biol.* (1971) **30**, 155.
606. Katzen, H. M., Buchanan, J. M., *J Biol. Chem.* (1965) **240,** 825.
607. Rowbury, R. J., Woods, D. D., *J. Gen. Microbiol.* (1961) **24**, 129.
608. Dickerman, H., Weissbach, H., *Biochem. Biophys. Res. Commun.* (1964) **16,** 593.
609. Greene, R. C., Su, C.-H., Holloway, C. T., *Biochem. Biophys. Res. Commun.* (1970) **38,** 1120.
610. Kutzbach, C., Galloway, E., Stokstad, E. L. R., *Proc. Soc. Exp. Biol. Med.* (1967) **124**, 801.
611. Kutzbach, C., Stokstad, E. L. R., *Biochim. Biophys. Acta* (1967) **139,** 217.
612. Dickerman, H., Redfield, B. G., Bieri, J. G., Weissbach, H., *J. Biol. Chem.* (1964) **239,** 2545.
613. Finkelstein, J. D., Kyle, W. E., Harris, B. J., *Arch. Biochem. Biophys.* (1971) **146,** 84.
614. Nixon, P. F., Bertino, J. R., *Amer. J. Med.* (1970) **48,** 555.
615. Sullivan, L. W., Liu, Y. K., McGeer, P. L., *Blood* (1966) **28**, 991.
616. Oace, S. M., Tarczy-Hornoch, K., Stokstad, E. L. R., *J. Nutr.* (1968) **95,** 445.
617. Lindegren, C. C., Lindegren, G., *Proc. Nat. Acad. Sci.* (1947) **33,** 314.
618. Arakawa, T., Narisawa, K., Tanno, K., Ohara, K., Higashi, O., Honda, Y., Tamura, T., Wada, Y., Mizuno, T., Hayashi, T., Hirooka, Y., Ohno, Y., Ikeda, M., *Tohoku J. Exp. Med.* (1967) **93,** 1.
619. Mudd, S. H., Levy, H. L., Abeles, R. H., *Biochem. Biophys. Res. Commun.* (1969) **35**, 121.
620. Levy, H. L., Mudd, S. H., Schulman, J. D., Dreyfus, P. M., Abeles, R. H., *Amer. J. Med.* (1970) **48,** 390.

Chapter

5

Inhibition of Purine Biosynthesis by Endproducts

ENDPRODUCT (OR FEEDBACK) inhibition of metabolic pathways is a now well studied and well accepted mechanism of biochemical regulation of cellular activities. Although this phenomenon can be expressed in several ways (*1*, *2*), the simplest form is inhibition of the first irreversible and specific reaction in a biosynthetic pathway by the principal endproduct of that pathway. In the case of purine biosynthesis the situation is complicated by the ready interconversion of inosinate, the actual endproduct, with other purine ribonucleotides; thus there are in fact nine purine ribonucleotides that are potential regulators of their own synthesis.

The study of endproduct inhibition of a pathway such as that of purine biosynthesis *de novo* may be thought of as taking place in three distinct phases. First, the inhibition of the pathway or some part of it in intact cells is observed following supplementation of culture or incubation media with endproducts or their proximal precursors (*e.g.*, purine bases, which are converted to ribonucleotides *via* the purine phosphoribosyltransferases). Next, endproducts are shown to inhibit one or more enzymes of the pathway in cell-free preparations. Finally, these observations are evaluated in terms of their physiological significance for the regulation of the pathway in intact cells grown under normal conditions, *i.e.*, without supplementation with added endproducts or their precursors.

The first phase, the demonstration of inhibition of purine biosynthesis *de novo* upon addition to media of purine bases and ribonucleosides, has been exhaustively explored in a wide number of biological systems and is not open to any question. The second phase, the study of inhibition of specific enzymes by purine ribonucleotides, has made considerable progress, but the detailed mechanisms of such inhibition have not yet been established. It is the third phase, that of evaluation of the physiological significance of the observations made in the first two stages of investigation, that is in a state of considerable uncertainty and confusion. The literature on this point contains few really hard data, and discussions of this matter sometimes involve unjustified generalization and oversimplification.

In this chapter an attempt will be made to evaluate critically the available information on endproduct inhibition of purine biosynthesis *de novo* and to assess the significance of these data for the physiological regulation of this process *in vivo*. Certain aspects of this subject have been reviewed by the author (*3*), Stadtman (*2*), Blakley and Vitols (*4*), and Momose (*5*).

Numerous purine analogs and derivatives inhibit purine biosynthesis by mimicking the normal endproduct inhibitory actions of naturally occurring purines; the discussion of these compounds and their effects on this pathway will for the most part be reserved until Chapter 8.

Experimental Systems for the Study of Endproduct Inhibition

The concept of endproduct inhibition of metabolic pathways was defined and concretely expressed in 1956 in the course of studies of isoleucine synthesis by Umbarger (*6*) and of pyrimidine biosynthesis by Yates and Pardee (*7*). Not unexpectedly, several observations during the five years preceding these studies had laid the groundwork for this concept, and indeed similar ideas had occasionally been expressed at least as far back as 1923 (*8*).

In 1957 Gots (*9*) published the first study of the regulation of purine biosynthesis *de novo* in which the term "feedback inhibition" was used, and detailed investigation of this topic may be said to date from this publication. In fact, however, endproduct inhibition of purine synthesis had been observed at least as early as 1946 (*10*), but the significance of most of these early findings went unrecognized. The following discussion of the development of the field of endproduct inhibition of purine biosynthesis illustrates not only the history of this subject but also the various experimental systems used to study this phenomenon; these systems will be briefly outlined.

Inhibition of Accumulation of Intermediates. The simplest and at the same time most definitive assays for the study of endproduct inhibition of purine biosynthesis *de novo* employ cells in which this pathway is blocked by genetic, pharmacological, or nutritional means and in which some intermediate (or a metabolite of it) accumulates as a consequence. Cessation of such accumulation when purines are added to incubation or growth media is then presumptive evidence of endproduct inhibition. This approach has proved extremely useful both in microorganisms and in animal cells.

Microorganisms. The earliest observations of endproduct inhibition of purine biosynthesis employed adenine-requiring strains of *Saccharomyces cerevisiae* and *Neurospora crassa* which under appropriate conditions accumulated the red or purple pigment formed from aminoimidazole or its ribosyl derivative (*see* Chapter 2); these mutants thus lacked either phosphoribosyl-aminoimidazole carboxylase or phosphoribosyl-aminoimidazole succinocarboxamide synthetase. The relative amounts of pigment formed under different conditions were estimated in early studies by visual inspection and only later was spectrophotometric determination used.

Purple mutants were used in early studies of microbial genetics, and Mitchell and Houlahan (*10*) observed in 1946 that such mutants of *Neurospora crassa* formed only a small amount of pigment when cultures were supplied with excess adenine. In the following few years Lindegren and Lindegren (*11*), Reaume and Tatum (*12*), Tavlitzky (*13*), and Abrams (*14*) also noted that excess adenine suppressed pigment formation in *Saccharomyces cerevisiae* mutants or that colorless colonies or cultures became pink when the growth-supporting purine was exhausted from the medium. These observations have been consistently confirmed in more recent work with this organism, and similar findings have been reported using the equivalent mutants of *Schizosaccharomyces pombe* (*15*).

Pigment derived from aminoimidazole is also produced by biotin-deficient *Saccharomyces cerevisiae,* as discussed in Chapter 4. Beginning in 1950, numerous studies (*16–20*) demonstrated clearly that pigment and aminoimidazole formation in yeast grown with sub-optimal concentrations of biotin were depressed when adenine was added to the culture media. Friedman and Moat (*21*) also studied a strain of *Vibrio comma* that synthesized aminoimidazole only in a purine-deficient medium and a pigment-producing mutant of *Neurospora crassa* that was pink only at low purine concentrations. Love and co-workers (*22, 23*) observed that the W-11 mutant of *Escherichia coli* K_{12} produced the maximum amount of aminoimidazole at a lower concentration of hypoxanthine than that required for optimum growth. Finally, purple mutants of *Candida albicans* were shown by Sarachek (*24*) not to produce pigment at high adenine concentrations.

It will be shown in Chapter 7 that the pyrimidine moiety of thiamine is synthesized from phosphoribosyl-aminoimidazole; numerous examples are discussed of growth inhibition in microorganisms due to thiamine deficiency which in turn was produced by inhibition of phosphoribosyl-aminoimidazole synthesis upon addition of purines to culture media.

Another intermediate of the purine biosynthetic pathway, phosphoribosyl-aminoimidazole carboxamide (or its dephosphorylated derivative and free base), accumulates in *Escherichia coli* cultures partially inhibited by sulfonamides and also in *p*-aminobenzoate-requiring mutants of this organism; these systems have been described in Chapter 4. Gots (*25, 26*) showed in 1950 that addition of purines in certain concentrations stimulated both growth and aminoimidazole carboxamide synthesis, but at higher concentrations growth was further stimulated whereas accumulation of aminoimidazole carboxamide was depressed. Sulfonamide inhibition and aminoimidazole carboxamide accumulation were later used in studies of endproduct inhibition in *Salmonella typhimurium* as well (*27*). Gots and Chu (*28*) also showed that whereas growth of a *p*-aminobenzoate auxotroph of *Escherichia coli* could be supported by a mixture of casein hydrolysate, thymine, and adenine accumulation of aminoimidazole carboxamide was markedly inhibited by adenine.

In studies of mutants of *Salmonella typhimurium* and *Escherichia coli* which lacked adenylosuccinate lyase, Gots and Gollub (*29*) demonstrated that the synthesis of phosphoribosyl-aminoimidazole succinocarboxamide was inhibited when the concentration of adenine in the medium was optimal for growth. In much later studies Bennett and Smithers (*30*) demonstrated endproduct inhibition of phosphoribosyl-formylglycineamide accumulation in azaserine-treated *Escherichia coli;* this system will be described in detail below. Finally, adenine has been shown to inhibit the accumulation of inosinate (or of inosine or hypoxanthine derived from it) in *Micrococcus glutamicus* (*31*), *Bacillus subtilis* (*32, 33*), *Brevibacterium ammoniogenes* (*34, 35*), and *Neurospora crassa* (*36*).

A great many of these observations of endproduct inhibition of purine biosynthesis *de novo* were published prior to or at about the same time as Gots' first deliberate study of this phenomenon in 1957 (*9*). He measured the accumulation of aminoimidazole carboxamide in the B-96 mutant of *Escherichia coli,* which lacks phosphoribosyl-aminoimidazole carboxamide formyltransferase; similar mutants were later used by Kalle and Gots (*27*) and Magasanik and Karibian (*37*). In this system maximal accumulation of aminoimidazole carboxamide occurred at an adenine concentration (4 μg/ml) which allowed only 30% of the maximal growth. At 20 μg/ml the growth was maximal, but the accumulation was completely suppressed. Inhibition was expressed immediately upon addition of the purine, and was substantially reversed when the medium was replaced with one lacking adenine.

Animal Cells. Mutants of animal cells which accumulate intermediates of purine biosynthesis *de novo* are not known, and attempts to block this pathway quantitatively by nutritional deprivation have not been reported. It is thus only by the use of drugs that intermediates can be made to accumulate and that inhibition of this accumulation by purines can be measured. The most useful drug in this regard has been azaserine (*O*-diazoacetyl-L-serine), which is a glutamine analog and which quantitatively inhibits phosphoribosyl-formylglycineamidine synthetase; it is discussed in Chapter 8. Phosphoribosyl-formylglycineamide accumulates in the presence of azaserine, and the incorporation of glycine-^{14}C or formate-^{14}C into this compound is a measure of the rate of the early reactions of the purine biosynthetic pathway. This system was first used to demonstrate inhibition of purine synthesis by 6-thioguanine (*38*), and development of simplified methods for the isolation of radioactive phosphoribosyl-formylglycineamide by LePage and Jones (*39*), Henderson (*40*), and Brockman and Chumley (*41, 42*) have led to its widespread use.

By the use of this method endproduct inhibition by naturally occurring purines has been demonstrated in Sarcoma 180 *in vivo* (*39*) and in culture (*43*), Adenocarcinoma 755 cells *in vivo* (*39*) and in culture (*42, 43*), 6C3HED cells *in vivo* (*39*), Mecca lymphosarcoma cells *in vivo* (*39*), Leukemia L1210 cells *in vivo* (*42*), Ehrlich ascites tumor cells *in vivo* (*39*) and *in vitro* (*40, 44–48*), H.Ep. #2 cells in culture (*30, 41, 42*), and human fibroblasts in culture (*49, 50, 51*).

Trachewsky and Johnstone (*52*) have also studied endproduct inhibition by measuring the synthesis of phosphoribosyl-formylglycineamide in cell-free extracts of Ehrlich ascites tumor cells which were incubated with nucleotide inhibitors, PP-ribose-P, glutamine, and other substrates and cofactors.

Inhibition of Precursor Incorporation. Endproduct inhibition of purine biosynthesis may also be detected by measurements of inhibition of the incorporation of radioactive glycine, formate, or other precursor into acid-soluble or nucleic acid purines upon addition of purines to the system. The purine nucleotide pools into which or through which the labeled compounds flow are often greatly enlarged because of the added purines, and dilution of the radioactivity may occur; the results of dilution may be indistinguishable from true inhibition. Such studies are inevitably somewhat ambiguous unless special precautions are taken, but the problem is somewhat less serious in studies of microorganisms than when animals or animal cells are used. Certainly, studies of inhibition of precursor incorporation have provided less information regarding mechanisms of endproduct inhibition of purine biosynthesis than have measurements of the accumulation of intermediates.

MICROORGANISMS. Inhibition of precursor incorporation into nucleotide or nucleic acid purines upon addition of unlabeled purine bases was frequently observed in early studies of purine biosynthesis in microorganisms. Thus Abrams (*14*) showed in 1952 that the incorporation of glycine-^{14}C into acid-soluble RNA and DNA purines was depressed as much as 92% in *Saccharomyces cerevisiae* when adenine was added to the medium. In the same year, purines were found to inhibit $^{15}NH_4^+$ (*52*) and $^{14}CO_2$ (*53, 54*) incorporation into purines in *Escherichia coli* and formate-^{14}C incorporation into nucleic acid purines in *Lactobacillus casei* (*55*). Soon afterwards Kerr and Chernigoy (*56*) also found that formate-^{14}C incorporation into nucleic acid adenine and guanine in *Torulopsis utilis* was depressed by addition of adenine. Addition of guanine, however, stimulated formate incorporation into nucleic acid adenine. Later, incorporation both of glycine-^{14}C (*57*) and formate-^{14}C (*58*) into nucleic acid purines in *Escherichia coli* was inhibited by high concentrations of adenine or guanine. Similar studies were also performed with *Bacillus subtilis* (*59, 60*) and *Pasteurella pestis* (*61*).

More detailed studies of what was then called preferential utilization of exogenous purine bases and ribonucleosides were reported by Roberts *et al.* (*62*) as part of their comprehensive study of biosynthesis in *Escherichia coli.* They found that addition of adenine or adenosine to growing cultures of this organism reduced the incorporation of $^{14}CO_2$ into nucleic acid adenine by 91–94%, and into nucleic acid guanine by 80–97%. Addition of guanine or guanosine, however, almost completely abolished incorporation into nucleic acid guanine but had almost no effect on incorporation into nucleic acid adenine. Similar results were used when glucose-^{14}C was used as precursor. Thus although adenine and adenosine may have produced real feedback inhibition, dilution or other effects have to be taken into account when considering the effects of guanine and guanosine.

Animal Cells. Inhibition of radioactive glycine and formate incorporation into purines upon injection of purines into animals was first observed in 1951 by Abrams (*63*) and by Furst and Brown (*64*). Abrams found that the administration of adenine to rats caused 31–42% inhibition of the incorporation of simultaneously injected glycine-^{15}N into RNA and DNA purines in small intestine, and 73–83% inhibition in liver. Administration of guanine had only a small effect on glycine incorporation. In discussing these results Abrams recognized that they could be caused by dilution, by inhibition of purine synthesis, or both, and he was unable to decide exactly what the basis of the apparent inhibition was. Furst and Brown (*64*) observed inhibition of glycine-^{15}N incorporation into nucleic acids of rat liver and regenerating liver following injection of adenine, and shortly thereafter Goldthwait and Bendich (*65*) clearly demonstrated that injection of adenine caused approximately a 60% inhibition of formate-^{14}C incorporation into unfractionated rat visceral nucleic acid. In later studies injection of adenine inhibited formate-^{14}C incorporation into nucleic acid purines in Sarcoma 180 and intestine in mice (*66*) and in rat brain (*67*) and liver (*68, 69*).

Similar observations have been made in man. In 1955 Seegmiller *et al.* (*70*) administered aminoimidazole carboxamide-^{13}C and glycine-^{15}N simultaneously and found that the conversion of the glycine into urinary uric acid was only 30–40% of that observed when the glycine was given alone. It was shown that the aminoimidazole carboxamide did not interfere with other aspects of glycine metabolism and that the results were not likely to be caused by dilution. More recently, similar results were obtained using adenine (*71*).

Studies of cells and tissues incubated *in vitro* soon followed these observations of apparent endproduct inhibition (or dilution) *in vivo.* Abrams and Goldinger (*72*) reported in 1952 that the addition of hypoxanthine inhibited the incorporation of formate-^{14}C into RNA and DNA purines in slices of erythroid rabbit bone marrow incubated with glucose. One year later LePage

(*73*) described extensive studies of the effects of added purines, purine nucleosides, and purine nucleotides on the incorporation of glycine-^{14}C into acid-soluble and nucleic acid purines in Ehrlich ascites tumor cells, Gardner (6C3HED) ascites lymphosarcoma cells, and mouse liver cell suspensions, all incubated *in vitro* with glucose. The very marked inhibitions of glycine incorporation observed under many of the conditions used were attributed entirely to dilution. Similar observations were later made using a variety of ascites tumor cells (*74–77*), L cells in culture (*78, 79*), human leukocytes (*80*), and rat kidney slices (*81*).

Inhibition of precursor incorporation by endproducts has also been observed using suitably fortified tissue extracts. Buchanan and Wilson (*82*), for example, reported in 1953 that the rate of purine biosynthesis *de novo* in pigeon liver extracts was markedly inhibited when inosinate was added. This system was later explored in more detail by Wyngaarden *et al.* (*83*). Adenine, xanthine, inosine, and inosinate inhibited glycine-^{14}C incorporation into inosinate when ribose 5-phosphate was used, but the latter three compounds were no longer inhibitory when PP-ribose-P was employed; xanthine and inosinate did not inhibit PP-ribose-P synthesis in a more purified system, however. No inhibitors of the conversion of phosphoribosyl-glycineamide-^{14}C to inosinate were identified. When the PP-ribose-P–dependent conversion of glutamine to glutamate (*i.e.*, the PP-ribose-P amidotransferase reaction) was assayed, adenylate and ATP were found to be very potent inhibitors, and their effects were partially reversed by increasing the concentration of PP-ribose-P. These studies formed the basis for more detailed examination of the regulation of the PP-ribose-P amidotransferase reaction; these are described below.

Identification of Inhibitory Metabolites

Because of the low permeability of most cells to ribonucleotides and the rapid dephosphorylation of these compounds at or near the cell membrane it has not been possible to use the actual endproducts of the purine biosynthetic pathway in studies of its regulation in intact cells. Instead purine bases or ribonucleosides have usually been injected or added to incubation media, with subsequent measurement of their effects on the rate of purine biosynthesis. These compounds are in general metabolized by the cells under investigation, and the identification of the compounds or metabolites which are the actual inhibitors of the purine biosynthetic pathway requires at the very least a knowledge of the metabolism of the compounds added and preferably means of qualitatively and quantitatively altering their metabolism.

Important as it is to identify the real intracellular inhibitors of purine biosynthesis for a thorough understanding of the physiology and mechanism of this mode of regulation, this question is not at all settled. Indeed, the studies discussed below suggest that the important inhibitors may very well vary from one cell to another.

Requirement for Nucleotide Formation. The first question is whether the added purine bases and nucleosides act as such or after conversion to nucleotides. Evidence on this point was first presented by Tavlitzky (*13*) in 1951 when he noted that only those purines that supported growth (*i.e.*, only those converted to nucleotides) would prevent pigment formation in *Saccharomyces cerevisiae*. Gots (*9*) later also showed a relationship between the ability of a purine to support growth and its ability to inhibit the accumulation of aminoimidazole carboxamide in *Escherichia coli* B-96.

Animal cells that cannot convert hypoxanthine or guanine to ribonucleotides have been isolated on the basis of their resistance to certain growth-inhibitory purine analogs or have been derived from humans who have a hereditary deficiency of hypoxanthine-guanine phosphoribosyltransferase. Studies that show that several purine analogs which are metabolized by this enzyme do not inhibit purine synthesis (or cell growth) in its absence are discussed in Chapter 8. A number of investigators have shown that in hypoxanthine-guanine phosphoribosyltransferase-deficient H.Ep. #2 cells in culture (*42*), Leukemia L1210 cells *in vivo* (*42*), Ehrlich ascites tumor cells *in vitro* (*45*), and human fibroblasts in culture (*49, 51*) hypoxanthine and guanine do not inhibit purine biosynthesis whereas they are inhibitory in lines of these cells that can convert them to nucleotides. Adenine is also less than normally effective as an inhibitor of phosphoribosyl-formylglycineamide synthesis in a line of H.Ep. #2 cells that dephosphorylated nucleotides at an unusually rapid rate (*84*).

There is thus quite strong evidence that nucleotide formation is required for the expression of endproduct inhibition of purine synthesis by the naturally occurring purine bases (and of nucleosides which are phosphorylyzed to purine bases). However, whether this means that the nucleotides thus synthesized inhibit an important enzyme (as is commonly thought) or whether it is the process of nucleotide synthesis that is inhibitory to the purine biosynthetic pathway, is not so clear. This point will be discussed later.

Studies of Purine Ribonucleotide Interconversion. Attempts to decide which of the nine common purine ribonucleotides is (or are) the principal inhibitor of purine biosynthesis have not yet come to a satisfactory conclusion. In the first study of this question Gots and Goldstein (*85*) compared the concentrations of adenine, hypoxanthine, guanine, and xanthine that would produce 50% inhibition of purine biosynthesis *de novo* in two mutants of *Escherichia coli.* The pathways of purine ribonucleotide interconversion in these mutants are as follows:

B-96: AMP ← IMP → XMP → GMP (GMP → IMP)

B-94: AMP ←-- missing --- IMP → XMP → GMP (GMP → IMP)

In B-96, all four purine bases are approximately equally potent inhibitors. In B-94, however, although adenine has about the same potency for inhibition as in B-96, hypoxanthine is only 1/12 as effective, guanine is 1/180 as effective, and xanthine is less than 1/300 as effective. These results were interpreted to mean that adenine nucleotides are the major inhibitors in these cells, and that hypoxanthine, xanthine, and guanine are effective only after conversion to adenine nucleotides.

Quite different results were obtained by Magasanik and Karibian (*37*), however, using different mutants of *Escherichia coli.* Thus both hypoxanthine and guanine were potent inhibitors of purine biosynthesis in mutant 31, which lacks guanylate reductase and hence cannot convert guanylate to adenylate; guanine nucleotides clearly must themselves be able to inhibit purine synthesis in this strain.

AMP ← IMP → XMP → GMP (GMP --- missing ---→ XMP)

Indeed, guanine inhibited growth in the related strain 316, presumably by preventing adenine nucleotide synthesis *de novo.* Adenine nucleotides required for growth could not be synthesized from guanine because of the lack of guanylate reductase; addition of hypoxanthine overcame the growth inhibition because it can be converted to both adenine and guanine nucleotides.

Adenine inhibits the growth of certain strains of *Staphylococcus aureus,* an organism in which adenine nucleotides cannot be converted to nucleotides of hypoxanthine or guanine. Presumably adenine nucleotides inhibit the synthesis of inosinate and guanine nucleotides *de novo,* and retardation of growth is a result (*86, 87, 88*). Guanine reverses this inhibition by supplying guanine nucleotides.

Mutant animal cells blocked in the pathways of purine ribonucleotide interconversion have not yet been isolated. However, in attempts to identify active endproduct inhibitory nucleotides both Brockman and Chumley (*42*) and Henderson and Khoo (*45*) have used the aspartate analog hadacidin (*N*-formylhydroxyaminoacetic acid), which inhibits adenylosuccinate synthetase and hence the conversion of inosinate to adenylate. Brockman and Chumley (*42*) used H.Ep. #2 cells in culture and were able to inhibit the adenylosuccinate synthetase reaction completely. Under these conditions hypoxanthine was as active an inhibitor of purine biosynthesis in the presence as in the absence of hadacidin; this indicates that inosinate and guanine nucleotides were as effective as adenine nucleotides.

Henderson and Khoo (*45*), in contrast, used Ehrlich ascites tumor cells *in vitro* and were able to inhibit adenylosuccinate synthetase by only 72%. Whereas 1 m*M* hypoxanthine produced 64% inhibition of purine biosynthesis in the absence of hadacidin, the inhibition caused by this purine was only 28% in the presence of this drug. In this case it was concluded that conversion of inosinate to adenine nucleotides was important for endproduct inhibition.

Finally, Burns (*89*) has measured the rate of accumulation of aminoimidazole in a mutant of *Saccharomyces cerevisiae* under conditions in which the concentrations of the various purine nucleotides could be altered by changes in the nutrient medium. Of the nucleotide concentrations measured, only that of inosinate consistently varied inversely with the rate of purine biosynthesis *de novo* as would be expected of an inhibitor of this pathway.

It appears from the results quoted above that the pathway of purine biosynthesis *de novo* can be inhibited by several different purine nucleotides and that the sensitivity of various cells to these endproducts differs considerably. At the present time no generalizations can be made on this point.

Sites of Inhibition

Studies of endproduct inhibition of purine biosynthesis by the method of inhibition of accumulation of intermediates have shown quite clearly that purines exert their inhibitory effects on this pathway at some point earlier than the synthesis of phosphoribosyl-formylglycineamide. In work with pigeon liver extracts inhibition by nucleotides was shown to be earlier than phosphoribosyl-glycineamide (*83*). All of these results are thus consistent with the hypothesis that PP-ribose-P amidotransferase, the first enzyme unique to the pathway of purine biosynthesis, is the site of inhibition by endproducts of this sequence of reactions. Although this hypothesis is taken as proved by many workers, there is actually little direct evidence on this point, and the possible role of reduced PP-ribose-P concentrations and of inhibition of PP-ribose-P synthetase must also be considered.

Competition for PP-Ribose-P. The possibility that PP-ribose-P "could be drained from the *de novo* pathway to be used preferentially for the incorporation of preformed purines" was suggested by Gots (*9*) in 1957 as a possible mechanism whereby addition of purine bases inhibited purine biosynthesis. That PP-ribose-P concentrations can be rate limiting for purine biosynthesis *de novo* has been shown in Chapter 4; unfortunately, PP-ribose-P concentrations are rather difficult to measure, and they have not been determined under conditions in which endproduct inhibition is measured. As a consequence only indirect evidence is available on this point.

Gots (*9*) observed that although aminoimidazole carboxamide synthesis was inhibited by exposure of *Escherichia coli* B-96 cells to adenine, the rate of its synthesis returned to about 75% of normal when this inhibitor was removed by resuspension of the cells in adenine-free medium. On the assumption that purine nucleotide concentrations did not change significantly during centrifugation and resuspension, this result suggests that most of the inhibition was not exerted by the increased concentration of purine nucleotides but rather by the process of their synthesis from adenine and PP-ribose-P. If the nucleotides themselves were the sole inhibitory factor, removal of adenine would not be expected to affect the rate of purine biosynthesis.

Inhibition by purine bases of inosinate synthesis in pigeon liver extracts was attributed by Wyngaarden *et al.* (*83*) to competition for PP-ribose-P, and the inhibition could be alleviated by increasing PP-ribose-P concentrations.

The concentration of glutamine (2 m*M*) used in studies of endproduct inhibition of purine biosynthesis in Ehrlich ascites tumor cells *in vitro* also reduced PP-ribose-P concentrations to very low levels (*90*); however, further changes in PP-ribose-P concentrations in the presence of glutamine and purine bases together were not investigated. Crabtree and Henderson (*91*), however, have shown that nucleotide formation from 100 μM hypoxanthine is inhibited as much as 40% upon addition of glutamine, and this is believed to reflect competition between PP-ribose-P amidotransferase and hypoxanthine phosphoribosyltransferase for their common substrate. At lower concentrations of hypoxanthine (*e.g.*, 50 μM), however, these processes did not appear to compete for PP-ribose-P.

Marko *et al.* (*81*) have studied the effect of anoxia and reoxygenation on the rate of purine biosynthesis in rat kidney slices and on the inhibition of this process by adenine. Endproduct inhibition by adenine was observed in both anoxic and recovery states, although purine biosynthesis was more rapid in reoxygenated slices than under anoxia, even when the pathway was inhibited under both conditions by adenine. However, the twofold increase in the rate of purine synthesis found in the reoxygenated slices was accompanied by a lowered conversion of adenine to nucleotides, and this was attributed by the authors to possible competition for PP-ribose-P.

Indirect evidence that adenine did not cause endproduct inhibition through depletion of PP-ribose-P was presented in the course of studies with *Saccharomyces cerevisiae* (*89*). This was based on the fact that PP-ribose-P is also required for tryptophan, and hence protein, synthesis, and the latter process did not appear to be inhibited upon addition of adenine.

These studies suggest that competition for PP-ribose-P by the purine phosphoribosyltransferases has to be taken seriously as a possible site of endproduct inhibition. In no case, however, can the evidence on this point be considered conclusive.

PP-Ribose-P Synthetase. The fact that PP-ribose-P synthetase is inhibited by purine ribonucleotides, particularly ADP and GTP, has been discussed in Chapter 4. This enzyme is, therefore, at least potentially a site of inhibition by nucleotides synthesized when purines are added to cell suspensions. No direct evidence on this point is available, however.

It will be shown in Chapter 8 that a number of drugs that inhibit purine biosynthesis by any of several mechanisms increase the availability of PP-ribose-P for other processes. In some cases this is believed to be due to release of endproduct inhibition of PP-ribose-P synthetase.

PP-Ribose-P Amidotransferase. Studies of this enzyme in crude tissue extracts and in partially purified preparations support the hypothesis that it is an important site of endproduct inhibition; this subject will be discussed below. There is, however, little evidence regarding the inhibition of this enzyme in intact cells; understandably, this is difficult to examine. Henderson and Khoo (*45*) assayed the activity of PP-ribose-P amidotransferase in Ehrlich ascites tumor cells *in vitro* by measuring the decline in PP-ribose-P concentrations that follows the addition of glutamine. The use of this assay requires that the experiments not use compounds which themselves reduce PP-ribose-P concentrations; this rules out the purine bases adenine, guanine, and hypoxanthine but permits the use of a compound such as 6-methylmercaptopurine ribonucleoside, which has a stable glycosidic bond and which is converted to its inhibitory nucleotide form by adenosine kinase. It was found that 6-methylmercaptopurine ribonucleoside inhibited the glutamine-dependent utilization of PP-ribose-P and hence clearly inhibited PP-ribose-P amidotransferase. It should be pointed out that this purine analog nucleoside is phosphorylated only to the monophosphate level; drugs that form analog nucleoside triphosphates frequently seem to inhibit PP-ribose-P synthetase rather than the amidotransferase (*see* Chapter 8). If there is any analogy between the actions of the analogs and those of natural purine bases, it should be noted that the latter are metabolized predominantly to the nucleoside triphosphate.

Alternative First Reactions. In their studies of the synthesis of phosphoribosylamine from ribose 5-phosphate and NH_3 (*see* Chapter 2) both LeGal *et al.* (*91*) and Reem (*92*) noted that adenylate and guanylate both inhibited this process. Purine nucleotides also inhibited the synthesis of phosphoribosyl-formylglycineamide in extracts of Ehrlich ascites tumor cells when NH_3 replaced glutamine as substrate (*51*). As stated in Chapter 2, the physiological significance of these observations remains to be ascertained.

PP-Ribose-P Amidotransferase: Enzyme Studies

PP-Ribose-P amidotransferase is the enzyme that catalyzes the following reaction:

$$\text{PP-Ribose-P} + \text{Glutamine} \xrightarrow{Mg^{2+}} \text{Phosphoribosylamine} + PP_i + \text{Glutamine}$$

It is the main focus of attention as far as endproduct inhibition of purine biosynthesis *de novo* is concerned. It catalyzes the first irreversible reaction specific to this pathway, it is inhibited by purine ribonucleotide endproducts, and it is believed to be the rate-limiting step in this sequence of reactions. Indeed, the idea that this enzyme is the sole site of endproduct inhibition and the principal locus of regulation of purine biosynthesis has almost reached the stature of an item of faith. Obviously this book would be incomplete without a thorough discussion of PP-ribose-P amidotransferase and its role in regulation.

As an enzyme, PP-ribose-P amidotransferase is unique in several ways. It catalyzes an amide transfer reaction that ordinarily would require ATP; PP-ribose-P thus serves as an energy source as well as a phosphoribosyl donor. It is a metalloenzyme of a rather unusual type, and the role of its iron moieties remains completely unclear. One of its products, phosphoribosylamine, is extremely unstable in aqueous solution, and its actual intracellular concentrations are unknown. In spite of a great deal of work the kinetic and catalytic mechanism of this reaction remains unclear. These features undoubtedly contribute to the experimental difficulties that have been encountered in the study of PP-ribose-P amidotransferase. It has been difficult to purify, most preparations have been quite unstable, and its assay is a problem.

The unique features of this enzyme, the great difficulties encountered in its study, the divergence among results obtained by various investigators and with different preparations, and the many questions which remain regarding its properties and function make a careful examination of its possible regulatory role necessary. This section is therefore devoted to a detailed and critical appraisal of the question: What do we really known about PP-ribose-P amidotransferase? Subsequently, we discuss whether the hard facts regarding this enzyme are consistent with its generally regarded position as the major site of regulation of purine biosynthesis *de novo*. In this close examination of the literature there is no intention of being critical of individual investigators, however.

The PP-ribose-P amidotransferase from pigeon liver has been most studied (*94–99*); chicken liver (*96, 100, 101, 102*) has been the other avian source. Mammalian preparations have included those from Adenocarcinoma 755 (*103*), rat liver (*96*), Ehrlich ascites tumor cells (*104* and L. W. Brox, personal communication), Lymphoma L5178Y cells (L. W. Brox, personal communication), human lymphoblasts in culture (*105*), and mouse spleen infected with Friend leukemia virus (*106*). Microbial sources have been *Bacillus subtilis* (*99, 107*), *Brevibacterium ammoniogenes* (*108*), *Saccharomyces cerevisiae* (*109*), *Schizosaccharomyces pombe* (*110*), and *Aerobacter aerogenes* (*111*). Not all of these studies are equally informative, but they will be referred to when appropriate.

Assays. The assay of PP-ribose-P amidotransferase activity in crude tissue extracts has proved to be quite difficult, and most preparations have had to be partially purified before detailed studies could be carried out.

A wide variety of assay methods and conditions have been employed; data describing these are presented in Table 5-1. Other methods and conditions have been used on a few occasions but will not be discussed in any detail. (*e.g., 100*).

Table 5-1. Assay of PP-Ribose-P Amidotransferase Activity

Method	*pH*	*$MgCl_2$, mM*	*PP-Ribose-P, mM*	*Glutamine, mM*	*Reference*
Glutamate dehydrogenase	8.0	3.3	3; Mg^{2+} salt	3	(*94*)
	8.0	3.3	0.25; Mg^{2+} salt	1	(*95, 96, 97*)
	8.0	10	0.5; Na^{+} salt	20	(*109*)
	7.5	3.3	0.25; Mg^{2+} salt	6	(*107*)
Pyrophosphate	8.0	5	5; K^{+} salt	15	(*100, 101*)
Glutamate-^{14}C	7.5	2	1; Mg^{2+} salt	3.3	(*103*)
Phosphoribosylglycineamide	7.5	6	4.5; Na^{+} salt	12	
	8.0	0.5	0.2; Mg^{2+} salt	1	(*108*)
	8.0	8	2; Mg^{2+} salt	20	(*110*)

It is apparent that the coupled assay employing glutamate dehydrogenase and reduction of the acetylpyridine analog of NAD has been most used. This method suffers from the general disadvantage of being an indirect assay and from the specific drawback that a lag in the reaction rate occurs before a linear rate of reaction is achieved. Hartman (*100*) and Brox (personal communication) state that although a lag was observed using the glutamate dehydrogenase procedure this was not found when other methods of measuring glutamate production were used. Li and Buchanan (*112*) have also experienced the same difficulty upon application of this method to the assay of glutamate formed in the formylglycineamidine synthetase reaction. Rowe *et al.* (*98*), in contrast, state that direct and indirect methods both showed the lag in initial rate. This is an extremely important difference of opinion. The common practice is to calculate enzyme velocity on the basis of rates obtained following the lag period; this may be valid, but this whole problem is at best unfortunate.

Another indirect assay is that which first converts phosphoribosylamine to phosphoribosyl-glycineamide in the presence of ATP and glycine; in a second step, this product is incubated with inosinate and the enzymes required to form phosphoribosyl-aminoimidazole carboxamide, which can be estimated colorimetrically. The following steps are involved:

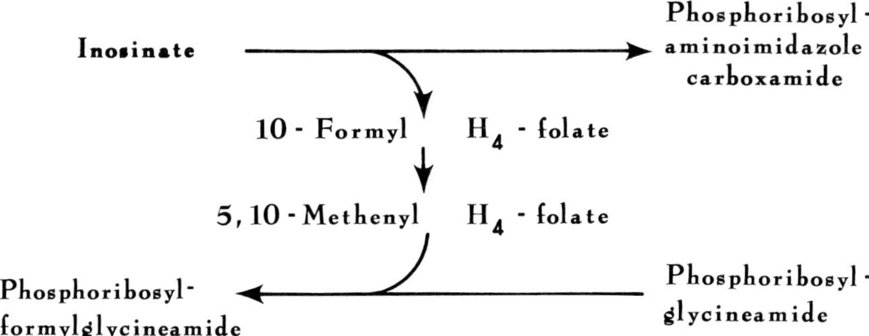

Thus four enzymes in addition to the amidotransferase and phosphoribosyl-glycineamide synthetase are required; this is inherently a drawback, although the procedure seems to work fairly well.

ATP is one of the substrates of the phosphoribosyl-glycineamide synthetase used in this system, and this nucleotide is supposed also to be an allosteric inhibitor of PP-ribose-P amidotransferase. Although Nierlich and Magasanik (*111*) used only 0.075 m*M* ATP, the concentration used by Nagy (*110*) was 1.0 m*M*; the complications introduced by the use of such concentrations of ATP have not been evaluated.

Of the direct assays used, precipitation of pyrophosphate as the manganous salt was very reliable in Hartman's hands (*100, 101*), but its lack of sensitivity has prevented its use for kinetic studies. Extraneous pyrophosphate contributed by use of impure preparations of PP-ribose-P may cause high blanks in this procedure.

The conversion of ^{14}C-glutamine to ^{14}C-glutamate appears to be the most simple and most sensitive assay method used. It suffers, however, from the disadvantage that commercial ^{14}C-glutamine may contain as much as 10% ^{14}C-glutamate. In addition, unless the specific activity of the material used is published, readers cannot calculate the actual sensitivity of the method in any particular case.

It will be shown below that the Michaelis constant of glutamine for PP-ribose-P amidotransferase is in most preparations about 1 m*M*. Many assays have employed concentrations of glutamine between 1 and 6 m*M*, however; at these concentrations this substrate may not be saturating. Similarly, many Michaelis constants for PP-ribose-P of around 2 to 3 $\times$ $10^{-4}M$ have been reported; concentrations of this substrate of less than 3 m*M* would probably not be saturating.

Determination of Substrate Concentration. Neither commercial PP-ribose-P nor glutamine (nor glutamine-^{14}C) are 100% pure, yet this point is not commented on nor apparently taken into consideration by most workers. Hartman (*100*) prepared his own PP-ribose-P which was about 80% pure; orthophosphate and pyrophosphate were the main contaminants. Wyngaarden and Ashton (*95*) and Nierlich and Magasanik (*111*) assayed their PP-ribose-P enzymatically but did not report their findings; Caskey *et al.* (*96*), Brox (personal communication), and the author find commercial PP-ribose-P to be only about 60% pure. As this has not been taken into account in most studies, reported substrate concentrations and Michaelis constants must be corrected accordingly.

Commercial glutamine and glutamine-^{14}C usually contain between 1 and 10% impurities which seem to consist of glutamate and a cyclized derivative of glutamate. This point has apparently been considered only by Hartman (*100*).

The effects of the impurities in the substrate preparations, particularly of the products pyrophosphate and glutamate, do not appear to have been studied; both are potential inhibitors of the amidotransferase.

The presence of glutaminase is a major obstacle to the accurate measurement of PP-ribose-P amidotransferase activity in crude tissue extracts. Partially purified preparations have been reported to be free of glutaminase activity (*95, 96, 103, 109*), or to contain low (*107*) or moderate (*111*) amounts of this enzyme. A difficulty encountered by some workers is that although phosphate-independent glutaminase may be absent phosphate contaminating the PP-ribose-P may activate the phosphate-dependent glutaminase of animal tissues. This has only recently been appreciated.

No investigator has checked for the presence of enzymes that degrade PP-ribose-P although Brox (personal communication) has found evidence for such activity in preparations from Ehrlich ascites tumor cells. Such activities might be the cause of the non-linear double reciprocal plots observed in some amidotransferase preparations when PP-ribose-P is the variable substrate (*e.g.*, *103, 110*).

Finally, the preponderance of evidence suggests that the monomagnesium salt of PP-ribose-P is the true substrate of the amidotransferase reaction rather than free PP-ribose-P or the dimagnesium salt. Table 5-2 shows the relative PP-ribose-P and Mg^{2+} concentrations used by various investigators, and it may be seen that the ratios of these components vary over a 20-fold range. In no case does an investigator state how the ratio used was chosen. Gadd and Henderson (*113*) have recently shown that the ratio of Mg^{2+} to PP-ribose-P which gives the maximum concentration of Mg-PP-ribose-P is a complex function of the absolute and relative concentrations of the two reactants, the pH, the ionic strength, and the concentration of other cations. In view of the complexity of this situation it is virtually impossible to tell what the concentration of the true substrate, Mg-PP-ribose-P, was in any of these studies or what the optimum Mg^{2+} concentration might really be.

In kinetic studies of the amidotransferase, PP-ribose-P concentrations were varied over approximately fivefold (*111*), 10-fold (*95*), 25-fold (*109, 110*), and 30-fold (*103*) ranges, but Mg^{2+} concentrations were kept constant at the values shown in Table 5-2. This certainly introduced some error.

Table 5-2. PP-Ribose-P and Mg^{2+} Concentrations Used in the Assay of PP-Ribose-P Amidotransferase

PP-Ribose-P, mM	*Mg^{2+} in PP-Ribose-P Salt*, mM	*Added Mg^{2+}*, mM	*Total Mg^{2+}*, mM	*Mg^{2+}/PP-Ribose-P*	*Reference*
0.25	0.5	3.3	3.8	14.8	(*95–99, 107*)
0.5	–	10	10	20	(*109*)
5	–	5	5	1	(*100, 101*)
1	2	2	4	4	(*103*)
4.5	–	6	6	1.33	(*111*)
0.2	0.4	0.5	0.9	4.5	(*108*)
2	4	8	12	6	(*110*)[a]

[a] 1 m*M* ATP also present

Kinetic Studies. Double reciprocal plots of initial velocity of PP-ribose-P amidotransferase as a function of substrate concentration have been linear for both PP-ribose-P and glutamine in studies of the enzyme from pigeon liver (*95, 96*), *Aerobacter aerogenes* (*111*), *Bacillus subtilis* (*107*), and *Saccharomyces cerevisiae* (*109*). The preparation from Adenocarcinoma 755 (*103*) gave linear plots for glutamine but nonlinear plots for PP-ribose-P; that from *Schizosaccharomyces pombe* (*110*) gave nonlinear plots for both substrates. Although the nonlinear plots have been interpreted in terms of homotrophic cooperativity in relation to the model of allosteric enzymes of Monod *et al.* (*114*), there are enough questions about the assay and about actual substrate concentrations to make further work necessary on this point. In the *Schizosaccharomyces pombe* system the presence of 1 m*M* ATP also is a complication. The most recent studies (*98*) of the pigeon liver enzyme used PP-ribose-P concentrations about one-tenth of those used in the work referred to above. At these low substrate concentrations double reciprocal plots were nonlinear, in contrast to the linear plots obtained earlier.

Table 5-3 lists the Michaelis constants that have been reported for the PP-ribose-P amidotransferase system. These are only apparent Michaelis constants, and the true values for the PP-ribose-P constant may be considerably lower than those reported. It is interesting that the PP-ribose-P constant for a highly purified pigeon liver enzyme (*98*) was one-fourth of those for less pure preparations from the same tissue.

Table 5-3. Michaelis Constants for PP-Ribose-P and Glutamine

	Michaelis Constants		
Source of Enzyme	*PP-Ribose-P*, M	*Glutamine*, M	*Reference*
Pigeon liver	2.3×10^{-4}	1.1×10^{-3}	(*95*)
Pigeon liver	2.4×10^{-4}	1.0×10^{-3}	(*96*)
Pigeon liver	6×10^{-5}	1×10^{-3}	(*98*)
Rat liver	8.6×10^{-5}	5.3×10^{-4}	(*96*)
Chicken liver	$2.5–5 \times 10^{-5}$	1.1×10^{-3}	(*100*)
Adenocarcinoma 755	4.7×10^{-4} ($S_{0.5}$)	1.8×10^{-3}	(*103*)
Human lymphoblasts	2.5×10^{-4}	4.4×10^{-4}	(*105*)
Aerobacter aerogenes	$2.3–3.0 \times 10^{-4}$	–	(*111*)
Bacillus subtilis	3×10^{-4}	–	(*99*)
Bacillus subtilis	8.6×10^{-5}	4.1×10^{-3}	(*107*)
Saccharomyces cerevisiae	1.1×10^{-4}	1.2×10^{-3}	(*109*)
Schizosaccharomyces pombe	3.5×10^{-4} ($S_{0.5}$)	5×10^{-3} ($S_{0.5}$)	(*110*)

Although an older method of kinetic analysis led some investigators to conclude that binding of substrates was random (*95, 96 107*), more recent

Table 5-4. Inhibition of PP-Ribose-P

Enzyme Sources	*Parameter Measured*	*AMP*	*ADP*
Pigeon liver	K_i (*M*)	9.0×10^{-5}	9.0×10^{-5}
Pigeon liver	K_i (*M*)	9.2×10^{-5}	3.8×10^{-5}
		2.5×10^{-3}	6.4×10^{-4}
Bacillus subtilis	K_i (*M*)	*ca.* 7×10^{-4}	
Aerobacter aerogenes	IC_{50} (*M*)	5.5×10^{-4}	1.3×10^{-3}
Bacillus subtilis	IC_{50} (*M*)	2×10^{-4}	2.7×10^{-4}
Schizosaccharomyces pombe	IC_{50} (*M*)	$>5 \times 10^{-3}$	
Saccharomyces cerevisiae	% inhibition at 5 m*M*	75	56
Brevibacterium ammoniogenes	% inhibition at 10^{-4}*M*	2.7	40.4
	10^{-3}*M*	78	79.8
Adenocarcinoma 755	% inhibition at	2.33 m*M* 30%	3.33 m*M* 40%
Human lymphoblasts	IC_{50} (*M*)	2×10^{-3}	

studies have shown that this is an ordered process with PP-ribose-P binding before glutamine (*100, 103, 107, 110*).

Kinetics of Inhibition by Purine Nucleotides. It is its sensitivity to inhibition by purine ribonucleotides that has caused so much attention to be paid to PP-ribose-P amidotransferase, and the potencies of various nucleotides in this regard are given in Table 5-4. These data must be interpreted in terms of the assay conditions used (*see* Table 5-1) and of the parameter measured; in addition, GTP is notoriously impure. These data are rearranged in Table 5-5 in an attempt to show the relative inhibitory activities of the different nucleotides in the various enzyme preparations studied; the studies which used only a few compounds have been omitted from this table. Where studied (*e.g.*, *95, 103, 109*), purine bases and ribonucleosides and pyrimidine bases, ribonucleosides, and ribonucleotides have never been found to inhibit PP-ribose-P amidotransferase. Finally, it should be noted that Hartman's highly purified chicken liver amidotransferase was not inhibited at all by 1 m*M* purine ribonucleotides (*100*).

In only two cases has the effect of Mg^{2+} concentration on the inhibitory activity of purine ribonucleotides been studied, and these produced apparently contradictory results. Wyngaarden and Ashton (*95*) stated that a threefold increase in Mg^{2+} concentration did not alter the inhibitory activity of ATP; their assay system ordinarily had a Mg^{2+} to PP-ribose-P ratio of about 15. In the Adenocarcinoma 755 system of Hill and Bennett (*105*), in which this ratio was four, the addition of concentrations of Mg^{2+} equal to those of the inhibitory nucleotides markedly reduced the effectiveness of

Amidotransferase by Purine Ribonucleotides

ATP	*GMP*	*GDP*	*GTP*	*IMP*	*Reference*
3.7×10^{-5}	8.6×10^{-5}	3.8×10^{-4}		1.8×10^{-4}	(*95*)
3.1×10^{-5}	8.6×10^{-5}	3.8×10^{-4}		1.8×10^{-4}	
1.1×10^{-3}	3.5×10^{-4}	5.4×10^{-3}		3.5×10^{-3}	(*96*)
					(*99*)
	4×10^{-4}		6.5×10^{-4}	1.8×10^{-3}	(*111*)
not inhib.	2×10^{-3}		$2–10 \times 10^{-4}$	not inhib.	(*107*)
	5×10^{-4}			5×10^{-4}	(*110*)
33	7	7	37	9	(*109*)
38.3	55.5				(*108*)
100	71.0				
2.00 m*M*	3.33 m*M*	3.33 m*M*	2.33 m*M*	6.67 m*M*	(*103*)
8%	36%	42%	17%	55%	
	1×10^{-3}				

Table 5-5. Relative Inhibitory Activities of Purine Ribonucleotides

	Relative Potency							
	Highest 1	2	3	4	5	6	*Lowest* 7	*Reference*
Pigeon liver	ATP	ADP	GMP	AMP	IMP	GDP		(*95, 96*)
Aerobacter aerogenes	GMP	AMP	GTP	IMP				(*111*)
Bacillus subtilis	AMP	ADP	GTP	GMP			ATP, IMP	(*107*)
Saccharomyces cerevisiae	AMP	ADP	GTP	ATP	IMP	GMP	GDP	(*109*)
Brevibacterium ammoniogenes	GMP	ADP	ATP	AMP				(*108*)
Adenocarcinoma 755	AMP	GDP	ADP	GMP	GTP	IMP	ATP	(*103*)

ADP and GDP and almost abolished the inhibition produced by GTP and ATP. These results make one question results obtained with purine ribonucleoside di- and triphosphates at relatively low Mg^{2+} concentrations (*see* Table 5-2); nucleoside monophosphates are only weak chelators of Mg^{2+}.

With these cautions in mind it is still clear that certain purine ribonucleotides are fairly potent inhibitors of PP-ribose-P amidotransferase. Enzymes from different sources vary in their sensitivity to inhibition, and the relative potency of various ribonucleotides vary from one preparation to another, but inhibition is still achieved. In most systems AMP and GMP are among the most active inhibitors.

Table 5-6 gives some information regarding the kinetics of inhibition of PP-ribose-P amidotransferases from different sources by purine ribonucleotides. It is apparent that inhibition can be either competitive or noncompetitive with respect to either substrate, depending on the system. In addition both linear and nonlinear double reciprocal plots have been obtained. It is very difficult to draw any general conclusions about the kinetic mechanism of inhibition, especially in view of the questions previously raised.

Nierlich and Magasanik (*111*) first studied the effects of pairs of purine ribonucleotides on the activity of PP-ribose-P amidotransferase, using a preparation from *Aerobacter aerogenes.* Having made certain assumptions about the activity of such combinations, they concluded that a mixture of AMP and GMP produced more inhibition than did either alone. In contrast inhibition by pairs of adenine nucleotides or by pairs of guanine nucleotides was additive. From these results they concluded both that the amidotransferase possesses separate allosteric binding sites for 6-aminopurine ribonucleotides and for 6-oxopurine ribonucleotides and that there is an interaction between these sites that can lead to an increase in apparent inhibitory activity when the two types of inhibitors are present together. Caskey *et al.* (*96*) reached similar conclusions on the basis of studies of the pigeon liver amidotransferase. In contrast, however, pairs of inhibitors caused only additive inhibition of the enzyme from Adenocarcinoma 755 (*103*), *Schizosaccharomyces pombe* (*110*), *Saccharomyces cerevisiae* (*109*), *Brevibacterium ammoniogenes* (*108*), and probably *Bacillus subtilis* (*99*).

It may be well to separate the question of the number of binding sites from that regarding the possible interaction of multiple sites. In addition to the evidence quoted above in support of multiple nucleotide binding sites, Caskey *et al.* (*96*) observed that gentle heating would desensitize the pigeon liver amidotransferase to inhibition by ATP whereas this treatment did not alter sensitivity to AMP. Nagy (*110*) found that a mutant amidotransferase from *Schizosacharomyces pombe* was less sensitive to IMP and GMP than the wild-type enzyme, while both were equally sensitive to AMP. Finally, Satyanarayana and Kaplan (*109*) found differences in the kinetics of inhibition by AMP and by ADP and suggested that these inhibitors are bound to separate sites. The whole question of the number of nucleotide binding sites and of their specificity remains open, therefore, as does the question of possible interactions among them.

Table 5-6. Kinetics of Inhibition by Purine Ribonucleotides

	PP-Ribose-P		*Glutamine*		
Enzyme Source	*Pattern*[a]	*Plot*[b]	*Pattern*[a]	*Plot*[b]	*Reference*
Pigeon liver	C	linear	NC	linear	(*95, 96*)
Pigeon liver	C	nonlinear	—	—	(*98*)
Adenocarcinoma 755	NC	nonlinear	—	—	(*103*)
Rat liver	C	linear	C	linear	(*96*)
Aerobacter aerogenes	C	nonlinear	—	—	(*111*)
Saccharomyces cerevisiae	NC	nonlinear	NC	linear	(*109*)
Schizosaccharomyces pombe	C	nonlinear	C	nonlinear	(*110*)
Bacillus subtilis	C	nonlinear	C (AMP, ADP) NC (GMP, GTP)	linear	(*107*)

[a] Pattern: C, competitive; NC, noncompetitive
[b] Plot: double reciprocal plot of velocity against substrate concentration in the presence of purine ribonucleotides

It has already been indicated that preparations of PP-ribose-P amidotransferase vary considerably in their sensitivity to inhibition by purine ribonucleotides. Although Hill and Bennett (*103*), Nagy (*110*), and Satyanarayana and Kaplan (*109*) found that their amidotransferase preparations were always sensitive to inhibition, Shiio and Ishii (*107*) observed that the degree of inhibition changed with the age of the preparation. Caskey *et al.* (*96*) have studied the matter of variation in sensitivity in some detail. Their pigeon liver amidotransferase varied greatly in sensitivity to inhibition by nucleotides from one preparation to another although no change in the

Michaelis constants occurred; upon extensive purification completely insensitive enzymes could be obtained. This is reminiscent of Hartman's observations (*100*) that a highly purified chicken liver amidotransferase was not inhibited by nucleotides, although Caskey *et al.* (*96*) stated that partially purified preparations from this source did respond to nucleotide inhibitors. By modifying their purification procedures Rowe and Wyngaarden (*97, 98*) were fortunately able to obtain a highly purified pigeon liver amidotransferase which was still sensitive to inhibition by purine ribonucleotides.

Finally, it should be pointed out that there is some evidence for binding of purine ribonucleotides to PP-ribose-P amidotransferase even when these do not inhibit this enzyme. Thus IMP, which inhibited the *Saccharomyces cerevisiae* enzyme only 7% at a concentration of 5 m*M*, markedly increased its rate of heat inactivation (*109*). Similarly AMP protected the highly purified pigeon liver amidotransferase against inhibition by *o*-phenanthroline even in preparations which were not sensitive to inhibition by this nucleotide (*97, 98*). The significance of these observations is at present unclear.

Purification and Physical Properties. Although in almost all studies of PP-ribose-P amidotransferase this enzyme has been purified to some degree, it has been purified to the point of homogeneity only by Hartman (*100*) and by Rowe and Wyngaarden (*97*); the former used chicken liver as source whereas the latter used pigeon liver.

Most preparations of PP-ribose-P have proved to be quite unstable (*95, 96, 97, 100, 103, 107, 111*), but mercaptoethanol or glutathione in most cases proved very effective as stabilizing agents (*96, 97, 100, 107*). Preparations in which dithiothreitol (*109*) or glycerol (*110*) were already present were reported to be quite stable. Hartman (*100*) also found that storage *in vacuo* helped prevent inactivation.

The amidotransferase is readily inactivated by heating but was protected by PP-ribose-P (*96, 109*). AMP had no effect on the rate of heat inactivation of a pigeon liver preparation (*96*), but AMP and ADP protected the enzyme from *Saccharomyces cerevisiae* (*109*) from heat inactivation.

Sulfhydryl reagents such as *p*-chloromercuribenzoate, *p*-hydroxymercuribenzoate, *N*-ethylmaleimide, and iodoacetate inhibited amidotransferases from various sources (*95, 96, 97, 100, 107*), and this inhibition could be prevented by glutathione (*95, 107*) or mercaptoethanol (*100*). In some cases amidotransferases inhibited by sulfhydryl reagents could be partially or completely reactivated by treatment with sulfhydryl compounds (*100, 107*). Inactivation by *p*-hydroxymercuribenzoate was also prevented by PP-ribose-P. Amino acid analysis revealed 18 cysteine residues per mole of which two were rapidly titrated; another six titrated slightly more slowly (*97*).

Hartman (*100*) first reported that PP-ribose-P amidotransferase contains non-heme iron, and this point has been further studied by Rowe and Wyngaarden (*97*), and Rowe *et al.* (*98*). Ten (*100*) to 12 (*97*) moles of iron, probably in the ferrous state, are bound per protein of 200,000 daltons. Iron chelators such as *o*-phenanthroline inhibit amidotransferase activity (*97, 98, 100*), and this can be prevented by addition of Fe^{2+} (*100*). As much as one-third of the iron can be removed by *o*-phenanthroline in the absence of reducing agents or by mercaptoethanol (*97, 100*); in fact iron is removed during purification when mercaptoethanol is used as a stabilizing agent (*97*). In the presence of mercaptoethanol *o*-phenanthroline treatment removes all of the iron, and the protein becomes irreversibly denatured and precipitates (*97, 100*). In the presence of Mg^{2+} both PP-ribose-P and AMP protect against inhibition by *o*-phenanthroline (*97, 98*).

The way in which iron participates in the structure of PP-ribose-P amidotransferase is unknown although Rowe and Wyngaarden (*97*) suggest that:

Protein - S - Fe - S - Protein

is a possible formulation. The function of the iron is also not known although at least part of it is required to preserve a catalytically active tertiary structure. Because mercaptoethanol removes iron under the same conditions that it causes subunit dissociation (*97*), the possibility exists that iron is involved in the subunit structure of this enzyme. Finally, the possibility must be kept in mind that the iron may play some role in the binding of PP-ribose-P and of purine ribonucleotide inhibitors because iron is known to bind to polyhydroxysugars.

The existence of iron in the amidotransferase may be the basis of the observations that divalent cations (besides Mg^{2+} and Mn^{2+}) inhibit this enzyme (*100, 103, 109*), possibly by replacement of iron by other ions. In addition, $(NH_4)_2SO_4$ is inhibitory (*103*), perhaps through the formation of ammonium-iron complexes.

In summary, about all that can be said about the iron content of PP-ribose-P amidotransferase is that its role is a mystery.

Hartman (*100*) and Rowe and Wyngaarden (*97*) agree that the molecular weight of PP-ribose-P amidotransferase is approximately 200,000 daltons. Wyngaarden and his colleagues (*96, 97, 98*) have been able to prepare subunits of 100,000 and 50,000 daltons which, under appropriate conditions, show enzymatic activity. Although the 100,000 unit can be formed upon dilution, the presence of mercaptoethanol is required for further halving. Electrophoretic studies and amino acid analyses suggest that the four 50,000 dalton subunits are identical, but small differences cannot be ruled out.

It is not certain whether or not all four subunits are enzymatically active. Hartman (*101*) had found that only one mole of diazooxonorleucine-^{14}C was bound per mole of 200,000 dalton size, an observation that suggests that there may be only one active site. Rowe and Wyngaarden (*97*) have detected enzymatic activity regardless of the molecular weight (50,000, 100,000, or 200,000 daltons) of the preparation. Because studies of physical properties and assays of activity are conducted under such different conditions, however, no definite conclusion can yet be reached regarding the possible enzymatic activity of the subunits.

Rowe *et al.* (*98*) have observed four different states of the highly purified pigeon liver PP-ribose-P amidotransferase with respect to the length of the lag period already referred to above and the velocity attained at the end of the lag period. Some of the physical properties of the enzyme differ in these states, but their relationship to subunit structure, to the activity of the enzyme *in vivo*, and to the mechanism of inhibition by purine ribonucleotides remains unknown.

Mutant PP-Ribose-P Amidotransferases. In 1966 Heslot *et al.* (*115*) described a mutant of *Schizosaccharomyces pombe* that was resistant to 8-azaguanine and whose production of purines could not be regulated in the normal way by endproduct inhibition. The genetic locus of the mutation was closely linked to that of PP-ribose-P amidotransferase, and some of the properties of this enzyme from normal and mutant cells were therefore compared (*110*); the properties of these enzymes are shown in Table 5-7. It should be noted that the specific activity of the mutant enzyme preparation was only about 40% that of the enzyme from the wild-type organism. Table 5-7 shows that several apparently significant differences between mutant and wild-type enzymes were detected, and these at least are in the direction predicted from the behavior of the intact cells. Reservations concerning the conditions of assay have been expressed above, however, and these enzymes should be subjected to much more detailed study.

Table 5-7. Properties of PP-Ribose-P Amidotransferases from Wild-type and Mutant *Schizosaccharomyces Pombe*

Property	*Wild-type*	*Mutant*
$S_{0.5}$,[a] PP-ribose-P	3.5×10^{-4} *M*	1×10^{-4} *M*
$S_{0.5}$, glutamine	5×10^{-3} *M*	5.5×10^{-3} *M*
Plots, PP-ribose-P	nonlinear	nonlinear
Plots, glutamine	nonlinear	linear
IC_{50},[b] AMP	*ca.* 5×10^{-3} *M*	*ca.* 4×10^{-3} *M*
IC_{50}, IMP	*ca.* 5×10^{-4} *M*	*ca.* 2×10^{-3} *M*
IC_{50}, GMP	*ca.* 5×10^{-4} *M*	*ca.* 1×10^{-3} *M*

[a] $S_{0.5}$ = Substrate concentration giving 50% of maximal activity
[b] IC_{50} = Inhibitor concentration giving 50% inhibition

The possible occurrence of altered amidotransferases in several animal cell lines has also been suggested, but no studies of the enzymes from these cells have yet been performed. In one case (*46*) a line of Ehrlich ascites tumor cells was identified in which guanine and 6-methylmercaptopurine ribonucleoside produced much less inhibition of phosphoribosyl-formylglycineamide synthesis than usual whereas adenine affected this process in a normal manner. No changes in the metabolism of these compounds were noted, but the basal rate of phosphoribosyl-formylglycineamide synthesis was accelerated twofold in the cells which were insensitive to inhibition.

In another study (*50*) purine synthesis appeared to be less than normally sensitive to inhibition by adenine, hypoxanthine, and 6-methylmercaptopurine ribonucleoside in cultured fibroblasts from two patients with gout and an overproduction of purines *in vivo*. As discussed in Chapter 9 it is premature as yet to associate these observations too closely.

Conclusions. It must be concluded that we know much less than is commonly thought about PP-ribose-P amidotransferase. A basic and serious difficulty is that almost all assay methods and conditions are open to criticism on one ground or another. What is urgently needed is a thorough and carefully controlled study of the initial velocity (and preferably also product inhibition) kinetics of amidotransferases from several sources. Such an investigation would determine whether reported differences were real or apparent and would permit evaluation of the seriousness of various potential sources of error. It would also provide information on the kinetic mechanism of this reaction on which studies of the inhibition of this enzyme by purine ribonucleotides must ultimately be based.

The second major question regarding PP-ribose-P amidotransferase concerns its iron content. Since the iron plays a potential role in the binding of PP-ribose-P and of purine ribonucleotide inhibition, an understanding of the mechanism of action of the latter may very well depend on a serious and thorough study of the structure and function of this metal ion.

This brings us to the question of the mechanism or mechanisms whereby purine ribonucleotides inhibit PP-ribose-P amidotransferase. In some—but certainly not all—cases this seems merely to be by competition with PP-ribose-P for a limited amount of Mg^{2+}. In other cases it may represent simple competition with PP-ribose-P or pyrophosphate for binding either on the free enzyme or on some intermediate in the kinetic mechanism. In view of the rather high concentrations of nucleotides used in some studies, these points—as well as possible complex formation with the iron—should be at least considered before recourse is made to more complex models, which are more difficult to prove or disprove. The question of the number, specificity, and possible interaction of nucleotide binding sites is in an unsettled state, with divergent results on record. At present it would seem that further studies of inhibition by purine ribonucleotides would not be particularly fruitful; instead, attention should be placed on the basic problems raised above.

Finally, one may ask: What might be the physiological role of inhibition of PP-ribose-P amidotransferase by purine ribonucleotides? A corollary that should be approached first is: Might the role of PP-ribose-P amidotransferase in the regulation of purine biosynthesis *de novo* be different in different cells? With respect to the possible regulatory role of this enzyme in livers of uricotelic animals Hartman (*100*) concluded, "The necessity for a control mechanism in avian liver of the type proposed [*i.e.*, endproduct inhibition] is not clear since, quantitatively, the major function of purine biosynthesis in these tissues is the formation of inosinic acid for nitrogen excretion." In a similar vein Caskey *et al.* (*96*) stated, "The existence of a control mechanism in avian liver potentially capable of regulating purine synthesis is clearly implied by the results reported [in their paper]. Since a major function of avian purine biosynthesis *de novo* is the disposition of excess nitrogen as uric acid, the functional role of such a control in avian liver is uncertain." As shown in Table 5-4 it is precisely the enzyme from pigeon liver that is most sensitive to inhibition by purine ribonucleotides although the commonly accepted extrapolation of these results to its function *in vivo* is extremely shaky. It must be pointed out, however, that Katunuma *et al.* (*102*) have recently stated that the IC_{50} for AMP for a chicken liver amidotransferase was about 20 times that for a rat liver enzyme; the details of the assay were not reported, and a more complete report of these studies is awaited with interest. In the meantime, it must be concluded that the biological role (if any) of the inhibition of avian liver PP-ribose-P amidotransferases is not known at present.

A much better case can be made for a real regulatory role of the amidotransferases in microorganisms, and the *Schizosaccharomyces pombe* mutant, which is defective in endproduct inhibition, is one of the most promising systems in which to study rigorously the function of this enzyme.

Finally, the amidotransferases from mammalian cells are something of an enigma and in reality have been very little studied. In spite of their potential regulatory role in these cells, they really are not very sensitive to inhibition by purine ribonucleotides. These enzymes require much further investigation.

Evidence for Regulation of Purine Biosynthesis by Endogenous Nucleotides

As indicated above most studies of endproduct inhibition of purine biosynthesis have measured either the effect of purine bases in intact cells or of purine nucleotides on PP-ribose-P amidotransferase activity in cell extracts. In only a very few cases has the rate of purine biosynthesis been related to endogenous concentrations of purine nucleotides in cells.

When rats are treated with ethionine, *S*-adenosylethionine is formed by reaction with ATP, and this analog is metabolized at a much lower rate than the naturally occurring *S*-adenosylmethionine. Consequently, ethionine acts as a trap for ATP, and its use results in lowered ATP concentrations.

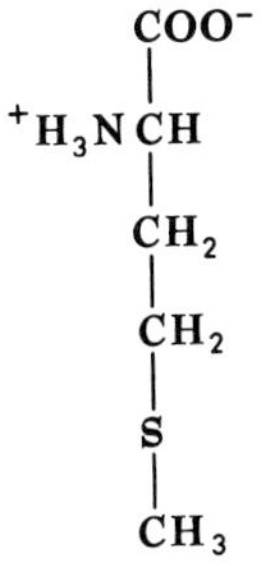

Methionine 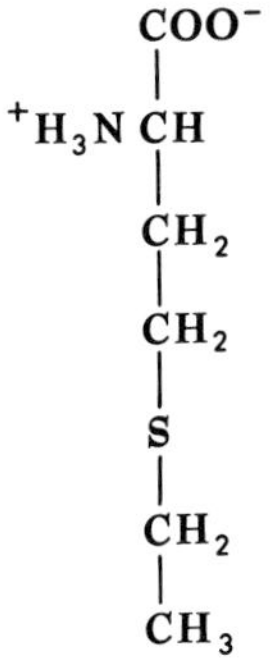 Ethionine 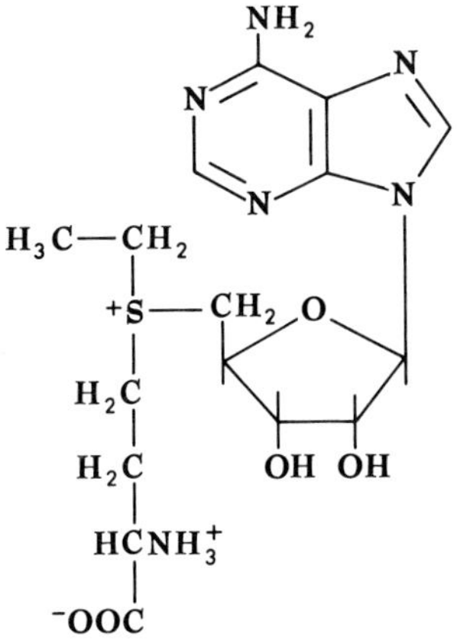 S - Adenosylethionine

Shull *et al.* (*68*), Stekol *et al.* (*116*), and Smith and Salmon (*69*) have observed that the rate of purine biosynthesis *de novo* increases following ethionine treatment, and they have attributed this change to release of endproduct inhibition by ATP. As much as a sixfold increase in the utilization of formate-^{14}C or glycine-^{14}C can occur as a response to ethionine treatment, and increased purine biosynthesis is detected whether total nucleotide radioactivity or nucleotide specific activity is determined. The increase occurs almost immediately upon administration of the analog and continues for a number of hours depending on the dose of ethionine. At certain doses the increased rate of purine biosynthesis can exactly compensate for the diversion of ATP; greater amounts of ethionine remove ATP more rapidly than it can be replaced.

Windmueller and Spaeth (*117*) have reported that accelerated rates of purine biosynthesis in rat liver followed feeding a diet containing 1% orotate for 72 hours. Orotate feeding led to a 40–50% reduction in the pools of acid-soluble purine nucleotides, and this was associated with a fivefold to 20-fold elevation in specific activity of acid-soluble purines following administration of formate-^{14}C and a 12- to 20-fold increase in the specific activity of nucleic acid purines. Similar results were obtained when glycine-^{14}C was used to measure the rate of purine biosynthesis *de novo,* although the kinetics of incorporation were slightly different from formate-^{14}C. The stimulatory effect of orotate was prevented by adenine. These workers concluded that the stimulation of purine biosynthesis observed in these studies probably represented release of the normal endproduct inhibitory activity of purine nucleotides.

It will be recalled that others (*e.g.*, *118*) have found that orotate inhibited purine biosynthesis in rat liver. However, these experiments were done under somewhat different conditions than those used by Windmueller and Spaeth, and the differences in results have not yet been reconciled.

ATP concentrations in rat liver also drop as much as 55% upon fasting, and Rajalakshmi and Handsschumacher (*118*) have reported that purine biosynthesis *de novo* is stimulated about twofold in fasted animals. Again, release of endproduct inhibition was believed responsible.

Burns (*89*) has performed some rather interesting experiments with *Saccharomyces cerevesiae* mutants with regard to the relationship between endproduct inhibition and concentrations of endogenous purine ribonucleotides. Although purine biosynthesis was completely inhibited when the medium contained 10 μg/ml adenine, it increased to its maximum rate within 10 minutes after changing the medium to one containing only 0.3 μg/ml adenine. After 15 to 20 minutes, however, the rate of purine biosynthesis began to decline and finally reached a new steady-state level about 25 to 30% of that attained immediately after the change of medium. During the course of these increases and decreases in the rate of purine biosynthesis the concentrations of several purine ribonucleotides were also measured, and the most rapid purine synthesis occurred at a time when the concentrations of AMP, IMP, and GMP declined markedly, although that of ATP rose slightly. As mentioned previously the only change in nucleotide concentrations that accompanied the subsequent decline in purine biosynthesis was an elevation in IMP levels.

These few papers apparently comprise the entire literature on this subject, and only the study of Burns (*89*) was deliberately designed for this purpose. Clearly, more work in this area is required.

Conclusions

The term "endproduct inhibition" can in the case of purine biosynthesis *de novo* refer to two somewhat different phenomena. The first is the inhibition observed when a purine base (or ribonucleoside) is presented to and utilized by a cell, and the second is inhibition presumed to be exerted by endogenous purine ribonucleotides in the absence of added purines.

Two basic alternatives exist regarding the site and mechanism of inhibition observed when a purine base is presented to a cell: either it is the process of nucleotide synthesis that is inhibitory through depletion of PP-ribose-P, or it is the newly formed ribonucleotides that inhibit PP-ribose-P synthetase or PP-ribose-P amidotransferase. The available evidence regarding the first point has been presented above; it is suggestive but far from conclusive.

It is often implicitly assumed that intracellular concentrations of purine ribonucleotides always increase when these potential endproduct inhibitors are formed from purine bases. Certainly this is so in the animal cells that have been studied (*e.g.*, *91*). The concentrations of nucleoside triphosphates are the only concentrations that increase significantly, however, and it is possible that there may be intracellular compartmentation of the newly formed purine ribonucleotides (*39*, *119*, and unpublished observations).

In contrast there is evidence (*120*) that purine bases enter *Escherichia coli* cells and are converted to ribonucleotides only at the same rate as the nucleotides are removed for nucleic acid synthesis. Thus over a range of extracellular concentrations of adenine and guanine there was no detectable expansion of nucleotide pools. In *Candida utilis* (*121*) the entry of purine bases into cells depends on their extracellular concentration, but the conversion of intracellular bases to ribonucleotides is regulated so that in this case also there is no actual increase in ribonucleotide concentrations. A so-called intracellular storage pool was also detected in *Saccharomyces cerevesiae* (*89*) although its chemical nature was not defined. Although the possibility of intracellular compartmentation again must be considered, these results at the very least do not support the hypothesis that increased purine ribonucleotide concentrations are the cause of endproduct inhibition in microbial systems through inhibition of an early enzyme in the pathway of purine synthesis.

Finally, the question must be asked whether endproduct inhibition by purine bases or ribonucleosides represents a physiologically significant process, or whether it is observed only in the laboratory. There is, for example, little evidence for the utilization of dietary nucleic acid purines by animals, and in fact Bowering *et al.* (*122*) failed to find any sign indicating endproduct inhibition of glycine-^{14}C incorporation into urinary uric acid in man upon feeding large amounts of RNA. It appears, however, that purine derivatives are transported among animal tissues *via* erythrocytes (*123–126*) and that these pass from erythrocytes to other cells in the form of purine bases (*127*). The extent of this process, its physiological role, and its possible influence on the rate of purine biosynthesis *de novo*, however, are not known.

It is supposed that purine bases may be available to many microorganisms in their natural habitats, although the only direct evidence on this point is the existence in nature of organisms that cannot synthesize purines *de novo*.

The second use of the term "endproduct inhibition" is inhibition presumed to be exerted by endogenous purine ribonucleotides (in the absence of added purines), which is detected by the acceleration of purine biosynthesis *de novo* when the concentrations of these nucleotides fall. This is the original sense of the concept of endproduct inhibition, and it must be assumed to occur in all cells that synthesize purines *de novo* which are not supplied with a surfeit of purine bases. As indicated above, however, this phenomenon has been little studied.

The site and mechanism of this second type of endproduct inhibition are not known. What little evidence is available in animal cells is mostly in favor of PP-ribose-P synthetase as the point of inhibition; there is no concrete evidence in any intact cell system for inhibition of PP-ribose-P amidotransferase although such inhibition may well occur.

Finally, it must be emphasized that the site, mechanism, and physiological importance of endproduct inhibition of purine biosynthesis *de novo* probably are different in microorganisms, ureotelic animals, and uricotelic animals. As pointed out previously there is no apparent biological role of this form of regulation in livers of uricotelic animals although it might have a function in their extrahepatic tissues. Presumably, it is physiologically significant in other organisms, and it seems likely that the rate of purine synthesis is controlled more tightly in microorganisms than in ureotelic animals. Nothing is known about endproduct inhibition in plants.

References

1. Umbarger, H. E., *Annu. Rev. Biochem.* (1969) **38,** 323.
2. Stadtman, E. R., *Advan. Enzymol. Relat. Subj. Biochem.* (1966) **28,** 41.
3. Henderson, J. F., *Progr. Exp. Tumor Res.* (1965) **6,** 84.
4. Blakley, R. L., Vitols, E., *Annu. Rev. Biochem.* (1968) **37,** 201.
5. Momose, H., *Protein Nucl. Acid Enzyme (Tokyo)* (1968) **13,** 781.
6. Umbarger, H. E., *Science* (1956) **123,** 848.
7. Yates, R. A., Pardee, A. B., *J. Biol. Chem.* (1956) **221,** 757.
8. Rose, W. C., *Physiol. Rev.* (1923) **3,** 544.
9. Gots, J. S., *J. Biol. Chem.* (1957) **228,** 57.
10. Mitchell, H. K., Houlahan, M. B., *Fed. Proc. Fed. Amer. Soc. Exp. Biol.* (1946) **5,** 370.
11. Lindegren, C., Lindegren, G., *Proc. Nat. Acad. Sci.* (1947) **33,** 314.
12. Reaume, S. E., Tatum, E. L., *Arch. Biochem. Biophys.* (1949) **22,** 331.
13. Tavlitzki, J., *Rev. Can. Biol.* (1951) **10,** 48.
14. Abrams, R., *Arch. Biochem. Biophys.* (1952) **37,** 270.
15. Heslot, H., Nagy, M., Whitehead, E., *C. R. Acad. Sci. Ser. D* (1966) **263,** 57.
16. Chamberlain, N., Cutts, N. S., Rainbow, C., *J. Gen. Microbiol.* (1952) **7,** 54.
17. Chamberlain, N., Rainbow, C., *J. Gen. Microbiol.* (1954) **11,** 180.
18. Moat, A. G., Wilkins, C. A., Jr., Friedman, H., *J. Biol. Chem.* (1956) **223,** 985.
19. Lones, D. P., Rainbow, C., Woodward, J. D., *J. Gen. Microbiol.* (1958) **19,** 146.
20. Rose, A. H., *J. Gen. Microbiol.* (1960) **23,** 143.
21. Friedman, H., Moat, A. G., *Arch. Biochem. Biophys.* (1958) **78,** 146.
22. Love, S. H., Gots, J. S., *J. Biol. Chem.* (1955) **212,** 647.
23. Love, S. H., Levenberg, B., *Biochim. Biophys. Acta* (1959) **35,** 367.
24. Sarachek, A., *Antonie van Leeuwenhoek J. Microbiol. Serol.* (1964) **30,** 289.
25. Gots, J. S., *Fed. Proc. Fed. Amer. Soc. Exp. Biol.* (1950) **9,** 178.
26. Gots, J. S., *Arch. Biochem.* (1950) **29,** 222.
27. Kalle, G. P., Gots, J. S., *Proc. Soc. Exp. Biol. Med.* (1962) **109,** 281.
28. Gots, J. S., Chu, E. C., *J. Bacteriol.* (1952) **64,** 537.
29. Gots, J. S., Gollub, E. G., *Proc. Nat. Acad. Sci.* (1957) **43,** 826.
30. Bennett, L. L., Jr., Smithers, D., *Biochem. Pharmacol.* (1964) **13,** 1331.
31. Nakayama, K., Suzuki, T., Sato, Z., Kinoshita, S., *J. Gen. Appl. Microbiol.* (1964) **10,** 133.
32. Aoki, R., *J. Gen. Appl. Microbiol.* (1963) **9,** 397.
33. Yamanoi, A., Konishi, S., Shiro, T., *J. Gen. Appl. Microbiol.* (1967) **13,** 365.
34. Furuya, A., Abe, S., Kinoshita, S., *Appl. Microbiol.* (1968) **16,** 981.

35. Furuya, A., Misawa, M., Nara, T., Abe, S., Kinoshita, S., "Fermentation Advances," Perlman, M., Ed., p. 177, Academic, New York, 1969.
36. Sugimoti, H., Iwasa, T., Ishiyama, J., Yokotsuka, T., *J. Agr. Chem. Soc. Jap.* (1962) **36,** 696.
37. Magasanik, B., Karibian, D., *J. Biol. Chem.* (1960) **235,** 2672.
38. Sartorelli, A. C., LePage, G. A., *Cancer Res.* (1958) **18,** 1329.
39. LePage, G. A., Jones, M., *Cancer Res.* (1961) **21**, 642.
40. Henderson, J. F., *J. Biol. Chem.* (1962) **237,** 2631.
41. Brockman, R. W., *Cancer Res.* (1963) **23,** 1191.
42. Brockman, R. W., Chumley, S., *Biochim. Biophys. Acta* (1965) **95,** 365.
43. Dixon, G. J., Dulmadge, E. A., Brockman, R. W., Shaddix, S., *J. Nat. Cancer Inst.* (1970) **45,** 681.
44. Henderson, J. F., *Biochim. Biophys. Acta* (1963) **76,** 173.
45. Henderson, J. F., Khoo, M. K. Y., *J. Biol. Chem.* (1965) **240,** 3104.
46. Henderson, J. F., Caldwell, I. C., Paterson, A. R. P., *Cancer Res.* (1967) **27,** 1773.
47. Caldwell, I. C., Henderson, J. F., Paterson, A. R. P., *Can. J. Biochem.* (1967) **45,** 735.
48. Henderson, J. F., *Cancer Chemother. Rep.* (Part 2) (1968) **1,** 375.
49. Rosenbloom, F. M., Henderson, J. F., Caldwell, I. C., Kelley, W. N., Seegmiller, J. E., *J. Biol. Chem.* (1968) **243,** 1166.
50. Henderson, J. F., Rosenbloom, F. M., Kelley, W. N., Seegmiller, W. N., *J. Clin. Invest.* (1968) **47,** 1511.
51. Rosenbloom, F. M., Henderson, J. F., Kelley, W. N., Seegmiller, J. E., *Biochim. Biophys. Acta* (1968) **161,** 258.
52. Trachewsky, D., Johnstone, R. M., *Can. J. Biochem.* (1969) **47,** 839.
53. Koch, A. L., Putnam, F. W., Evans, E. A., Jr., *J. Biol. Chem.* (1952) **197,** 105.
54. Bolton, E. T., Abelson, P. H., Aldous, E., *J. Biol. Chem.* (1952) **198,** 179.
55. Balis, M. E., Levin, D. H., Brown, G. B., Elion, G. B., VanderWerff, H., Hitchings, G. H., *J. Biol. Chem.* (1952) **196,** 729.
56. Kerr, S. F., Chernigoy, F., *J. Biol. Chem.* (1953) **200,** 887.
57. Koch, A. L., *J. Biol. Chem.* (1955) **217,** 931.
58. Koch, A. L., Levy, H. R., *J. Biol. Chem.* (1955) **217,** 947.
59. Zimmerman, E. F., Mandel, H. G., *Exp. Cell Res.* (1964) **33,** 130.
60. Zimmerman, E. F., Mandel, H. G., *Exp. Cell Res.* (1964) **33,** 138.
61. Bekker, M. L., *Biochemistry (USSR)* (1967) **32,** 518.
62. Roberts, R. B., Abelson, P. H., Cowie, D. B., Bolton, E. T., Britten, R. J., *Carnegie Inst. Wash. Publ.* (1955) No. 607.
63. Abrams, R., *Arch. Biochem. Biophys.* (1951) **33,** 436.
64. Furst, S. S., Brown, G. B., *J. Biol. Chem.* (1951) **191**, 239.
65. Goldthwait, D. A., Bendich, A., *J. Biol. Chem.* (1952) **196,** 841.
66. Bennett, L. L., Jr., Smithers, D., Teague, C., Baker, H. T., Stutts, P., *Biochem. Pharmacol.* (1962) **11,** 81.
67. Held, I., Wells, W., *J. Neurochem.* (1969) **16,** 529.
68. Shull, K. H., McConomy, J., Vogt, M., Castillo, A., Farber, E., *J. Biol. Chem.* (1966) **241**, 5060.
69. Smith, R. C., Salmon, W. D., *Arch. Biochem. Biophys.* (1969) **129,** 554.
70. Seegmiller, J. E., Laster, L., Stetten, D. W., Jr., *J. Biol. Chem.* (1955) **216,** 653.
71. Seegmiller, J. E., Klinenberg, J. R., Miller, J., Watts, R. W. E., *J. Clin. Invest.* (1968) **47,** 1193.
72. Abrams, R., Goldinger, J. M., *Arch. Biochem. Biophys.* (1952) **35,** 243.
73. LePage, G. A., *Cancer Res.* (1953) **13,** 178.
74. Edmonds, M., LePage, G. A., *Cancer Res.* (1956) **16,** 222.
75. Williams, A. M., LePage, G. A., *Cancer Res.* (1958) **18,** 548.

76. Thomson, R. Y., Smellie, R. M. S., Davidson, J. N., *Biochim. Biophys. Acta* (1958) **29,** 308.
77. Klenow, H., *Biochim. Biophys. Acta* (1959) **35,** 412.
78. Thomson, R. Y., Paul, J., Davidson, J. N., *Biochem. J.* (1958) **69**, 553.
79. McFall, E., Magasanik, B., *J. Biol. Chem.* (1960) **235,** 2103.
80. Diamond, H. S., Friedland, M., Halberstam, D., Kaplan, D., *Ann. Rheum. Dis.* (1969) **28,** 275.
81. Marko, P., Gerlach, E., Zimmer, H.-G., Pechan, I., Cremer, T., Trendelenburg, C., *Z. Physiol. Chem.* (1969) **350,** 1669.
82. Buchanan, J. M., Wilson, D. W., *Fed. Proc. Fed. Amer. Soc. Exp. Biol.* (1953) **12**, 646.
83. Wyngaarden, J. B., Silberman, H. R., Sadler, J. H., *Ann. N.Y. Acad. Sci.* (1958) **75,** 45.
84. Bennett, L. L., Jr., Allan, P. W., Smithers, D., Vail, M. H., *Biochem. Pharmacol.* (1969) **18,** 725.
85. Gots, J. S., Goldstein, J., *Science* (1959) **130,** 622.
86. DeRepentigny, J., Grimard, S., Turgeon, S., Sonea, S., *J. Bacteriol.* (1966) **91,** 2099.
87. DeRepentigny, J., Labelle, C., Sonea, S., *Can. J. Microbiol.* (1967) **13,** 919.
88. DeRepentigny, J., Mathieu, L. G., Turgeon, S., Sonea, S., *Can. J. Microbiol.* (1968) **14,** 39.
89. Burns, V. W., *Biophys. J.* (1964) **4,** 151.
90. Henderson, J. F., Khoo, M. K. Y., *J. Biol. Chem.* (1965) **240,** 2358.
91. Crabtree, G. W., Henderson, J. F., *Cancer Res.* (1971) **31,** 985.
92. LeGal, M.-L., LeGal, Y., Roche, J., Hedegaard, J., *Biochem. Biophys. Res. Commun.* (1967) **27**, 618.
93. Reem, G. H., *J. Biol. Chem.* (1968) **243,** 5695.
94. Hartman, S. C., Buchanan, J. M., *J. Biol. Chem.* (1958) **233,** 451.
95. Wyngaarden, J. B., Ashton, D. M., *J. Biol. Chem.* (1959) **234,** 1492.
96. Caskey, C. T., Ashton, D. M., Wyngaarden, J. B., *J. Biol. Chem.* (1964) **239,** 2570.
97. Rowe, P. B., Wyngaarden, J. B., *J. Biol. Chem.* (1968) **243,** 6373.
98. Rowe, P. B., Coleman, M. D., Wyngaarden, J. B., *Biochemistry* (1970) **9,** 1498.
99. Rottman, F., Guarino, A. J., *Biochim. Biophys. Acta* (1964) **89,** 465.
100. Hartman, S. C., *J. Biol. Chem.* (1963) **238,** 3024.
101. Hartman, S. C., *J. Biol. Chem.* (1963) **238,** 3036.
102. Katunuma, N., Matsuda, Y., Kuroda, Y., *Advan. Enzyme Regul.* (1970) **8,** 73.
103. Hill, D. L., Bennett, L. L., Jr., *Biochemistry* (1969) **8,** 122.
104. Tay, B. S., Lilley, R. M., Murray, A. W., Atkinson, M. R., *Biochem. Pharmacol.* (1969) **18,** 936.
105. Woods, A. W., Seegmiller, J. E., *Fed. Proc. Fed. Amer. Soc. Exp. Biol.* (1971) **30,** 1113.
106. Reem, G. H., Friend, C., *Science* (1967) **157,** 1203.
107. Shiio, I., Ishii, K., *J. Biochem. Tokyo* (1969) **66,** 175.
108. Nara, T., Komuro, T., Misawa, M., Kinoshita, S., *Agr. Biol. Chem.* (1969) **33,** 739.
109. Satyanarayana, T., Kaplan, J. G., *Arch. Biochem. Biophys.* (1971) **142,** 40.
110. Nagy, M., *Biochim. Biophys. Acta* (1970) **198,** 471.
111. Nierlich, D. P., Magasanik, B., *J. Biol. Chem.* (1965) **240,** 358.
112. Li, H.-C., Buchanan, J. M., *J. Biol. Chem.* (1971) **246,** 4713.
113. Gadd, R. E. A., Henderson, J. F., *Can. J. Biochem.* (1970) **48,** 302.
114. Monod, J., Wyman, J., Changeux, J. P., *J. Mol. Biol.* (1965) **12,** 88.
115. Heslot, H., Nagy, M., Whitehead, E., *C. R. Acad. Sci. Ser. D* (1966) **263,** 57.
116. Stekol, J. A., Utsonomiya, T., Bulba, S., *Fed. Proc. Fed. Amer. Soc. Exp. Biol.* (1967) **26,** 864.

117. Windmueller, H. G., Spaeth, A. E., *J. Biol. Chem.* (1965) **240,** 4398.
118. Rajalakshmi, S., Handschumacher, R. E., *Biochim. Biophys. Acta* (1968) **155,** 317.
119. Henderson, J. F., *Biochim. Biophys. Acta* (1962) **65,** 824.
120. Buchwald, M., Britten, R. J., *Biophys. J.* (1963) **3,** 155.
121. Cowie, D. B., Bolton, E. T., *Biochim. Biophys. Acta* (1957) **25,** 292.
122. Bowering, J., Calloway, D. H., Margen, S., Kaufmann, N. A., *J. Nutr.* (1970) **100,** 249.
123. Lajtha, L. G., Vane, J. R., *Nature (London)* (1958) **182,** 191.
124. Henderson, J. F., LePage, G. A., *J. Biol. Chem.* (1959) **234**, 3219.
125. Mager, J., Hershko, A., Zeitlin-Bech, R., Shoshani, T., Razin, A., *Biochim. Biophys. Acta* (1967) **149,** 50.
126. Pritchard, J. B., Chavez-Peon, F., Berlin, R. D., *Amer. J. Physiol.* (1970) **219,** 1263.
127. Brown, R. B., Paterson, A. R. P., *Can. J. Biochem.* (1971) **49**, 1251.

Chapter

6 Regulation of Enzyme Amount and Genetic Regulation

RELATIVELY LITTLE is known about the regulation of the amounts of the enzymes of purine biosynthesis *de novo* or of the relative amounts of the 10 enzymes of this pathway. This situation exists in large part because these enzymes are somewhat difficult to assay and particularly because their substrates are not, for the most part, commercially available. In addition, intermediates which may accumulate in microbial mutants are usually not excreted as such but are dephosphorylated and sometimes are metabolized more extensively. In spite of these difficulties a good beginning has been made.

Regulation of enzyme amount may be divided into two parts. One is the limitation placed on enzyme amount by the genetic constitution of the cell, with respect both to the structural gene for each enzyme and to any regulatory genes which may exist. The second is the regulation of enzyme amount within these limits, usually in response to nutrient or endproduct concentrations.

Repression and Derepression in Microorganisms

PP-Ribose-P Amidotransferase. The first studies of repression and depression of the enzymes of purine biosynthesis *de novo* were briefly reported in 1965 by Nierlich and Magasanik (*1*), and more details of this work have recently become available (*2*). The specific activity of PP-ribose-P amidotransferase could be reduced from seven to 1.5 units in wild-type *Aerobacter aerogenes* by growth in the presence of either adenine or guanine. Enzyme levels in the purine-requiring mutant strain PD-1 were between 0.8 and 2.5 units in the presence of adenine, guanine, or both together. When strain PD-1 was grown with limiting amounts of either adenine or guanine, derepression occurred and the specific activity of this enzyme rose to between 24.0 and 29.9 units. Similar studies were made by Westby and Gots (*3*) with wild-type *Salmonella typhimurium* and various purine-requiring mutants grown on limiting amounts of xanthine. Under these conditions the specific activity of PP-ribose-P amidotransferase rose from 800 to as much as 1100 units. Purine biosynthesis *de novo* in wild-type cells of both organisms apparently produced enough nucleotides to cause repression.

Momose *et al.* (*4*) caused repression of PP-ribose-P amidotransferase activity in purine-requiring mutants of *Bacillus subtilis* by adding adenosine or guanosine to culture media. Later studies (*5*) were conducted with double mutants which were blocked both in the latter stages of the *de novo* pathway and also at various points in the pathways of purine ribonucleotide interconversion. In these cases the relative specific activity of PP-ribose-P amidotransferase was found to vary both with the mutant studied and with the purine ribonucleoside supplied as repressor. Thus, compared with the enzyme activity of controls grown without added purines, enzyme activity was 28% in mutant MX-354 grown with guanosine, 21% in mutant MX-37 grown with adenosine, 46% in mutant NG-88 grown with inosine, and 80% in mutant NG-388 grown with xanthosine. Because adenine and guanine nucleotides could not be interconverted in mutants MX-354 and MX-37, it was concluded that both classes of nucleotides could independently repress PP-ribose-P amidotransferase. It has also been shown that PP-ribose-P amidotransferase is repressed up to 65% in *Brevibacterium ammoniagenes* grown with adenine (*6, 7*).

Phosphoribosyl-Glycineamide Synthetase. Repression and derepression of phosphoribosyl-glycineamide synthetase have also been observed. Thus in one study of *Aerobacter aerogenes* strain PD-1 grown with a limiting supply of adenine the specific activity of this enzyme rose fourfold over that in wild-type cells (*8*). In another investigation with the same organism (*2*) synthetase activities rose from 7.5 to between 15.3 and 18.1 units when strain PD-1 was grown with limiting amounts of either adenine and guanine; excess amounts of these purines led to repression of this enzyme to specific activities of between 1.0 and 4.3 units.

Westby and Gots (*3*) found that the specific activity of phosphoribosyl-glycineamide synthetase rose from 34 units in wild-type *Salmonella typhimurium* to between 88 and 179 units (in different experiments) in a mutant which lacked PP-ribose-P amidotransferase and which was grown on limiting amounts of xanthine.

In combined assays of PP-ribose-P amidotransferase plus phosphoribosyl-glycineamide synthetase in mutants of *Salmonella typhimurium* blocked at various late stages of purine biosynthesis *de novo* the specific activity was 41 in wild-type cells, and 72, 98, 101, and 127 in different mutants when they were grown with limiting supplies of purine (*3*).

Phosphoribosyl-Formylglycineamidine Synthetase. Nierlich and Magasanik (*1, 2*) showed that whereas the specific activity of phosphoribosyl-formylglycineamidine synthetase in wild-type *Aerobacter aerogenes* was 2.9 units, it could be repressed to 0.5 unit, or derepressed to 20.1 units in strain PD-1 grown on excess or limiting purines, respectively.

Adenylosuccinate Lyase. Adenylosuccinate lyase has been found to be repressed in *Bacillus subtilis* when grown with adenosine or guanosine (*9, 10*); this enzyme was not nearly as sensitive to repression as were other enzymes of purine biosynthesis, however. This was also true of *Aerobacter aerogenes* (*2*), in which its activity could be decreased only from 3.5 to 1.1 units by growth in adenine or guanine and derepressed to 11.6 units when these purines were limiting. It must be rememberd, of course, that this enzyme is also required for the synthesis of adenylate from inosinate in addition to its role in inosinate synthesis.

Phosphoribosyl-Aminoimidazole Carboxamide Formyltransferase and Inosinate Cyclohydrolase. Levin and Magasanik (*11*) studied the combined activities of phosphoribosyl-aminoimidazole carboxamide formyltransferase and inosinate cyclohydrolase in wild-type *Salmonella typhimurium* and *Aerobacter aerogenes* and in different purine-requiring mutants grown with limiting or excess purine supplements. In both organisms the combined specific activities of these enzymes was greater (up to fivefold) in most purine-requiring mutants grown with limiting purine than in wild-type cells grown without purines. Addition of excess purines resulted in repression of these enzymes, their specific activities decreasing as much as 85%. In the case of a guanine-requiring mutant of *Aerobacter aerogenes* grown with limiting supplies of guanine, however, further addition of adenine led to a 30% increase in the specific activities of these enzymes.

Phosphoribosyl-aminoimidazole carboxamide formyltransferase and inosinate cyclohydrolase were repressed completely in *Bacillus subtilis* grown either with adenosine or with guanosine (*9*). They were also repressed in experiments in which mutants blocked in purine ribonucleotide interconversions were used to show that both adenine and guanine nucleotides were active independently (*10*).

Other Measurements. Other studies of repression of purine biosynthesis *de novo* have used measurements of isotope incorporation or of accumulation of intermediates as indicators of the rate of this pathway instead of enzyme assays. Thus Bekker (*12*) found that the incorporation of radioactive precursors into purine nucleotides was much reduced in *Pasteurella pestis* cells previously grown with excess adenine or guanine. Love and Remy (*13*), in contrast, studied growth and accumulation of aminoimidazole carboxamide (and its ribosyl derivative) in an adenylosuccinate lyase-deficient strain of *Escherichia coli* grown with 6-methoxypurine and related compounds. Although these substrates were converted to inosinate and hence supported growth, this process was sufficiently slow to permit an increase in the accumulation of aminoimidazole carboxamide, presumably because of derepression of the early enzymes of the purine biosynthetic pathway.

Coordinate Repression. Nierlich and Magasanik (*1, 2*) have demonstrated that the ratio of activities of PP-ribose-P amidotransferase and phosphoribosyl-formylglycineamidine synthetase in extracts of *Aerobacter areogenes* is constant when these enzyme activities are repressed and derepressed over a 30-fold range. Under similar conditions the relationship between PP-ribose-P amidotransferase and phosphoribosyl-glycineamide synthetase activities was more complex, and the latter enzyme seemed less responsive to regulation than the former. It is shown below that the genetic loci for these three enzymes are not closely linked.

Conclusions. The observations quoted above leave no doubt that at least six of the 10 enzymes of the purine biosynthetic pathway can be regulated by repression and derepression. It is also apparent that some enzymes are more responsive to the addition of exogenously supplied purines than are others and that the synthesis of any single enzyme may be regulated differently in different microorganisms. Thus Nierlich and Magasanik (*2*) have concluded that in *Aerobacter aerogenes* the synthesis of three early enzymes of the pathway is regulated primarily by adenine nucleotides and possibly in a coordinate manner. In contrast, adenylosuccinate lyase is equally sensitive to both adenine and guanine whereas inosinate cyclohydrolase is responsive mainly to supplementation with guanine. In *Bacillus subtilis* adenosine and guanosine independently affect the synthesis of both PP-ribose-P amidotransferase and adenylosuccinate lyase (*5, 10*).

It is difficult to draw any general conclusions about the mechanism and actual physiological significance of repression and derepression for the regulation of purine biosynthesis at the present time. Further studies of this subject should be rewarding.

Repression and Derepression in Animal Cells

As might be expected, much less work has been done on repression and derepression of the enzymes of the purine biosynthetic pathway in animal cells than in microorganisms. Nevertheless, following suggestive evidence by McFall and Magasanik (*14*) that repression of purine biosynthesis *de novo* might have occurred in L cells grown in culture with excess adenine, Nierlich and McFall (*15*) showed that the specific activity of phosphoribosyl-glycineamide synthetase was reduced to about half the control value by this treatment.

Although details are most unclear, it appears that PP-ribose-P amidotransferase activity increases dramatically in mouse spleen following infection with Friend leukemia virus (*16*). This may be a form of derepression.

Katunuma *et al.* (*17*) have recently shown that PP-ribose-P amidotransferase is induced in chicken liver by high-protein diets. Thus the specific activity of this enzyme rose 3.5-fold when the diet of chickens was changed from 5% to 50% protein; it also rose slightly when the birds were fasted. In contrast, PP-ribose-P amidotransferase activity in rat liver did not change under the same conditions, and its total activity was only about 10% that of chicken liver with a 5% protein diet. The induction by high-protein diets of PP-ribose-P amidotransferase in chicken liver is of course consistent with the role of the purine biosynthetic pathway in the excretion of amino acid nitrogen in uricotelic animals. Whether other enzymes of purine synthesis also respond to nitrogen intake is not yet known.

Relative Activities of the Enzymes of Purine Biosynthesis

Information regarding the maximum potential rate of purine biosynthesis, and potential rate-limiting reactions in this pathway, might be deduced from measurements of the total activities of each of the constituent enzymes. Unfortunately, in only a few cases have even two of these enzymes been assayed by the same investigator at the same time and in the same preparation. The available data are given in Table 6-1.

Mapping of Genetic Loci of the Enzymes of Purine Biosynthesis

Studies of the genetic regulation of enzyme amount require, or are at least greatly facilitated by, identification of the loci for each structural gene for the enzymes of the purine biosynthetic pathway. If possible, these should also be located on the genetic map of the organism. The available data regarding identification and mapping of genetic loci for the enzymes of purine biosynthesis are given in Table 6-2; the enterobacteria have been most thoroughly studied. In addition, two loci have been identified in *Aspergillus nidulans* (*20*): *ade1* for phosphoribosyl-aminoimidazole carboxylase, and *ade3* = *adeA* for adenylosuccinate lyase.

Mutations Affecting Regulation of Purine Biosynthesis

Recent developments suggest that genetic studies of the regulation of the amounts of the enzymes of purine biosynthesis and of specifically genetic mechanisms of regulation will be a fruitful but complex field. The beginnings of this work are recorded here.

Bacterial Mutants Used for Fermentative Production of Purine Nucleotides. The commercial use of guanylate, inosinate, and xanthylate as flavoring agents for foods, and the potential medical use of purine nucleotides,

Table 6-1. Relative Activities of Enzymes of Purine Biosynthesis

Salmonella typhimurium (*3*)			
PP-ribose-P-aminotransferase			800
Phosphoribosyl-glycineamide synthetase			34.4
Salmonella typhimurium (*18*)			
Phosphoribosyl-aminoimidazole carboxamide formyltransferase			1.45
Inosinate cyclohydrolase			1.38
Aerobacter aerogenes (*1*)			
PP-ribose-P amidotransferase			7
Phosphoribosyl-glycineamide synthetase			28
Aerobacter aerogenes PD-1, derepressed (*6*)			
PP-ribose-P amidotransferase			28
Phosphoribosyl-glycineamide synthetase			112
Bacillus subtilis (*19*)			
PP-ribose-P amidotransferase			4.4
Phosphoribosyl-aminoimidazole carboxamide formyltransferase plus inosinate cyclohydrolase			3.8
Bacillus subtilis mutant G-6 (*10*)			
PP-ribose-P amidotransferase			2.94
Phosphoribosyl-aminoimidazole carboxamide formyltransferase plus inosinate cyclohydrolase			2.22
Adenylosuccinate lyase			3.21
Aerobacter aerogenes (*2*)			
PP-ribose-P amidotransferase	7.5[a]	0.8[b]	28.2[c]
Phosphoribosyl-glycineamide synthetase	7.5	1.1	16.7
Phosphoribosyl-formylglycineamide synthetase	2.9	0.5	20.1
Adenylosuccinate lyase	3.8	1.1	11.6

[a] Wild type
[b] Strain PD-1, repressed
[c] Strain PD-1, derepressed

has led to successful efforts to produce these compounds in large quantities by microbial fermentative processes. Some of these studies have been reviewed by Demain (*49*) and by Furuya *et al.* (*7*). Although the purine ribonucleotides may be produced by a number of different mechanisms, in some cases mutants appear to have been selected which are deficient in the regulation of the purine biosynthetic pathway. Unfortunately, the mechanisms by which purine synthesis is accelerated are in most cases not certain, nor are the genetic loci involved identified.

PP-ribose-P amidotransferase, adenylosuccinate lyase, and phosphoribosyl-aminoimidazole carboxamide formyltransferase plus inosinate cyclohydrolase are normally repressed when *Bacillus subtilis* is grown in the presence of guanosine; in the absence of guanylate reductase this effect of guanosine causes growth inhibition because of a lack of adenine nucleotides. Momose

Table 6-2. Genetic Loci of the

	Escherichia coli[a]	
PP-Ribose-P amidotransferase	*purF*	44[f]
Phosphoribosyl-glycineamide synthetase	*purD*	78
Phosphoribosyl-glycineamide formyltransferase		
Phosphoribosyl-formylglycineamidine synthetase	*purG*	49
Phosphoribosyl-aminoimidazole synthetase	*purI*	
Phosphoribosyl-aminoimidazole carboxylase	*purE*	15
Phosphoribosyl-aminoimidazole succinocarboxamide synthetase	*purC*	48
Adenylosuccinate lyase	*purB*	23
Phosphoribosyl-aminoimidazole carboxamide formyltransferase	*purH*	78
IMP cyclohydrolase	*purJ*	78

[a] Reviews: (*21–24*)
[b] Reviews: (*3, 18, 25, 26, 27*)
[c] (*28–34*)

et al. (*9*) isolated a number of guanosine-resistant mutants, and Momose (*10*) has shown that in various mutants one or more of the above-mentioned enzymes of purine biosynthesis is no longer repressed. Unfortunately, it is not known if each of the bacterial strains is the result of a single mutational event or of more than one mutation.

***Ade4* Mutants in *Schizosaccharomyces pombe*.** Heslot *et al.* (*50*) selected for mutants of *Schizosaccharomyces pombe* which were resistant to 8-azaguanine and excreted hypoxanthine. Because they showed no requirement for adenine, the overproduction of hypoxanthine appeared to rise from accelerated purine biosynthesis *de novo* and loss of adenylosuccinate synthetase. Genetic analysis of such cultures showed that mutation had occurred in the gene for PP-ribose-P amidotransferase (the *ade4* locus), resulting in an active but altered enzyme which is not subject to normal feedback inhibition. Studies of this enzyme have recently been reported by Nagy (*51*), and it appears to be one-tenth as sensitive to inhibition by guanylate and inosinate as is the PP-ribose-P amidotransferase from wild-type cells (Chapter 5).

***Ade12* Mutants in *Saccharomyces cerevisiae*.** *Ade12* is the locus for adenylosuccinate synthetase in yeast (*52*), and mutants which lack this enzyme require adenine for growth. They also excrete hypoxanthine, which is derived from the inosinate that cannot be converted to adenylate. Double

Enzymes of Purine Biosynthesis *de novo*

Salmonella typhimurium[b]		Saccharomyces cerevisiae[c]	Schizosaccharomyces pombe[d]	Neurospora crassa[e]
purF	73[f]	*ade4*	*ade4*	
purD	129	*ade5*	*ade1A*	
				D
purG	80	*ade6*		I
purI	79	*ade7*	*ade1B*	H
purE	19	*ade2*	*ade6*	*ade3B, B*
purC	79	*ade1*	*ade7*	*ade3A, A*
purB	43	*ade13*	*ade8*	*ade4, F*
purH	129		*ade10* (purH, purJ)	*J* (purH, purJ)
purJ	129			

[d] *(35–41)*
[e] *(32, 38, 42–48)*
[f] Map distances

mutants of the type *ade2 ade12* or *ade1 ade12,* which in addition are blocked at the phosphoribosyl-aminoimidazole carboxylase or phosphoribosyl-aminoimidazole succinocarboxamide synthetase steps of the purine biosynthetic pathway, accumulate the red or purple pigment which is formed from aminoimidazole. Dorfman (*52*) observed that concentrations of adenine which in simple *ade2* or *ade1* mutants or in other double mutants such as *ade2 ade13* would inhibit pigment formation through endproduct inhibition, failed to affect pigment synthesis in the presence of mutations at the *ade12* locus. Because of this so-called constitutive purine biosynthesis in *ade12* mutants it was concluded that in addition to its catalytic activity, adenylosuccinate synthetase has a regulatory function. Auxotrophic *ade12* mutants which excrete hypoxanthine have also been isloated by Armitt and Woods (*53*).

Dorfman *et al.* (*54, 55*) obtained a number of revertants of *ade12* mutants which apparently had adenylosuccinate synthetase activity (because they no longer required adenine for growth) but continued to synthesize excessive amounts of purines *de novo.* Thus the enzymatic and regulatory functions associated with the *ade12* locus are mutationally separable, and this locus appears to code for a single protein with both catalytic and regulatory functions. Lomax and Woods (*56*) have confirmed these findings. These workers have also shown that the *pur1* prototrophic mutants previously isolated by Armitt and Woods (*53*), which are defective in the control of purine synthesis, are a type of *ade12* mutants in which adenylosuccinate synthetase activity is retained but in which its regulatory function is impaired. Genetic studies suggest that the regulatory function of adenylosuccinate synthetase "may be exerted through a complex involving the products of at least two genes in addition to *ade12 pur1*."

Pur* Loci in *Saccharomyces cerevisiae. Of the six unlinked loci (*pur1 to pur6*), which Armitt and Woods (*53, 57*) found to regulate purine biosynthesis *de novo* in prototrophic *Saccharomyces cerevisiae, pur1* has been identified as the regulatory portion of adenylosuccinate synthetase. The biochemical sites of action of the *pur2, pur3, pur4,* and *pur5* loci unfortunately remain unknown. They do not appear to be closely linked to those loci for the enzymes of purine biosynthesis which have so far been identified or for the loci *ade9, ade5,* or *ade7,* which induce an adenine requirement but about which little is known.

The *pur6* locus includes both dominant (*PUR6*) and recessive (*pur6*) alleles. In addition a gene (*su-pur*) was identified (*58*) which suppressed the overproduction of purines in other regulatory mutants but not in *pur6;* it did not recombine with alleles of *pur6. Pur6* also did not recombine with *ade4,* which has recently (*34*) been shown to affect PP-ribose-P amidotransferase activity, although previously (*31*) this locus had been thought to code for phosphoribosyl-glycineamide formyltransferase.

Lomax and Woods (*59*) subsequently isolated yeast mutants that are sensitive to growth inhibition by 2,6-diaminopurine. The responsible locus (*dap*) appears to regulate the enzyme hypoxanthine-guanine phosphoribosyltransferase, and has also (*60*) been found not to recombine with *su-pur* alleles. These and other studies showed that mutants of types *dap, su-pur, ade4, pur6,* and *PUR6* are all alleles of the same gene, but the exact relationship among them remains unclear at the present time.

Loss of Enzymes of Purine Biosynthesis during the Maturation of the Mammalian Erythrocyte

Mammalian reticulocytes possess the ability to synthesize purine ribonucleotides *de novo,* but this ability is lost during the process of maturation to form mature erythrocytes (*61, 62, 63, 64*). Not all of the 10 enzymes of the purine biosynthetic pathway are missing in mature cells, however; they readily convert aminoimidazole carboxamide to purine nucleotides (*62, 63*), a process requiring the activity of the last two enzymes in the pathway.

Adenylosuccinate lyase is required both for purine biosynthesis *de novo* and for the conversion of inosinate to adenylate. The process of adenylate synthesis from inosinate is lost during the maturation of human erythrocytes (*62, 64*) but is retained in rabbit erythrocytes (*65, 66, 67*). The presence of adenylosuccinate lyase activity in both human and rabbit erythrocytes has recently been demonstrated (*68*), and this enzyme therefore is not the basis of the inability of both cell types to synthesize purines *de novo.*

Fontenelle and Henderson (*69*) have shown that mouse erythrocytes do not accumulate phosphoribosyl-formylglycineamide in the presence of azaserine, and they have presented presumptive evidence that PP-ribose-P amidotransferase is missing from these cells. Direct assays of the latter enzyme in extracts of human erythrocytes have shown that it indeed is absent (*70*).

It is not yet known whether other enzymes in addition to PP-ribose-P amidotransferase are missing in the mature mammalian erythrocyte or the mechanism by which such an enzyme is lost.

References

1. Nierlich, D. P., Magasanik, B., *J. Biol. Chem.* (1965) **240,** 358.
2. Nierlich, D. P., Magasanik, B., *Biochim. Biophys. Acta* (1971) **230,** 349.
3. Westby, C. A., Gots, J. S., *J. Biol. Chem.* (1969) **244,** 2095.
4. Momose, H., Nishikawa, H., Shiio, J., *J. Biochem. (Tokyo)* (1966) **59,** 325.
5. Nishikawa, H., Momose, H., Shiio, J., *J. Biochem. (Tokyo)* (1967) **62,** 92.
6. Nara, T., Komura, T., Misawa, M., Kinoshita, S., *Agr. Biol. Chem.* (1969) **33,** 739.
7. Furuya, A., Misawa, M., Nara, T., Abe, S., Kinoshita, S., "Fermentation Advances," Perlman, M., Ed., p. 177, Academic, New York, 1969.
8. Nierlich, D. P., Magasanik, B., *J. Biol. Chem.* (1965) **240,** 366.
9. Momose, H., Nishikawa, H., Katsuya, N., *J. Gen. Appl. Microbiol.* (1965) **11,** 211.
10. Momose, H., *J. Gen. Appl. Microbiol.* (1967) **13,** 39.
11. Levin, A. P., Magasanik, B., *J. Biol. Chem.* (1961) **236,** 184.
12. Bekker, M. L., *Biochemistry (USSR)* (1967) **32,** 518.
13. Love, S. H., Remy, C. N., *J. Bacteriol.* (1966) **91,** 1037.
14. McFall, E., Magasanik, B., *J. Biol. Chem.* (1960) **235,** 2103.
15. Nierlich, D. P., McFall, E., *Biochim. Biophys. Acta* (1963) **76,** 469.
16. Reem, G. H., Friend, C., *Science* (1967) **157,** 1203.
17. Katunuma, N., Matsuda, Y., Kuroda, Y., *Advan. Enzyme Regul.* (1970) **8,** 73.
18. Gots, J. S., Dalal, F. R., Shumas, S. R., *J. Bacteriol.* (1969) **99,** 441.
19. Nishikawa, H., Momose, H., Shiio, J., *J. Biochem. (Tokyo)* (1968) **63,** 149.
20. Foley, J. M., Giles, N. H., Roberts, C. F., *Genetics* (1965) **52,** 1247.
21. Taylor, A. L., Trotter, C. D., *Bacteriol. Rev.* (1967) **31,** 332.
22. Taylor, A. L., *Bacteriol. Rev.* (1970) **34,** 155.
23. Stouthamer, A. H., de Haan, P. G., Nykamp, H. J., *Genet. Res.* (1965) **6,** 442.
24. Tritz, G. J., Matney, T. S., Chandler, J. L. R., Gholson, R. K., *J. Bacteriol.* (1970) **102,** 881.
25. Sanderson, K. E., *Bacteriol. Rev.* (1967) **31,** 354.
26. Sanderson, K. E., *Bacteriol. Rev.* (1970) **34,** 176.
27. Ozeko, H., *Genetics* (1959) **44,** 457.
28. Armitt, S., Woods, R. A., *Genet. Res.* (1970) **15,** 7.
29. Dorfman, B., *Genetics* (1963) **48,** 887.
30. Levinthal, M., Fogel, S., Hurst, D. D., *Genetics* (1962) **47,** 967.
31. Silver, J. M., Eaton, N. R., *Genetics* (1968) **60,** 225.
32. Mazlen, A. S., Eaton, N. R., *Biochem. Biophys. Res. Commun.* (1967) **26,** 590.
33. Silver, J. M., Eaton, N. R., *Biochem. Biophys. Res. Commun.* (1969) **34,** 301.
34. Gross, T. S., Woods, R. A., *Biochim. Biophys. Acta* (1971) **247,** 13.
35. Heslot, H., Nagy, M., Whitehead, E., *C. R. Acad. Sci. Ser. D.* (1966) **263,** 57.

36. Fisher, C. R., *Biochem. Biophys. Res. Commun.* (1969) **34**, 306.
37. Leupold, U., Gutz, H., *Proc. Int. Cong. Genet. 11th* (1963) **2,** 31.
38. Giles, N. H., *Proc. Int. Cong. Genet. 11th* (1963) **2,** 17.
39. Nagy, M., Heslot, H., Poirier, L., *C. R. Acad. Sci. Ser. D.* (1969) **269,** 1268.
40. Whitehead, E., Nagy, M., Heslot, H., *C. R. Acad. Sci. Ser. D.* (1966) **263,** 819.
41. Flury, R., Flury, U., Coddington, A., *Heredity* (1971) **27,** 311.
42. Buchanan, J. M., *Harvey Lect.* (1960) **54**, 104.
43. Barrett, R. W., Newmeyer, D., Perkins, D. D., Gamjobst, L., *Advan. Genet.* (1954) **6,** 1.
44. Fisher, C. R., *Biochim. Biophys. Acta* (1969) **178,** 380.
45. Bernstein, H., *J. Gen. Microbiol.* (1961) **25,** 41.
46. De Serres, F. J., *Mutat. Res.* (1966) **3,** 3.
47. De Serres, F. J., Jr., *Genetics* (1956) **41,** 668.
48. Giles, N. H., Partridge, C. W. H., Nelson, N. J., *Proc. Nat. Acad. Sci.* (1957) **43,** 305.
49. Demain, A. L., "Progress in Industrial Microbiology," Hockenhull, D. J. D., Ed., Vol. 8, p. 35, Churchill, London, 1968.
50. Heslot, H., Nagy, M., Whitehead, E., *C. R. Acad. Sci. Ser. D* (1966) **263,** 57.
51. Nagy, M., *Biochim. Biophys. Acta* (1970) **198,** 471.
52. Dorfman, B.-Z., *Genetics* (1969) **61**, 377.
53. Armitt, S., Woods, R. A., *Genet. Res.* (1970) **15,** 7.
54. Dorfman, B.-Z., Goldfinger, B. A., Berger, M., *Science* (1970) **168,** 1482.
55. Dorfman, B.-Z., *J. Bacteriol.* (1971) **107,** 646.
56. Lomax, C. A., Woods, R. A., *Nature (London) New Biology* (1971) **229,** 116.
57. Armitt, S., Woods, R. A., *Heredity* (1968) **23**, 468.
58. Woods, R. A., Armitt, S., *Heredity* (1968) **23,** 467.
59. Lomax, C. A., Woods, R. A., *J. Bacteriol.* (1969) **100,** 817.
60. Lomax, C. A., Ph.D. Thesis, Sheffield University, 1970.
61. Lowy, B. A., Ramot, B., London, I. M., *Ann. N.Y. Acad. Sci.* (1958) **75,** 148.
62. Lowy, B. A., Williams, M. K., London, I. M., *J. Biol. Chem.* (1962) **237,** 1622.
63. Lowy, B. A., Williams, M. K., *J. Biol. Chem.* (1960) **235,** 2924.
64. Lowy, B. A., Cook, J. K., London, I. M., *J. Biol. Chem.* (1961) **236,** 1442.
65. Lowy, B. A., Williams, M. K., London, I. M., *J. Biol. Chem.* (1961) **236,** 1439.
66. Mager, J., Hershko, A., Zeitlin-Beck, R., Shoshani, T., Razin, A., *Biochim. Biophys. Acta* (1967) **149,** 50.
67. Hershko, A., Razin, A., Shoshani, T., Mager, J., *Biochim. Biophys. Acta* (1967) **149**, 59.
68. Lowry, B. A., Dorfman, B.-Z., *J. Biol. Chem.* (1970) **245,** 3043.
69. Fontenelle, L. J., Henderson, J. F., *Biochim. Biophys. Acta* (1969) **177,** 175.
70. Brox, L. W., personal communication.

Chapter

7

Branches of the Pathway of Purine Synthesis and Their Regulation

THE PATHWAY OF purine biosynthesis from phosphoribosylamine to inosinate is unbranched in animal cells—*i.e.*, no intermediate has any other anabolic fate, and none has any physiological origin other than the preceding compound in this pathway. Branches are introduced into this pathway, however, in organisms which synthesize the vitamin thiamine and the amino acid histidine. The regulation of the purine biosynthetic pathway consequently becomes of interest in relation to the synthesis of these two compounds, and regulation of the pathways of thiamine and histidine biosynthesis may affect the rate of purine synthesis.

Thiamine Biosynthesis

Studies of microbial genetics, and of certain types of purine toxicity in microorganisms, first showed that a close relationship must exist between purine metabolism and the biosynthesis of thiamine. Later, the biosynthesis

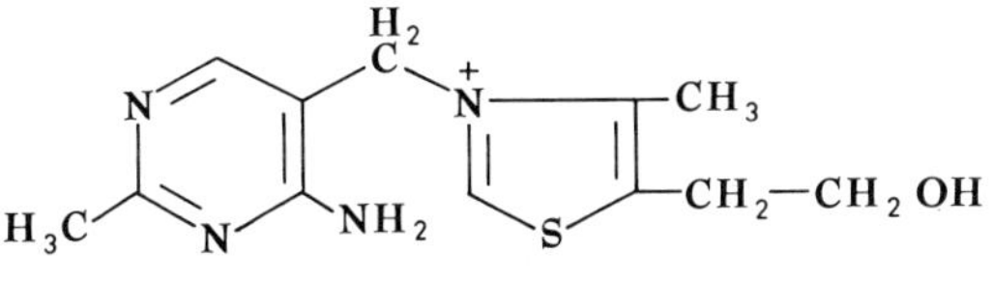

Thiamine

of purines *de novo* and that of the pyrimidine ring of thiamine were recognized as interrelated pathways, and finally it became clear that the latter process is really a branch from the purine biosynthetic pathway.

Pathway of Synthesis of the Pyrimidine Moiety of Thiamine. The early genetic studies of Yura (*1*) with *Salmonella typhimurium* showed that all mutants blocked before phosphoribosyl-aminoimidazole in the purine biosynthetic pathway required both adenine and thiamine for growth. Most mutants blocked at later stages of purine biosynthesis *de novo* required only adenine; the exceptions will be discussed below. Many subsequent investigations have confirmed these findings.

Studies incorporating radioactive precursors into the pyrimidine ring of thiamine showed that the regular pathway of nucleic acid pyrimidine biosynthesis was not followed; rather, glycine and formate were used for this purpose as they also are for purine synthesis. In addition, aspartate contributed three of its carbon atoms. The extensive work in this area has been reviewed by Newell and Tucker (*2*) in the course of their own investigations. Although many details still remain unclear, the present view of the pathway of synthesis of the pyrimidine ring of thiamine is outlined in Figure 7-1.

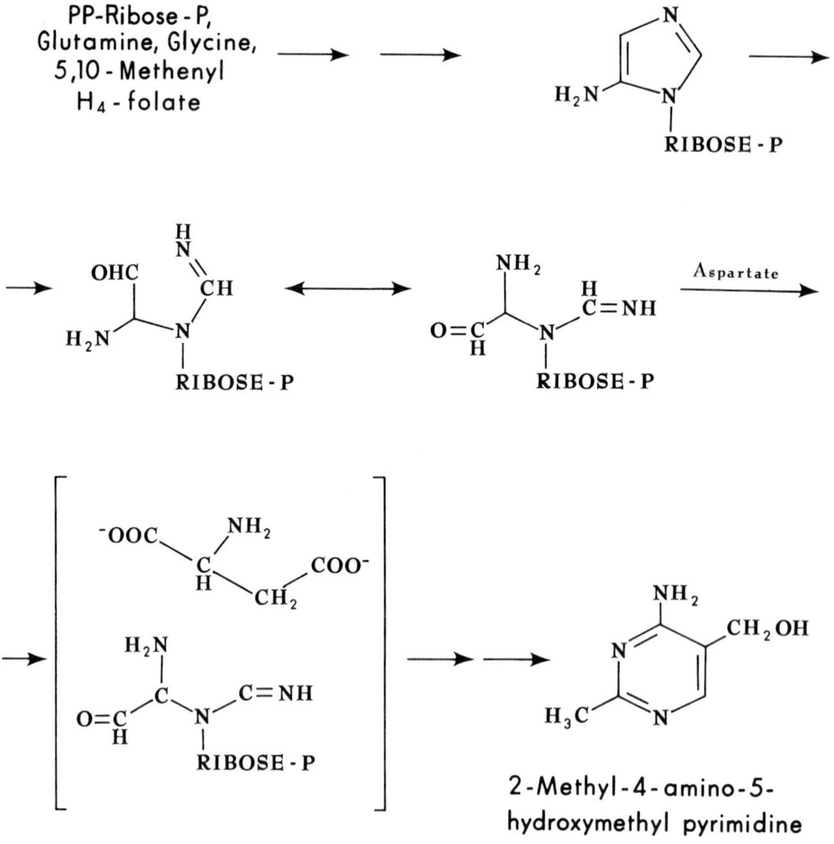

PP-Ribose-P,
Glutamine, Glycine,
5,10-Methenyl
H_4-folate

RIBOSE-P

Aspartate

RIBOSE-P

RIBOSE-P

RIBOSE-P

2-Methyl-4-amino-5-
hydroxymethyl pyrimidine

Figure 7-1. Biosynthesis of the pyrimidine moiety of thiamine

Regulation of the Pathway. Obviously, those factors which regulate the synthesis of phosphoribosyl-aminoimidazole as an intermediate in the pathway of purine biosynthesis *de novo* will also regulate the formation of the pyrimidine ring of thiamine. This point will be discussed further below. In addition, the branch pathway leading from phosphoribosyl-aminoimidazole to 4-amino-5-hydroxymethyl-2-methylpyrimidine is under specific regulatory control by thiamine itself. Newell and Tucker (*3, 4*) have shown, for example, that addition of more than 40 ng of thiamine per ml to cultures of *Salmonella typhimurium* mutants led to repression of pyrimidine synthesis whereas derepression occurred when thiamine concentrations fell below 30 ng per ml.

Purine Toxicity and Thiamine Biosynthesis. The growth of wild-type *Salmonella typhimurium* is inhibited by adenine, and in 1962 Kalle and Gots (*5*) found that addition to culture media of thiamine or its pyrimidine moiety reversed this inhibitory effect. Later studies with mutants of this organism which were hypersensitive to inhibition by adenine showed that thiamine could reverse completely the effect of adenine regardless of its concentration (*6*). Such results have been amply confirmed in further studies with this organism (*e.g., 2, 4*).

Strains of *Escherichia coli* (*7, 8*), *Aerobacter aerogenes* (*7, 9*), and *Micrococcus sodonensis* (*10, 11*) are also inhibited by adenine; this inhibition is prevented or overcome by thiamine.

Inhibition by adenine of strains of *Escherichia coli* and *Aerobacter aerogenes* was reversed not only by thiamine but also by succinate or by a mixture of amino acids (*7*). It will be recalled that thiamine pyrophosphate is the cofactor for pyruvate decarboxylase, and the effects of these compounds were thought to reflect decreased conversion of pyruvate to Krebs cycle intermediates arising from an adenine-induced thiamine deficiency. In an *Escherichia coli* mutant (*7*) evidence was also obtained that adenine toxicity was accompanied by a deficiency of ribose, although addition of this sugar supported only RNA synthesis and not growth. Presumably the supply of thiamine was limiting for ribose phosphate synthesis *via* transketolase, the cofactor of which is thiamine pyrophosphate. Later studies of other mutants of *Aerobacter aerogenes* (*8*) and *Escherichia coli* (*9*) found that succinate and histidine each could partially reverse adenine toxicity; considerable variation was observed from one experiment to another.

It was Moyed (*9*) who, in 1964, discovered that addition of adenosine and several other purines to cultures of *Aerobacter aerogenes* inhibited the synthesis of the pyrimidine portion of thiamine. In addition to studying the reversal of purine toxicity by thiamine and its pyrimidine moiety, he showed that the synthesis both of the vitamin and its pyrimidine portion were actually inhibited. Subsequent studies by Newell and Tucker (*2*) in 1966 with *Salmonella typhimurium* and by Shobe (*11*) with *Micrococcus sodonensis* also demonstrated that adenosine inhibited the synthesis of the pyrimidine ring of thiamine.

When Newell and Tucker (*4*) established that the pathway of biosynthesis of the pyrimidine moiety of thiamine coincided with the early reactions of purine biosynthesis *de novo,* the actual mechanism of the inhibitory effect of adenosine and other purines on its synthesis became clear. The inhibitory purines caused feedback inhibition or repression of the purine biosynthetic pathway at a point prior to phosphoribosyl-aminoimidazole, the last compound common to both pathways. Some other mutants, of a type described earlier by Yura (*1*), accumulated phosphoribosyl-aminoimidazole carboxamide, which itself exerted feedback inhibition both of purine and thiamine synthesis.

There is no evidence that high concentrations of thiamine or of its pyrimidine moiety have any effect on the rate of purine biosynthesis. When low concentrations of the vitamin are present, some phosphoribosyl-aminoimidazole is diverted to pyrimidine synthesis instead of to purine synthesis; however, this is probably a small percentage of the phosphoribosyl-aminoimidazole formed. It is interesting, however, that purines have such a potent controlling influence on this metabolically unrelated compound.

Histidine Biosynthesis

Actual or potential relationships between histidine and purines have been studied for many years. Ackroyd and Hopkins (*12*) proposed as early as 1916 that histidine might be a major precursor of at least the imidazole ring of purines. This was supported by nutritional studies of Rose and Cook (*13*) in 1925, and it was not until the investigations of Barnes and Schoenheimer (*14*) and Tesar and Rittenberg (*15*) with ^{15}N-labeled compounds in the 1940s that this hypothesis was shown to be incorrect, at least as originally formulated. The original hypothesis was partly true, however, and the conversion of the C-2 of the histidine ring to the C-2 and C-8 positions of the purine ring has been amply demonstrated, as discussed in Chapter 4.

In 1926 Cox and Rose (*16*) first investigated the possibility that purines might be precursors of histidine. Unfortunately the experimental system chosen to test this hypothesis was the rat, which does not synthesize the carbon skeleton of histidine. This idea lay dormant until the early 1950s, when work with appropriate microbial histidine auxotrophs showed that purines did indeed contribute to the biosynthesis of the imidazole ring of this amino acid; phosphoribosyl-aminoimidazole carboxamide was formed as the portion of the purine nucleotide precursor that was not used for histidine synthesis. Histidine formation, then, introduces into purine metabolism a loop or cycle which includes both fully formed purine ribonucleotides and the last stages of the pathway of purine biosynthesis *de novo.* The existence of such a cycle

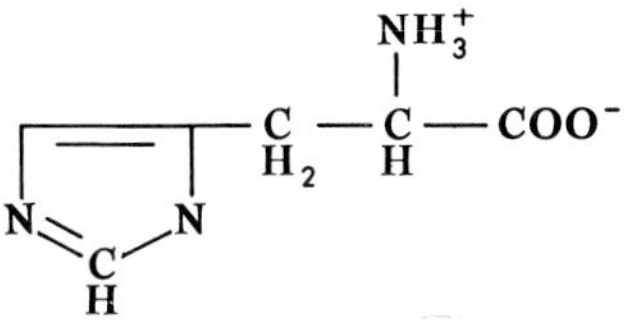

$$\mathrm{(C_3H_3N_2)-\underset{H_2}{C}-\underset{H}{\overset{NH_3^+}{C}}-COO^-}$$

L-Histidine

poses certain unique problems of regulation of purine nucleotide biosynthesis and metabolism, which are illustrated in the following discussion.

Pathway of Histidine Biosynthesis. In 1949, Broquist and Snell (*17*) showed that addition of either purine bases or histidine stimulated growth of *Lactobacillus arabinosus.* In further studies they concluded that, because the histidine requirement of *Streptococcus faecalis* was the same whether it synthesized purines *de novo* or obtained them preformed from the medium, histidine could not be a precursor of the purines. However, addition of histidine to cultures of *Lactobacillus casei* approximately halved the concentration of guanine required to support half-maximal growth. On the basis of these results it was concluded that purines were precursors of histidine in some organisms and that xanthine, guanine, adenine, and hypoxanthine were all active in this respect.

Isotope Incorporation Studies. It was established early in the study of histidine synthesis that the entire imidazole ring of purines was not transferred intact to histidine. Levy and Coon (*18*), for example, showed that although formate-^{14}C was well incorporated into histidine in *Saccharomyces cerevisiae,* glycine-^{14}C was not a precursor of this amino acid. Both, of course, go into the imidazole ring of purines. Mitoma and Snell (*19*) and Magasanik *et al.* (*20*) later found that radioactivity from guanine-2-^{14}C was well incorporated into C-2 of the imidazole ring of histidine in *Lactobacillus casei, Escherichia coli,* and *Aerobacter aerogenes.* Magasanik (*21*) also suggested that guanine was the source of the histidine ring N-1; this was demonstrated conclusively by Neidel and Waelsch (*22*). Using guanine and xanthine labeled with ^{15}N, the latter investigators, together with Magasanik and Karibian (*8*), showed that the amino group of guanine was not transferred to histidine but that either the guanine N-1 or N-3 was. Indirect evidence pointed to guanine N-1 as the precursor of the histidine ring N-1, and this conclusion was confirmed by the elucidation of the early reactions in the pathway.

Identification of Intermediates. Until it was recognized that phosphoribosyl-aminoimidazole carboxamide could be synthesized both *via* the pathway of purine biosynthesis *de novo* and *via* the pathway of histidine synthesis, measurements of its accumulation in bacterial mutants and in cell extracts led to some confusion. In their early study of factors which influenced accumulation of aminoimidazole carboxamide in *Escherichia coli* B-96 (blocked at the formyltransferase step), Gots and Love (*23*) showed that addition of histidine stimulated this process, which indicates that the aminoimidazole carboxamide was in this case being formed through the purine biosynthetic pathway. However, Love (*24*) later found that aminoimidazole carboxamide was even formed in extracts of *Escherichia coli* W-11, a mutant which had previously (*25*) been shown to be blocked several steps earlier in the pathway of purine synthesis. ATP, ribose 5-phosphate, glutamine, glycine, formate, bicarbonate, and aspartate were added to the extracts to support aminoimidazole carboxamide synthesis; of these ATP, glutamine, and ribose 5-phosphate were most critical. In subsequent studies (*26*) it was found that glycine-^{14}C was not incorporated into aminoimidazole carboxamide in this system. Clearly, there was a source of this compound other than the purine biosynthetic pathway, but its identity was not known at that time.

This puzzle was clarified when Moyed and Magasanik (*27, 28*) observed that imidazoleglycerol-phosphate, which was already known to be an intermediate in histidine synthesis, was formed in extracts of *Salmonella typhimurium* in amounts which were approximately equal to that of the aminoimidazole carboxamide synthesized. In the absence of glutamine a compound was formed which could be cleaved to aminoimidazole carboxamide upon mild acid hydrolysis; this was at first thought to be 1-(5″-phosphoribosyl)-adenylate but was probably phosphoribosyl-formimino-aminoimidazole carboxamide ribonucleotide (called Compound III in the early literature). These results were confirmed by others (*26, 29, 30*), and Ames and his colleagues subsequently worked out the other early steps in the pathway of histidine biosynthesis (*e.g., 30, 31*). The entire scheme is shown in Figure 7.2.

Regulation of Histidine and Phosphoribosyl-Aminoimidazole Carboxamide Synthesis. Observations that addition of histidine inhibited the synthesis of phosphoribosyl-adenylate in extracts of *Salmonella typhimurium* (*28*) and of phosphoribosyl-aminoimidazole carboxamide in extracts of *ade3* mutants of *Saccharomyces cerevisiae* (*29*) were shown in 1961 by Ames *et al.* (*31*) to arise from feedback inhibition of the first enzyme of the histidine biosynthetic pathway, ATP phosphoribosyltransferase. The enzymology of the inhibition of this enzyme by histidine has been studied in some detail (*32, 33*), and mutants of *Salmonella typhimurium* containing ATP phosphoribosyltransferases that are resistant to feedback inhibition (*34, 35, 36*) or hypersensitive to feedback inhibition (*35*) have been isolated.

Histidine analogs such as thiazolealanine also inhibit ATP phosphoribosyltransferase (*e.g., 34*), and Whitehead *et al.* (*37*) reported that the enzyme from *Schizosaccharomyces pombe* was also inhibited by phosphoribosyl-aminoimidazole carboxamide; this was not the case in *Saccharomyces cerevisiae* (*38*). Klungsoyr *et al.* (*36*) have observed that the inhibitory effects of histidine on the enzyme from *Escherichia coli* are enhanced by adenylate and by phosphoribosyl-ATP and that the enzyme activity is also affected by

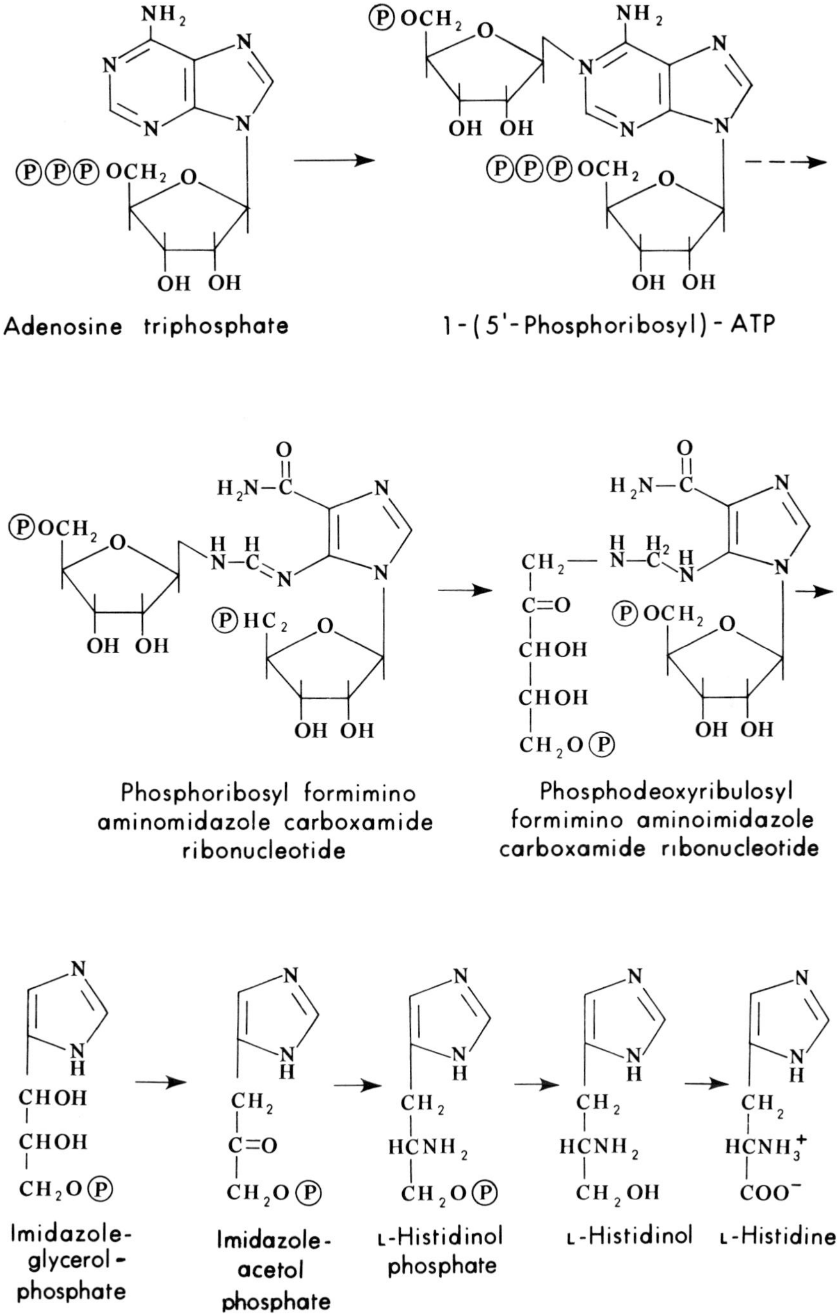

Adenosine triphosphate → 1-(5'-Phosphoribosyl)-ATP - - →

Phosphoribosyl formimino aminomidazole carboxamide ribonucleotide → Phosphodeoxyribulosyl formimino aminoimidazole carboxamide ribonucleotide →

Imidazole-glycerol-phosphate → Imidazole-acetol phosphate → L-Histidinol phosphate → L-Histidinol → L-Histidine

Figure 7-2. Histidine biosynthesis

the "energy charge" of the system, both in the presence and absence of histidine.

The regulation of histidine biosynthesis in a number of microorganisms thus appears to be a classical example of feedback inhibition of a biosynthetic pathway, in which the endproduct inhibits the first specific enzyme of the pathway.

Effects of Histidine on Purine Biosynthesis and Metabolism. As far as histidine biosynthesis is concerned, the precursor purine ribonucleotide molecule (*i.e.*, ATP) simply acts as a carrier of an –N–C– group derived from the amino group of aspartate and 10-formyl H_4-folate. This moiety plus PP-ribose-P and glutamine gives imidazoleglycerol-phosphate plus phosphoribosyl-aminoimidazole carboxamide:

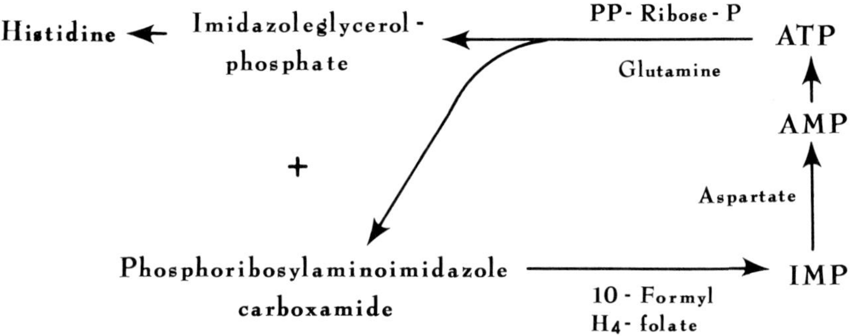

The fumarate and H_4-folate produced in the regeneration of ATP can be converted again to aspartate and 10-formyl H_4-folate for another cycle of purine biosynthesis.

It is apparent that if the conversion of phosphoribosyl-aminoimidazole carboxamide back to ATP were for any reason slower than its production from this nucleotide, then there would be a net loss of purine nucleotide; ultimately this would be detrimental to the cell. If under such conditions histidine were added to the medium, then the loss of ATP would cease because its conversion to phosphoribosyl-ATP is inhibited by the amino acid endproduct of the pathway. That such control is significant for purine metabolism has been shown in a number of cases.

In the absence of folate *Lactobacillus casei* can be made to depend on purines for growth if thymine, glycine, methionine, and so forth are supplied; it does not require exogenous histidine. Under such conditions addition of histidine reduced to about one-half the concentration of guanine required for half-maximal growth (*17*). Presumably there would be a deficiency of 10-formyl H_4-folate in these cells in the absence of this amino acid. A similar phenomenon was noted in *Escherichia coli* strain HP-1, which lacks the last enzyme in the purine biosynthetic pathway, inosinate cyclohydrolase. It excreted ribosyl-aminoimidazole carboxamide into the medium when grown with purines, but this ceased when histidine was added. Similarly, the concentration of guanine required to support growth to a density of about 4.5×10^8 cells per ml was reduced from 8 to 3 μg per ml when histidine was added (*8, 20*).

Magasanik and Karibian (*8*) have also shown that in *Escherichia coli,* which lacks adenylate deaminase, a major route of conversion of free adenine into guanine nucleotides is the following:

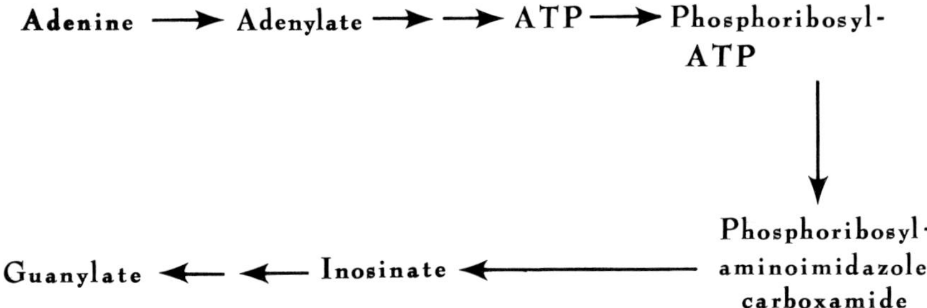

This pathway should of course be inhibited by histidine, and this was indeed demonstrated by the use of radioactive adenine (*8*). Studies which suggested the same conclusion had been reported earlier by Balis *et al.* (*39*).

Competition for H_4-folate coenzymes between histidine biosynthesis (*i.e.,* the recycling of phosphoribosyl-aminoimidazole carboxamide *via* its formyltransferase) and other processes has also been shown by Broquist (*40*), using the H_4-folate dehydrogenase inhibitor, aminopterin. The toxicity of low doses of this drug for the growth of *Torula cremoris* was overcome by methionine; adenine plus methionine reversed the effects of higher drug concentrations, and histidine plus adenine plus methionine allowed growth in still higher concentrations of aminopterin. The addition of adenine (and methionine) therefore spared the requirements of the cell for one-carbon units; however, at the highest drug concentrations the H_4-folate coenzyme requirement for formylation of phosphoribosyl-aminoimidazole carboxamide for histidine biosynthesis eventually either became rate-limiting for growth or competed for the scarce H_4-folate coenzymes with reactions such as thymidylate synthetase. In the same study, aminopterin was found to be more toxic for *Lactobacillus arabinosus* when histidine was being synthesized than when it was supplied in the medium. Studying strains of *Saccharomyces cerevisiae* that require *p*-aminobenzoate, Cutts and Rainbow (*41*) have also observed that addition of histidine stimulated growth provided that methionine and adenine were already present.

Addition of histidine stimulated purine biosynthesis *de novo* in *Escherichia coli* B-96 (*23, 42*), under conditions such that a shortage of H_4-folate coenzymes is unlikely. Purine synthesis was also stimulated by glucose under these conditions, however, and it is possible that inhibition of ATP phosphoribosyltransferase made more PP-ribose-P available for the first enzyme of the purine biosynthetic pathway. Inhibition by adenine of phosphoribosyl-aminoimidazole carboxamide synthesis *via* the histidine pathway in extracts of *Escherichia coli* W-11 may also have been caused by competition for PP-ribose-P (*26*).

Finally, the interesting case of *Escherichia coli* W-74 must be mentioned. Although it was originally described as a leaky histidine auxotroph (*43*), Luzzati and Guthrie (*44*) and Balis *et al.* (*39*) later showed that purines would replace histidine for growth although the cells grew faster on histidine. In a strict auxotroph, histidine and adenine should not be able to replace each other, and this strain remained an enigma for a number of years. Finally, Shedlovsky and Magasanik (*45, 46*) found that one of the two enzymes (they were never distinguished) which converts phosphoribosyl-formimino-aminoimidazole carboxamide ribonucleotide (Compound III) to imidazoleglycerol-phosphate plus phosphoribosyl-aminoimidazole carboxamide was unstable, and these cells had only about 20% of the normal activity. As a consequence histidine concentrations became too low to cause feedback inhibition of the ATP phosphoribosyltransferase reaction, and Compound III accumulated and leaked out of the cells. This process was stopped by addition either of histidine or of the histidine analog thiazolealanine to the medium; addition of adenine had no effect on excretion of the intermediate.

These results strongly suggest that *Escherichia coli* W-74 cells ordinarily grow slowly because they lose adenine nucleotides to the medium *via* Compound III. Addition of adenine replaces this loss and supports growth. Loss of purine nucleotides can also be prevented by inhibition or retardation of the synthesis of Compound III by histidine, thiazolealanine, or an appropriate mutation. A similar explanation may account for the observations of Hartman *et al.* (*47*) that adenine stimulated the growth of a number of leaky histidine auxotrophs of *Salmonella typhimurium*.

The interrelationship of histidine and purine synthesis and metabolism is obviously much more complex than is that of thiamine and purines; it would probably repay more detailed study in a wider variety of organisms and mutants.

References

1. Yura, T., *Carnegie Inst. Wash. Publ.* (1956) No. 612, 63.
2. Newell, P. C., Tucker, R. G., *Biochem. J.* (1968) **106,** 271.
3. Newell, P. C., Tucker, R. G., *Biochem. J.* (1966) **100,** 517.
4. Newell, P. C., Tucker, R. G., *Biochem. J.* (1968) **106,** 279.
5. Kalle, G. P., Gots, J. S., *Proc. Soc. Exp. Biol. Med.* (1962) **109,** 277.
6. Dalal, F. R., Gots, R. E, Gots, J. S., *J. Bacteriol.* (1966) **91,** 507.
7. Neidhardt, F. C., *Biochim. Biophys. Acta* (1963) **68,** 365.
8. Magasanik, B., Karibian, D., *J. Biol. Chem.* (1960) **235,** 2672.

9. Moyed, H. S., *J. Bacteriol.* (1964) **88,** 1024.
10. Campbell, J. N., Evans, J. B., Perry, J. J., Niven, C. F., *J. Bacteriol.* (1961) **82,** 823.
11. Shobe, C. R., Ph.D. Thesis, University of Alberta, 1970.
12. Ackroyd, H., Hopkins, F. G., *Biochem. J.* (1916) **10,** 551.
13. Rose, W. C., Cook, K. G., *J. Biol. Chem.* (1925) **64,** 325.
14. Barnes, F. W., Jr., Schoenheimer, R., *J. Biol. Chem.* (1943) **151,** 123.
15. Tesar, C., Rittenberg, D., *J. Biol. Chem.* (1947) **170,** 35.
16. Cox, G. J., Rose, W. C., *J. Biol. Chem.* (1926) **68,** 769.
17. Broquist, H. P., Snell, E. E., *J. Biol. Chem.* (1949) **180,** 59.
18. Levy, L., Coon, M. J., *J. Biol. Chem.* (1951) **192,** 807.
19. Mitoma, C., Snell, E. E., *Proc. Nat. Acad. Sci.* (1955) **41,** 891.
20. Magasanik, B., Moyed, H. S., Karibian, D., *J. Amer. Chem. Soc.* (1956) **78,** 1510.
21. Magasanik, B., *J. Amer. Chem. Soc.* (1956) **78,** 5449.
22. Neidle, A., Waelsch, H., *J. Biol. Chem.* (1959) **234,** 589.
23. Gots, J. S., Love, S. H., *J. Biol. Chem.* (1954) **210,** 395.
24. Love, S. H., *J. Bacteriol.* (1956) **72,** 628.
25. Love, S. H., Gots, J. S., *J. Biol. Chem.* (1955) **212,** 647.
26. Love, S. H., Boyles, P. D., *Biochim. Biophys. Acta* (1959) **35,** 374.
27. Moyed, H. S., Magasanik, B., *J. Amer. Chem. Soc.* (1957) **79,** 4812.
28. Moyed, H. S., Magasanik, B., *J. Biol. Chem.* (1960) **235,** 149.
29. Klopotowski, T., Luzzati, M., Slonimski, P. P., *Biochem. Biophys. Res. Commun.* (1960) **3,** 150.
30. Smith, D. W. E., Ames, B. N., *J. Biol. Chem.* (1964) **239,** 1846.
31. Ames, B. N., Martin, R. G., Garry, B. J., *J. Biol. Chem.* (1961) **236,** 2019.
32. Martin, R. G., *J. Biol. Chem.* (1963) **238,** 257.
33. Voll, M. J., Appella, E., Martin, R. G., *J. Biol. Chem.* (1967) **242,** 1760.
34. Moyed, H. S., *J. Biol. Chem.* (1961) **236,** 2261.
35. O'Donovan, G. A., Ingraham, J. L., *Proc. Nat. Acad. Sci.* (1965) **54,** 451.
36. Klungsoyr, L., Hageman, J. H., Fall, L., Atkinson, D. E., *Biochemistry* (1968) **7,** 4035.
37. Whitehead, E., Nagy, M., Heslot, H., *C.R. Acad. Sci. Ser. D* (1966) **263,** 819.
38. Mazlen, A. S., Eaton, N. R., *Biochem. Biophys. Res. Commun.* (1967) **26,** 590.
39. Balis, M. E., Levin, D. H., Luzzati, D., *J. Biol. Chem.* (1955) **216,** 9.
40. Broquist, H. P., *Arch. Biochem. Biophys.* (1957) **70,** 210.
41. Cutts, N. S., Rainbow, C., *J. Gen. Microbiol.* (1950) **4,** 150.
42. Burton, K., *Biochem. J.* (1957) **66,** 48 P.
43. Witkin, E. M., Kennedy, F. L., *Amer. Natur.* (1951) **85,** 141.
44. Luzzati, D., Guthrie, R., *J. Biol. Chem.* (1955) **216,** 1.
45. Shedlovsky, A. E., Magasanik, B., *J. Biol. Chem.* (1962) **237,** 3725.
46. Shedlovsky, A. E., Magasanik, B., *J. Biol. Chem.* (1962) **237,** 3731.
47. Hartman, P. E., Loper, J. C., Serman, D., *J. Gen. Microbiol.* (1960) **22,** 323.

Chapter

8

Inhibition and Stimulation of Purine Biosynthesis by Drugs

INHIBITION OF purine biosynthesis by drugs such as cycloserine and the sulfonamides has already been mentioned in the course of previous chapters. In this chapter the inhibitory actions on this pathway of three major classes of drugs will be discussed in some detail: the folate analogs, glutamine analogs, and purine analogs and derivatives. All are of pharmacological importance. In addition, some miscellaneous inhibitors of uncertain mechanisms of action are also mentioned more briefly.

Certain drugs stimulate purine biosynthesis rather than inhibit it, and these also will be discussed; their mechanisms of action are not known.

There are numerous reviews of the actions of most of the drugs mentioned here; the most recent are the monographs of Balis (*1*), Langen (*2*), and Roy-Burman (*3*), which may be consulted for other references.

Stimulatory Drugs

The stimulation of purine biosynthesis produced under certain conditions by some drugs is dramatic and intriguing. At the least it demonstrates that the full potential of the pathway is not ordinarily used, but as yet it is not known how this result is achieved.

Nicotinamide. In 1956 Kaplan *et al.* (*4*) reported that the injection of nicotinamide into mice resulted in a ninefold to 12-fold increase in the concentration of NAD in liver, twofold to threefold increases in kidney and spleen, and small increases, if any, in other tissues. Maximum NAD concentrations were detected eight to 12 hours after treatment, by which time no free nicotinamide could be detected. The increased synthesis of NAD was associated with an increase in total acid-soluble adenine, ribose, and organic phosphate and was inhibited by 6-mercaptopurine. Ricci *et al.* (*5*) found

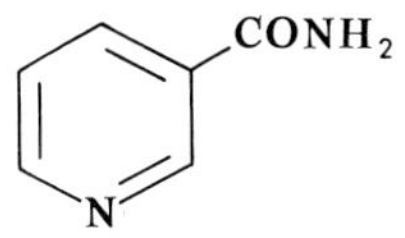

Nicotinamide

that the concentration of adenylate was increased in rat liver following injection of nicotinamide whereas that of ATP was decreased somewhat.

Further studies by Shuster and his co-workers (*6–9*) show clearly that net purine biosynthesis *de novo* had occurred. The incorporation of labeled glycine and formate into the adenine of NAD was increased fivefold to 10-fold although the stimulation of formate incorporation responded more rapidly than did that of glycine. The incorporation of formate-^{14}C into other acid-soluble purine derivatives was also stimulated by nicotinamide, although it had no effect on the incorporation of formate into protein. Injection of nicotinamide stimulated incorporation of both ribose-^{14}C and glucose-^{14}C into NAD; in the latter case incorporation into the AMP moiety of NAD was stimulated eightfold whereas that into the nicotinamide mononucleotide portion was increased only threefold. The stimulatory effect of nicotinamide could not be demonstrated when slices of mouse liver were incubated with it *in vitro*.

Thiadiazoles. Krakoff and Magill (*10*) observed in 1956 that following the administration of 2-ethylamino-1,3,4-thiadiazole to man there was a prompt elevation in serum uric acid concentration from 6 to 15 mg per 100 ml and an increase in urinary uric acid excretion from 350 to 1500 mg per day. An equal weight of nicotinamide did not alter this response.

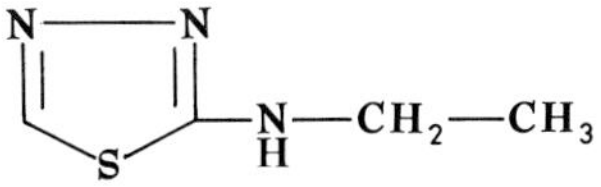

2 - Ethylamino - 1,3,4-thiadiazole

Subsequent studies (*11, 12*) showed that the incorporation of radioactive glycine and formate into urinary uric acid was increased and hence that this drug caused accelerated purine biosynthesis *de novo*. The increase in uric acid excretion produced by ethylamino-thiadiazole was prevented by treatment with the glutamine analogs azaserine and diazooxonorleucine (*12*) and by 6-mercaptopurine (*13*).

The ethylamino-thiadiazole–induced stimulation of purine biosynthesis *de novo* was also prevented or suppressed by amounts of nicotinamide four times larger than those of the drug (*11–14*) and by nicotinate and tryptophan (*13*). Ethylamino-thiadiazole itself had no effect on NAD synthesis (*13*) nor did it change blood concentrations of NAD (*12*); the effects of its toxicity did not resemble pellagra. Lest too much attention be given to possible effects of ethylamino-thiadiazole on pyridine nucleotide-requiring reactions related to purine metabolism, Krakoff and Balis warned "It should be noted that nicotinamide opposes the action of a wide variety of chemicals which do not appear to have a common mechanism of action" (*12*).

The mechanism of action of ethylamino-thiadiazole on purine biosynthesis *de novo* remains entirely unknown. However, Seegmiller *et al.* (*15*) showed that not only did this drug stimulate the incorporation of glycine-^{14}C into urinary uric acid in man but it also caused increased incorporation of this precursor into urinary hippurate and creatinine. Although these results tend to suggest a generalized disturbance in glycine metabolism, this point has not been pursued.

Ethylamino-thiadiazole also markedly stimulates purine biosynthesis *de novo* in the developing chick embryo (*16*), a uricotelic system with a high basal rate of this process. It also stimulated purine synthesis in ureotelic systems with unusually rapid rates of the *de novo* pathway. Thus Shuster and Goldin (*14*) showed that although high doses of nicotinamide inhibited the response to ethylamino-thiadiazole, low doses increased its effect. For example, although 125 mg per kg of nicotinamide stimulated the incorporation of formate-^{14}C into acid-soluble adenine compounds 1.5-fold and 500 mg per kg of ethylamino-thiadiazole stimulated this process five times, the two together produced a 15-fold increase.

Nyhan *et al.* (*17*) studied the effect of ethylamino-thiadiazole in patients with the Lesch-Nyhan syndrome, in which the rate of glycine-^{14}C incorporation into urinary uric acid was already 20 times higher than normal. Incorporation of glycine-^{14}C was increased to 30 times normal following administration of ethylamino-thiadiazole, serum uric acid concentrations increased from 11 to 25.4 mg per 100 ml, and urinary uric acid excretion rose from 900 to 4000 mg per day.

Folate Analogs

Analogs of folate such as aminopterin and amethopterin are potent inhibitors of H_4-folate dehydrogenase activity and are believed to inhibit growth as a consequence of this effect.

From one point of view they may be considered to be inhibitors of H_4-folate synthesis both from guanosine triphosphate and from folate itself. However, they may also be considered to inhibit the interconversion of folate coenzymes, in light of the conversion of H_4-folate to H_2-folate in the thymidylate synthetase reaction. The consequences for purine metabolism of the enzyme inhibition produced by aminopterin, amethopterin, and related compounds have been demonstrated by a variety of studies.

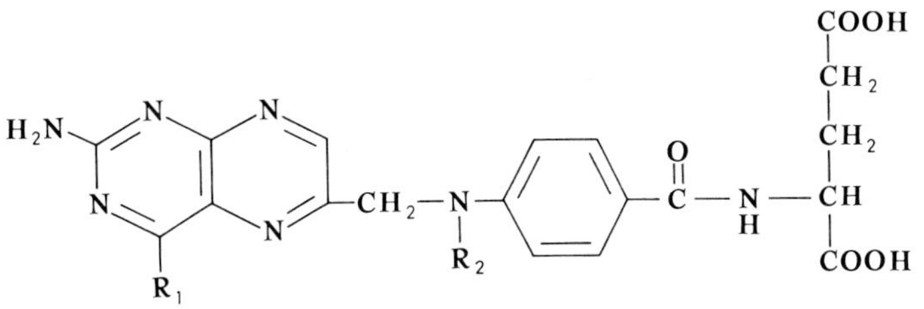

	R_1	R_2
Amethopterin (Methotrexate)	OH	CH_3
Folate	NH_2	H
Aminopterin	NH_2	H

Reversal of Growth Inhibition by Purines. The growth-inhibitory effects of "methylfolate" on *Lactobacillus casei* were antagonized by purines in some of the first studies of this class of drugs (*18, 19*). Adenine (*20, 21*) reversed growth inhibition by aminopterin in cultures of *Aerobacter aerogenes*, and adenine prevented the toxic effects of amethopterin on *Bacillus subtilis* (*22*).

In similar studies with Sarcoma 180 cells in tissue culture Hakala and Taylor (*23, 24*) have shown that the toxicity of amethopterin can be completely reversed by combinations of purines, thymidine, and glycine. Any one of these alone gives only partial antagonism. A variety of compounds could supply the purine requirement.

Hakala (*25*) has recently reported studies of homofolate and H_4-homofolate, each of which has an additional methylene bridge between the pteridine and *p*-aminobenzoate moieties of folate. They are about equally inhibitory to Sarcoma 180 cells in culture, and the concentrations required for 50% inhibition are not substantially increased when thymidine and glycine are present; the synthesis of the latter compounds therefore does not seem to be affected. When the medium is supplemented either with hypoxanthine or with aminoimidazole carboxamide, which eliminate the need for purine biosynthesis *de novo*, the concentration of analogs had to be raised 20-fold to achieve the same degree of inhibition. This indicates that the most sensitive site of inhibition by homofolate and H_4-homofolate is purine biosynthesis. Because aminoimidazole carboxamide is almost as effective as hypoxanthine as a reversing agent, Hakala suggested that these drugs are probably inhibitors of phosphoribosyl-glycineamide formyltransferase rather than of the synthesis of 5,10-methenyl H_4-folate.

Accumulation of Aminoimidazole Carboxamide. Woolley and Pringle (*26*) first demonstrated the accumulation of aminoimidazole carboxamide in cultures of aminopterin-inhibited *Escherichia coli*, and similar results were later obtained when amethopterin was used (*27*); this also occurred in cultures of *Aerobacter aerogenes* inhibited by aminopterin (*20*).

Rats to which amethopterin was administered in a single large dose excreted two to seven times the normal amount of aminoimidazole carboxamide in their daily urine (*28, 29*). However, rats given repeated smaller doses of this drug did not excrete increased amounts of this compound, possibly because under these conditions purine biosynthesis might have been blocked more at an earlier step (*29*). The accumulation of phosphoribosyl-aminoimidazole carboxamide labeled from formate-^{14}C was observed in the intestine and liver, as well as Leukemia L1210 cells, from tumor-bearing mice treated with amethopterin (*30*). Similar observations were made using *Escherichia coli* (*31*).

Metabolism of Aminoimidazole Carboxamide. Weaver and Shive (*32*) studied the utilization (*i.e.*, disappearance) of aminoimidazole carboxamide by disrupted preparations of *Lactobacillus casei* 17-5 to which glucose, phosphate, and formate were added. Aminopterin severely inhibited this utilization. In later studies Deodhar and Pittman (*33*) studied the effect of amethopterin on the urinary excretion by rats of a loading dose of aminoimidazole carboxamide. Whereas control rats excreted 18% of the administered dose in 24 hours, those treated with the antimetabolite excreted 55% of the load.

Effects on Isotope Incorporation. Finally, folate analogs that inhibit H_4-folate dehydrogenase have also been shown to inhibit the incorporation of radioactive formate and other precursors into purines in normal and neoplastic tissues. Thus in early experiments it was shown that amethopterin almost completely inhibited the incorporation of formate-^{14}C into nucleic acid purines of pooled mouse viscera and drug-sensitive Leukemia L1210 cells (*34, 35*). Inhibition of incorporation into DNA purines was greater than that into RNA purines in rat viscera (*36*), and inhibition was greater in small intestine and spleen than in liver and other organs (*36, 37, 38*). A small degree of inhibition was observed in rabbit bone marrow slices incubated *in vitro* (*39*). Wada and Arakawa (*40*) have shown that 24 hours following administration of amethopterin to pregnant rats purine synthesis in the brains of the fetuses was strongly inhibited.

Amethopterin inhibited the incorporation of formate-^{14}C into purines in undifferentiated human acute leukemic leukocytes and chronic granulocytic leukemic leukocytes, but it had no effect on this process in normal leukocytes or chronic lymphocytic leukemic leukocytes incubated *in vitro* (*41, 42*). Similar inhibition of purine biosynthesis *de novo* was observed in mouse leukemia cells (*43*), TA3 mouse ascites carcinoma cells (*44*), and Ehrlich ascites tumor cells (*45, 46*).

The amethopterin derivative, 3′,5′-dichloroamethopterin, also inhibited purine biosynthesis *de novo* in normal and neoplastic mouse tissues (*38, 45, 46, 47, 48*).

Administration either of folate (*49*) or of 5-formyl H_4-folate (*46*) together with or after treatment with amethopterin markedly reduced the effect of this drug on purine biosynthesis *de novo.*

TA3 ascites carcinoma cells resistant to amethopterin (*44*) and Leukemia L1210 cells dependent on this drug (*35*) both incorporated substrates of the purine biosynthetic pathway into endproducts at faster rates than parent sensitive lines of tumor cells. However, there was no change in the rate of purine synthesis in a drug-resistant subline of the Ehrlich ascites carcinoma (*45*).

Glutamine Antimetabolites

Several antimetabolites of glutamine are among the many growth-inhibitory compounds that have been isolated from *Streptomyces* and related organisms in recent years. One effect of these antibiotics is inhibition of the purine biosynthetic pathway and consequent decline in the intracellular concentrations of purine nucleotides essential for normal cellular growth and function. Some of these glutamine antimetabolite antibiotics have found limited use in cancer chemotherapy.

Azaserine and Diazooxonorleucine. Azaserine and diazooxonorleucine (often abbreviated DON), the two most important antibiotics of this category from both biochemical and pharmacological points of view, were shown by Hartman *et al.* (*50*) to be antimetabolites of glutamine in experiments concerned with the enzymatic synthesis of inosinic acid *de novo* in pigeon liver extracts.

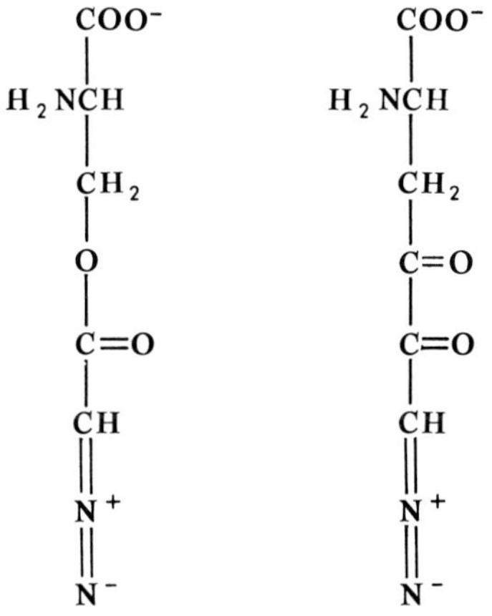

```
      COO⁻             COO⁻
       |                |
   H₂NCH            H₂NCH
       |                |
      CH₂              CH₂
       |                |
       O               C=O
       |                |
      C=O              C=O
       |                |
      CH               CH
      ||               ||
      N⁺               N⁺
      ||               ||
      N⁻               N⁻
```

Azaserine — Diazooxonorleucine

Only the effects of these drugs on purine biosynthesis will be discussed here; more complete reviews of other biochemical actions and of the biological effects of these drugs have been prepared by Mandel (*51*) and by the Cancer Chemotherapy National Service Center (*52, 53*). They are also discussed in the monographs of Langen (*2*) and Balis (*1*) and by Stock (*54*). A bibliography on azaserine has recently been made available (*55*).

INHIBITION OF PRECURSOR INCORPORATION. The first indication that azaserine was an inhibitor of purine biosynthesis was the brief report of Skipper *et al.* (*56*) in 1954 that it inhibited the incorporation of formate-^{14}C into nucleic acid purines in several normal and neoplastic mouse tissues. In more complete studies the same investigators later showed (*57*) that azaserine treatment inhibited purine synthesis from formate-^{14}C and glycine-^{14}C in mouse intestine, liver, and spleen, in mouse tumors Sarcoma 180 and Adenocarcinoma Eo771, and in rat intestine and transplanted human Sarcoma HS-1 in the rat. Because the incorporation into nucleic acids of radioactive aminoimidazole carboxamide was not inhibited by azaserine, it was concluded that the site of inhibition by this drug was relatively early in the pathway of purine biosynthesis.

Numerous studies by LePage and his collaborators during 1956–58 (*58–63*) also clearly demonstrated the inhibitory effect of azaserine on glycine-^{14}C incorporation into acid-soluble and nucleic acid purines in a variety of normal mouse tissues; in Ehrlich carcinoma, Sarcoma 180, TA3 Carcinoma, and 6C3HED Lymphosarcoma *in vivo;* and in the Ehrlich ascites carcinoma both *in vivo* and *in vitro.* Inhibition in the latter tumor was also reported by Smellie *et al.* (*64*), and this system was used by Henderson *et al.* (*61*) to measure azaserine concentrations in human and mouse serum.

Diazooxonorleucine was shown to inhibit purine biosynthesis in intact animal tissues by Barclay *et al.* (*65*) and by Moore and LePage (*62*). The former observed that formate-^{14}C incorporation into RNA and DNA purines of rat intestine was almost completely inhibited by treatment with this drug, while the latter investigators measured its inhibitory effects on glycine-^{14}C incorporation into purines in a number of normal and neoplastic mouse tissues.

Numerous subsequent studies have confirmed these initial demonstrations of inhibition of purine biosynthesis in animal tissues by azaserine and diazooxonorleucine and have extended these observations to other mouse tumors (*e.g., 66, 67*), other normal mouse tissues including brain (*e.g., 68*), and animal cells in culture (*69, 70*). Both azaserine and diazooxonorleucine at LD_{50} doses also reduced plasma concentrations of uric acid and urinary excretion of uric acid in chickens, pigeons, and cormorants (*71*), although studies with labeled precursors were not performed in these animals.

In man, Grayzel and Seegmiller (*72*) observed that diazooxonorleucine inhibited glycine-^{14}C incorporation into urinary uric acid and depressed both serum uric acid concentrations and urinary excretion of this purine. Similar studies with azaserine were reported by Zuckerman *et al.* (*73*), with the same results. In contrast to these reports Krakoff and Balis (*74*) found that neither azaserine nor diazooxonorleucine, at the doses used, had any effect on formate-^{14}C incorporation into urinary uric acid or on serum or urinary uric acid concentrations. However, under the same conditions these drugs did markedly inhibit the stimulation in purine biosynthesis caused by administration of ethylamino-thiadiazole. The basis of this differential effect has not been explained. Inhibition of glycine-^{14}C incorporation into purines by azaserine has also been demonstrated in cultured human fibroblasts (*75*).

Diazooxonorleucine has consistently been found to be a more potent inhibitor of purine biosynthesis than azaserine in every system so far studied. This has been most thoroughly investigated by Moore and LePage (*62*), who carried out a careful dose-response study of the inhibitory effects of both drugs in several normal mouse tissues and solid Ehrlich carcinoma. The wide range of drug doses required to give 90% inhibition of glycine-^{14}C incorporation into purines and the relative potency of azaserine and diazooxonorleucine in each tissue are shown in Table 8-1. These differences are presumably due to differences in drug distribution and destruction, to variations in concentrations of protective metabolites (*e.g.*, glutamine), and to differences in binding constants of the two drugs.

Table 8-1. Dose Required for 90% Inhibition[a]

Tissue	*Azaserine, mg/kg*	*Diazooxonorleucine, mg/kg*
Ehrlich carcinoma	180	18
Spleen	110	11
Intestine	57	3.6
Lung	14	0.72
Kidney	7.2	0.36
Liver	2.9	0.14

[a] From Moore and LePage (*62*)

Studies with labeled compounds have also demonstrated inhibition of purine biosynthesis by azaserine and diazooxonorleucine in wild-type *Escherichia coli* and in mutants B-96 and W-11, in which aminoimidazole carboxamide and aminoimidazole derivatives, respectively, accumulate (*76–82*). Such studies showed clearly that the sites of action of these drugs were early in the pathway of purine biosynthesis.

Reversal of Inhibition. Other information regarding the inhibitory effects of azaserine and diazooxonorleucine came from attempts to prevent or reverse their growth-inhibitory actions.

Animal Cells. The interference of the glutamine antimetabolites with purine biosynthesis suggested that exogenous purines should overcome their inhibitory effects, and this proved to be the case with animal cells. Thus adenine, hypoxanthine, and aminoimidazole carboxamide partially reversed the carcinostatic effects of azaserine and diazooxonorleucine on Sarcoma 180 in mice but did not appreciably affect their toxicity to normal mouse tissues (*83*). Similarly, inhibition of the growth of the RC mammary carcinoma in mice by diazooxonorleucine was partially overcome by adenine (*84*). Thiersch (*85*) has reported that the toxicity to rats *in vitro* of diazooxonorleucine was partially reversed by adenine, but this treatment did not affect the toxicity of azaserine in this system. Finally, some partially successful attempts have been made to alleviate the oral toxicity of diazooxonorleucine in man by the concomitant administration of adenine (*86*).

These results are clearly compatible with the conclusion that inhibition of purine biosynthesis *de novo* is a major site of action of the glutamine antimetabolites.

Microorganisms. Reversal studies in microorganisms have presented a much more confusing picture than those in animals. In most cases amino acids were the most effective reversing agents whereas purines were either completely or partially ineffective. Thus leucine was the most potent reversing agent for the growth-inhibitory actions of azaserine against *Saccharomyces cerevisiae* (*87*), alanine and arginine for *Kloeckera brevis* (*88*), glutamine and arginine for *Gaffkya homari* (*89*), and tryptophan, phenylalanine, and tyrosine for *Escherichia coli* (*76–80, 88*). Purines were either ineffective (*77, 89*) or only partially effective (*57*) in reversing the growth-inhibitory effects of azaserine.

In apparent contrast to these results with azaserine, inhibition of *Escherichia coli* growth by diazooxonorleucine was reversed better by arginine and glutamine than aromatic amino acids (*78*), and its actions in this system were also reversed by purines.

These studies have usually been interpreted as indicating that azaserine interferes with amino acid metabolism as well as purine biosynthesis in microorganisms and that these effects on amino acid metabolism are the more important for its growth-inhibitory actions. Unfortunately this subject has not been studied in any more depth, and many of the questions raised by these reversal studies remain unanswered.

ACCUMULATION OF PHOSPHORIBOSYL-FORMYLGLYCINEAMIDE. In 1955–56 Hartman *et al.* (*50, 90*) observed that the accumulation of phosphoribosylglycineamide and phosphoribosyl-formylglycineamide in a fortified extract of pigeon liver was considerably increased when azaserine was added to the system; in fact the use of this drug greatly aided the original isolation and identification of these intermediates. These experiments first established that azaserine and diazooxonorleucine are antimetabolites of glutamine. At about the same time Greenlees and LePage (*60*) also observed that in the presence of azaserine a glycine-^{14}C-containing compound accumulated in Ehrlich ascites tumor cells and that the extent of its formation was proportional to the extent of inhibition of glycine incorporation into purines. This compound was later conclusively identified as phosphoribosyl-formylglycineamide by Moore and LePage (*62*); accumulation of a small amount of phosphoribosyl-glycineamide was also detected. Moore and LePage (*62*) also measured the extent of accumulation of phosphoribosyl-formylglycineamide in several normal mouse tissues and in solid Ehrlich carcinoma after treatment with a range of doses of azaserine and diazooxonorleucine. In a few tissues (*e.g.*, liver) this intermediate did not accumulate even when there was strong inhibition of purine biosynthesis; presumably it was broken down in these tissues, but the products of its metabolism have never been identified.

The methods used for the measurement of phosphoribosyl-formylglycine-amide accumulation after azaserine treatment were simplified successively by LePage and Jones (*91*), Henderson (*92*), and Brockman and Chumley (*70*), and such measurements have subsequently been used by a number of investigators to study rates of the early reactions of the purine biosynthetic pathway in a variety of animal cells.

Tomisek and his associates (*76, 79, 81*) have demonstrated with *Escherichia coli* that incorporation of formate-^{14}C into phosphoribosyl-formylglycineamide and its dephosphorylated derivative occurred concomitantly with the inhibition by azaserine and diazooxonorleucine of formate incorporation into purines.

Thus both in animal and microbial cells a major site of action of both azaserine and diazooxonorleucine was localized at the phosphoribosyl-formyl-glycineamidine synthetase reaction.

MECHANISM OF INHIBITION. Following the discovery that an important site of inhibition by azaserine and diazooxonorleucine is the phosphoribosyl-formylglycineamidine synthetase reaction, further studies were conducted to elucidate in more detail the mechanism by which this inhibition was accomplished. The reaction is:

$$\begin{array}{l} \text{Phosphoribosyl-} \\ \text{formylglycineamide} \\ + \text{glutamine} + \text{ATP} \end{array} \longrightarrow \begin{array}{l} \text{Phosphoribosyl} \\ \text{formylglycineamidine} \\ + \text{glutamate} + \text{ADP} + P_i \end{array}$$

Competitive Inhibition with Respect to Glutamine. Glutamine, a substrate of the phosphoribosyl-formylglycineamidine synthetase reaction, was among the amino acids that were shown in early studies to give at least partial protection against the growth-inhibitory effects of azaserine and diazo-oxonorleucine in *Escherichia coli* (*57, 77, 78*) and *Gaffkaya homari* (*89*). With Ehrlich ascites tumor cells *in vitro*, addition of glutamine (*60*), serum (*61*), or liver extract (*61, 64*) at the same time as azaserine also partially prevented its inhibitory effect on glycine-^{14}C incorporation into purines (the serum and liver extract contain glutamine as well as other metabolites and perhaps drug-inactivating enzymes). However, injection of glutamine intraperitoneally had no effect on the inhibitory effects of azaserine on purine synthesis in normal mouse tissues or a solid tumor (*59*).

Levenberg *et al.* (*93*) showed in 1957 that azaserine and glutamine were kinetically competitive for phosphoribosyl-formylglycineamidine synthetase activity in pigeon liver extracts, and the diazooxonorleucine was probably also a competitive inhibitor with respect to glutamine in this system. Chu and Henderson (*94*) have more recently studied the kinetics of inhibition by asaserine and diazooxonorleucine of a partially purified enzyme from Ehrlich ascites tumor cells and have confirmed their competitive relationship with respect to glutamine. The inhibition constants for these two drugs, as well as the Michaelis constants for glutamine in these two experimental systems, are presented in Table 8-2. It may be seen that the glutamine antimetabolites were more potent in the mammalian cell system.

Table 8-2. Inhibition Constants for Phosphoribosyl-Formylglycineamidine Synthetase

Source of Enzyme	K_m *Glutamine*, M	K_i *Azaserine*, M	K_i *Diazooxonorleucine*, M
Pigeon liver (*93*)	6.2×10^{-4}	3.4×10^{-5}	1.1×10^{-6}
Ehrlich ascites tumor cells (*94*)	1.0×10^{-4}	2.3×10^{-6}	4.0×10^{-7}

Inhibition in Microorganisms. It has already been mentioned that inhibition by azaserine and diazooxonorleucine of purine biosynthesis *de novo* in microorganisms is prevented, and sometimes reversed, by phenylalanine and other amino acids apparently unrelated to glutamine. Tomisek *et al.* (*79*) studied this phenomenon with *Escherichia coli* and found that radioactive phosphoribosyl-formylglycineamide accumulated when cells were incubated with azaserine and formate-^{14}C, but this was much decreased in the presence of phenylalanine. Radioactivity was found in the purine nucleotides both in the absence of azaserine and in the presence of azaserine plus phenylalanine. Thus it appeared that this aromatic amino acid could either prevent or reverse the binding of azaserine to phosphoribosyl-formylglycineamidine synthetase.

That the protective effect of phenylalanine was probably not on the entry of azaserine into cells was deduced from the observations of Tomisek *et al.* (*79*) that phenylalanine also prevented the azaserine-induced inhibition of phosphoribosyl-aminoimidazole carboxamide synthesis in a suitable cell-free extract of *Escherichia coli* B-96. Gots and Gollub (*77*) observed also that phenylalanine could still reverse the growth-inhibitory action of azaserine when added to cultures of this organism as long as two hours after addition of azaserine. How phenylalanine might affect the binding of azaserine to an enzyme is not at all clear and has not been investigated since these early studies. That azaserine can bind irreversibly to the phosphoribosyl-formylglycineamidine synthetase of microorganisms has been shown by Dawid *et al.* (*95*) with a highly purified enzyme preparation from *Salmonella typhimurium.*

Irreversible Binding in Animal Cells. Azaserine has consistently been shown to be an irreversible inhibitor in animal cells. Thus LePage and his associates (*58, 60*) demonstrated that the inhibitory action of azaserine on glycine-^{14}C incorporation into purines could not be reversed by repeated washing of Ehrlich ascites tumor cells, even though this procedure removes most other amino acids. Similarly, the relationship between azaserine inhibition and the mass of tumor cells present also suggested drug binding to some tissue component. Finally, the addition of glutamine after cells had been exposed to azaserine did not alter its inhibitory effect whereas prior addition of glutamine gave at least partial protection.

Studies with pigeon liver extracts by Levenberg *et al.* (*93*) also indicated that azaserine and diazooxonorleucine were bound tightly to phosphoribosylformylglycineamidine synthetase. Thus although these drugs were competitive inhibitors with respect to glutamine if all components were added simultaneously, the kinetics of the inhibition changed to noncompetitive if the drug were added to the preparation prior to glutamine. The change from competitive to noncompetitive inhibition under similar conditions has also been demonstrated using a partially purified enzyme preparation from Ehrlich ascites tumor cells (*94*).

Nature of Binding to Phosphoribosyl-Formylglycineamidine Synthetase. The nature of the binding of azaserine to phosphoribosyl-formylglycineamidine synthetase has been most thoroughly studied with a highly purified enzyme from *Salmonella typhimurium* (*96*). Azaserine-^{14}C was allowed to bind to the enzyme; the complex was then digested with papain, and the fragment containing the radioactivity was characterized (*95, 97*). By such studies it was established that azaserine had been linked covalently to a sulfhydryl group of a cysteine residue with the displacement of the diazo moiety. Thus a *S*-(carboxymethylseryl)cysteine compound was formed. These workers postulated that the sulfhydryl group to which the asaserine was bound is the nucleophilic group that displaces the amide nitrogen from the carboxyl group of glutamine in the normal catalytic reaction of the enzyme. Only 0.3 mole of azaserine-^{14}C was bound per mole of enzyme, but this was undoubtedly a minimal value.

In later studies with a highly purified enzyme from chicken liver, Mizobuchi and Buchanan (*98, 99*) found that azaserine inhibited the formation of an enzyme-glutamine complex, but its binding did not affect the subsequent formation of an enzyme-ATP-phosphoribosyl-formylglycineamide complex. The latter complex was relatively unstable in the presence of azaserine, however. The addition of ATP, Mg^{2+}, and phosphoribosyl-formylglycineamide to the enzyme had no effect on the binding of azaserine (*100*).

Binding to PP-Ribose-P Amidotransferase. Azaserine and diazooxonorleucine can inhibit not only purine biosynthesis but also most other glutamine amidotransferase reactions (*cf. 101,* p. 637). Phosphoribosyl–formylglycineamidine synthetase seems to be the most sensitive target for these drugs, however, but diazooxonorleucine is less specific for this enzyme than is azaserine.

Moore and LePage (*62*) first observed that although phosphoribosyl-formylglycineamide accumulated in mouse tissues *in vivo* at certain doses of azaserine and diazooxonorleucine higher doses sometimes led to less accumulation of this intermediate, suggesting that some reaction prior to phosphoribosyl-formylglycineamidine synthetase was also being inhibited. Inhibition of phosphoribosyl-formylglycineamide accumulation has subsequently also been observed in Ehrlich ascites tumor cells *in vitro* treated with very high concentrations of azaserine (*92*) and in *Escherichia coli* treated with high concentrations of diazooxonorleucine (*81*).

These observations are believed to be the result of inhibition of PP-ribose-P amidotransferase, another glutamine-requiring reaction, by these glutamine antimetabolites. Weak inhibition of this reaction by azaserine in pigeon liver extracts had been demonstrated in the early studies of Levenberg *et al.* (*93*), and the effect of diazooxonorleucine on this enzyme was later studied in detail by Hartman (*102, 103*). Hartman found that inhibition by this drug of a highly purified PP-ribose-P amidotransferase from chicken liver began with a reversible binding to the glutamine binding site, and this binding was competitively prevented by this amino acid. Once bound, however, a covalent attachment took place, presumably with a sulfhydryl group with displacement of the diazo group; one mole of diazooxonorleucine was bound per mole of enzyme of 200,000 daltons.

Hartman (*102, 103*) observed that the inhibition constant of diazooxonorleucine for PP-ribose-P amidotransferase was decreased about 100 times in the presence of PP-ribose-P. It was suggested that the binding of this substrate put the enzyme in a conformation which was more favorable for diazooxonorleucine binding. This fact may explain the observation of Henderson and Khoo (*104*) that inhibition of PP-ribose-P amidotransferase in intact Ehrlich ascites tumor cells by this antimetabolite was greater when glucose was added and PP-ribose-P was being synthesized than under conditions in which PP-ribose-P concentrations would have been very low.

Inhibition by diazooxonorleucine has also been reported for PP-ribose-P amidotransferases from Adenocarcinoma 755 (*105*) and *Aerobacter aerogenes* (*106*).

Azaserine is a comparatively weak inhibitor of pigeon liver PP-ribose-P amidotransferase, with an inhibition constant of $4.6 \times 10^{-3} M$; the inhibition constant for diazooxonorleucine was $2.2 \times 10^{-6}M$ (*107*). Wyngaarden and Ashton (*108*) also detected inhibition of the pigeon liver enzyme by azaserine, but it did not inhibit the amidotransferase from Adenocarcinoma 755 cells even at a concentration of 10 m*M* (*105*).

CONSEQUENCES OF INHIBITION OF PURINE BIOSYNTHESIS BY GLUTAMINE ANTIMETABOLITES. Inhibition by azaserine and diazooxonorleucine of purine biosynthesis, and in particular of phosphoribosyl-formylglycineamidine synthetase, would be expected both to increase the concentration of glutamine and to lower the concentrations of purine nucleotides, and both predictions have been confirmed in one or another experimental system. Barker *et al.* (*109*), for example, observed elevated glutamine concentrations in *Scenedesmus* following treatment with azaserine, and similar observations were made by Tomisek *et al.* (*79*) with *Escherichia coli.* Increased isotope incorporation into glutamine from bicarbonate (*109*) or formate (*79*) were observed in both systems.

Sartorelli and his co-workers (*110, 111*) have measured up to 60% decreases in the concentrations of adenine nucleotides in ascites Sarcoma 180 cells following intraperitoneal injection of azaserine into tumor-bearing mice, and Hyams *et al.* (*112*) found a 37% drop in ATP concentrations in rat liver following treatment with azaserine. No change in rat liver ATP was observed by Marchetti *et al.* (*113*), but they used a lower dose of azaserine than did other investigators.

Effect on Thymidine Kinase Activity. A rather unexpected consequence of inhibition of purine biosynthesis by azaserine was observed by Sartorelli and Booth (*110*). After noting that incorporation of radioactive thymidine into DNA was inhibited by azaserine in Sarcoma 180 cells, they found that the activity of thymidine kinase in cell-free extracts had declined from 18.8 to 2.5 units and that of thymidylate kinase had changed from 110 to 43.9 units. Cramer and Sartorelli (*111*) later found that simultaneous injection of adenine, thymidine, or deoxycytidine with the azaserine prevented the loss of thymidine kinase activity (and presumably that of thymidylate kinase as well). It was concluded that thymidine kinase was stabilized by its substrates and that azaserine treatment led to a decline in the concentration of ATP and hence to accelerated denaturation or catabolism of this enzyme. This is a very interesting example of a quite secondary, but still important, effect of a drug.

Effect on Nucleotide Synthesis from Purine Bases. Apparent stimulation of incorporation of purine bases (adenine, guanine, hypoxanthine) into nucleic acids or acid-soluble purine nucleotides following treatment with azaserine and other glutamine antimetabolites has been observed by several investigators using a variety of normal and neoplastic animal cells (*59, 61, 65, 68, 114, 115*). These results have often been assumed to arise from a decrease in the dilution of radioactive precursor because of the lowered intracellular concentrations of purine nucleotides already described; the specific activity of the labeled purine nucleotides and nucleic acid purines would increase as a consequence. This must indeed be at least partly the basis of the observed stimulation of purine base incorporation. However, stimulation of nucleotide synthesis from 6-mercaptopurine (*116, 117*), 6-thioguanine (*118–123*), and 4-aminopyrazolopyrimidine (*124*) has also been measured following treatment of cells with azaserine. These results cannot be ascribed to dilution effects.

It is believed that the lowered purine ribonucleotide content of cells treated with azaserine leads to decreased endproduct inhibition of PP-ribose-P synthetase. Concentrations of PP-ribose-P would increase as a consequence, and this would cause an acceleration of purine phosphoribosyltransferase activity.

Other Drugs. The effects on purine biosynthesis of several other glutamine analogs have also been studied. In general, these have not been found to be potent inhibitors of this pathway, and for this or other reasons they have not received much attention.

Duazomycin A has been characterized as the *N*-acetyl derivative of diazo-oxonorleucine and apparently can be an active inhibitor of purine biosynthesis in the acetylated as well as unacetylated form. Anderson and Brockman (*125*) showed that it strongly inhibited incorporation of formate-^{14}C into acid-soluble and nucleic acid purines in the mouse plasma cell tumor 70429. Phosphoribosyl-formylglycineamide accumulated at low doses of duazomycin, but this was prevented by high concentration of the drug; diazooxonorleucine acted in the same way. Adams (*115*) also demonstrated inhibition of formate-^{14}C incorporation into nucleic acids by duazomycin, using mouse brain.

Mor (*126*) has recently reported that *N*-alkyl-glutamine derivatives could inhibit purine biosynthesis in a suitably fortified extract of pigeon liver, and this effect was overcome by increasing the concentration of glutamine; the ethyl derivative was most active. Carbobenzoxyglutamine was also an effective inhibitor in this system.

Levenberg *et al.* (*93*) showed that *O*-carbamyl-L-serine and γ-glutamylhydrazide were only weak inhibitors of the pigeon liver phosphoribosylformylglycineamidine synthetase, but in later studies by Schroeder *et al.* (*100*) albiziin (β-ureido-L-alanine) was identified as another irreversible inhibitor for this enzyme. As with azaserine one mole of albiziin was bound per mole of enzyme, and the inhibition was competitive with respect to glutamine.

Purine Analogs

Purine analogs and derivatives exhibit a wide range of pharmacological activities and are used at least experimentally in the chemotherapy of cancer, the chemotherapy of certain parasitic and viral infections, and for suppression of immune responses; they may also cause vasodilation, cause or prevent platelet aggregation, and antagonize or potentiate the actions of some hormones. It is quite clear that such a wide range of biological activities must reflect an equally wide number of biochemical sites of action of these drugs. One of these—but only one—is the pathway of purine biosynthesis *de novo,* which has been known for many years to be inhibited by a variety of purine analogs and derivatives. It must be emphasized from the outset, however, that some drugs that inhibit purine biosynthesis actually exert their dominant pharmacological effects through other, and sometimes quite unrelated, biochemical effects. This section will first describe the actions of this class of drugs on the purine biosynthetic pathway without reference to the biological effects which may or may not result from such inhibition. A brief discussion of the possible relationship between these facets of drug action will then follow. This topic has previously been reviewed by the author (*127, 128*).

The term purine analogs will be used for brevity and convenience to include purines, purine derivatives, purine nucleosides and their derivatives, analogs of purines and their derivatives and nucleosides.

Identification of Purine Analog Inhibitors of Purine Biosynthesis. Several inhibitors of purine biosynthesis *de novo* have been discovered in the course of wider studies of their biochemical effects; these will be mentioned below. A number of investigations, however, have been conducted in specific attempts to identify compounds which would affect this pathway of metabolism. This work may be said to have begun in 1955, with the use of glycine-^{14}C and formate-^{14}C incorporation into nucleic acid purines as assays (*129, 130*). More specific tests for inhibition of purine biosynthesis were eventually designed, and screening studies for inhibitors of this pathway have continued up to the present time; these are described briefly in Table 8-3.

Differences in the response of different cells to potential purine analog inhibitors of purine biosynthesis, together with differences in the expression of results by different investigators, make a systematic analysis of structure activity relationships rather difficult. Another point hindering analysis of these results is that there may be at least three different mechanisms by which such inhibition is produced; these will be discussed below. It should be pointed out, however, that a surprisingly high percentage of the compounds tested produced marked inhibition of this pathway; this varied from 20 to 40% in several of the larger series.

A point of continuing interest is whether purine analogs must be converted to nucleotide derivatives in order to inhibit purine biosynthesis. LePage and Jones (*91*), for example, found that nucleotide formation and inhibitory activity were related in the series of compounds studied by them, and Brockman and Chumley (*70*) and Caldwell *et al.* (*136*), among others, showed that a variety of purine analogs were inactive in cells that could not convert them to nucleotides. In contrast Henderson (*104, 132*) found that drug nucleotide synthesis was often necessary but not sufficient and in a few cases was not even necessary.

Sites of Inhibition. Inhibitors of purine biosynthesis *de novo* may at least potentially inhibit any of the 10 enzymes of this pathway or may act to decrease the availability of any of the substrates of these enzymes. The earliest studies, in which glycine (*129*) or formate (*130*) incorporation into nucleic acid purines was measured, gave no information regarding site of inhibition. Gots and Gollub (*131*), however, had originally set out to find

Table 8-3. Screening

Purine Analogs That Inhibit

System	*Assay*
Ehrlich ascites tumor cells *in vitro*	Glycine-$^{14}C \rightarrow$ nucleic acid purines
Flexner-Jobling carcinoma and rat spleen *in vitro*	Formate-$^{14}C \rightarrow$ nucleic acid purines
Escherichia coli B-96	Accumulation of amino-imidazole carboxamide
Ehrlich ascites carcinoma, Sarcoma 180, TA3 Carcinoma, Adenosarcoma 755, 6C3HED Lymphosarcoma, Mecca lymphosarcoma; all *in vivo*	Glycine-$^{14}C \rightarrow$ phosphoribosyl-formylglycineamide
Ehrlich ascites carcinoma *in vitro*	Glycine-$^{14}C \rightarrow$ phosphoribosyl-formylglycineamide
H.Ep. #2 cells in culture	Glycine-$^{14}C \rightarrow$ phosphoribosyl-formylglycineamide
Ehrlich ascites carcinoma *in vitro*	Glycine-$^{14}C \rightarrow$ phosphoribosyl-formylglycineamide
H.Ep. #2 cells and Adenocarcinoma 755 cells in culture; Leukemia L1210 *in vivo*	Glycine-$^{14}C \rightarrow$ phosphoribosyl-formylglycineamide
Ehrlich ascites carcinoma *in vitro*	Glycine-$^{14}C \rightarrow$ phosphoribosyl-formylglycineamide
Ehrlich ascites carcinoma *in vitro*	Glycine-$^{14}C \rightarrow$ phosphoribosyl-formylglycineamide

purine analogs that would prevent the normal endproduct inhibitory action of naturally occurring purines. When purine analogs were themselves found to be inhibitory, it was natural to conclude that they were acting in the same way as were the naturally occurring purines. Furthermore, the assay in this case was accumulation of aminoimidazole carboxamide, which conclusively localized the inhibition at some step in the pathway earlier than phosphoribosyl-aminoimidazole carboxamide formyltransferase. Gots and Gollub also suggested the possibility that some inhibitory purine analogs acted by trap-

Studies for Inhibitors

Purine Biosynthesis *de novo*

Compounds Tested	*Investigators*	*Reference*
4	LePage and Greenlees	(*129*)
4	Heidelberger and Keller	(*130*)
14	Gots and Gollub	(*131*)
8	LePage and Jones	(*91*)
37	Henderson	(*132*)
15	Bennett and Smithers	(*133*)
16	Henderson and Khoo	(*104*)
9	Brockman and Chumley	(*70*)
71	Henderson	(*134*)
164	Henderson *et al.*	(*135*)

ping PP-ribose-P in the course of their own conversion to ribonucleotides.

By the time of the study of Gots and Gollub in 1959 Sartorelli and LePage (*137*) had used another assay, glycine-^{14}C incorporation into phosphoribosylformylglycineamide in the presence of azaserine, to show that thioguanine inhibited purine biosynthesis at a point prior to the fourth reaction in this biosynthetic pathway. From this time on it was assumed, at least implicitly, that such inhibitors acted on the PP-ribose-P amidotransferase reaction and that they were bound to some "allosteric" site. This presumption was strengthened when McCollister *et al.* (*138*) demonstrated in 1964 that ribonucleotides of certain purine analogs did indeed inhibit a partially purified PP-ribose-P amidotransferase from pigeon liver.

In 1964–65, however, certain purine analogs were reported to inhibit PP-ribose-P synthetase, and this was not unexpectedly shown to result in inhibition of purine biosynthesis. Soon afterward the original suggestion that this class of drugs might act by reducing the availability of PP-ribose-P began to be taken more seriously (*e.g.*, *104*).

Thus there seem to be three possible sites of action of purine analogs which block purine biosynthesis *de novo*, and the most common assay for such inhibition, which measures the synthesis of phosphoribosyl-formylglycineamide, cannot distinguish among these. It must be strongly emphasized that at the present time the sites of action of the vast majority of purine analogs which have been identified as inhibitors of purine biosynthesis simply are not known.

The three sites of action identified so far, PP-ribose-P utilization, PP-ribose-P synthetase, and PP-ribose-P amidotransferase, will be discussed next, together with the drugs which have been shown to be involved at each step. Some drugs are involved to some degree at two or more of these sensitive sites, but the relative importance of each is not known; in other cases, the effect of a drug has been studied only on one of the three sites, and information regarding its potential range of actions remains incomplete.

UTILIZATION OF PP-RIBOSE-P. It is very difficult to prove or disprove that a purine analog might inhibit purine biosynthesis *de novo* by lowering intracellular concentrations of PP-ribose-P in the course of its conversion to ribonucleotide. Two groups of compounds may, however, be excluded from consideration in this regard: those which cannot be converted to nucleotides (*e.g.*, 9-alkylpurines) and those nucleosides which are not subject to phosphorolysis (*e.g.*, 6-methylmercaptopurine ribonucleoside). Only a few inhibitory compounds in each of these classes are known.

A major difficulty in the evaluation of this site of action is that PP-ribose-P concentrations have been measured in only a few cells, and they have most commonly been measured when glutamine concentrations were low or in cells such as erythrocytes which apparently lack PP-ribose-P amidotransferase. Both conditions are atypical, but they are chosen because PP-ribose-P concentrations are highest under these conditions. A decline in PP-ribose-P concentration upon addition of a purine analog under these conditions suggests but does not prove that this is how the drug inhibits purine synthesis. An indirect assay for PP-ribose-P availability which can sometimes be used is the inhibition in intact cells of adenine nucleotide synthesis from radioactive adenine, as this process also requires PP-ribose-P. In this case controls must be run for inhibition of adenine phosphoribosyltransferase and of PP-ribose-P synthetase.

Table 8-4. Effects of Purine Analogs on Accumulation of PP-Ribose-P and Phosphoribosyl-Formylglycineamide[a]

Purine Analog	*PP-Ribose-P (% of Control)*	*Phosphoribosyl-Formylglycineamide (% Inhibition)*
2,6-Diaminopurine	2.6	84.7
6-Methylthioinosine	102.3	84.2
6-Methylpurine	1.0	81.2
4-Aminopyrazolopyrimidine	58.8	64.4
Decoyinine	70.5	63.4
Purine	22.7	62.5
6-Benzylthioguanine	102	54.6
6-Chloropurine ribonucleoside	12.4	40.7
6-Chloropurine	60.3	39.5
6-Thioguanosine	15.6	30.8
6-Thioguanine	17.4	30.4
Adenine arabinoside	106	24.5
6-Chloroguanine ribonucleoside	5.2	11.7
Psicofuranine	105	10.5
6-Mercaptopurine	48.9	10.0
6-Methylthiopurine	1.6	−2.1

[a] From Henderson and Khoo (*104*)

The data of Henderson and Khoo (*104*) may be used to illustrate these points. In Table 8-4 the inhibition of phosphoribosyl-formylglycineamide synthesis and the inhibition of PP-ribose-P accumulation produced by a series of 16 purine analogs are compared. It may be seen that there was no general correlation between inhibition of purine biosynthesis and PP-ribose-P concentrations. It was also observed that a 95% decline in this concentration was still compatible with only a 10% inhibition of phosphoribosyl-formylglycineamide synthesis. The latter measurements were carried out after incubation with glutamine whereas in the former case this amino acid was omitted.

Effect of 2,6-Diaminopurine. Diaminopurine was shown in 1955 to inhibit the incorporation of glycine-^{14}C into nucleic acid purines (*129*), and it has subsequently been found to inhibit aminoimidazole carboxamide accumulation in *Escherichia coli* (*131*) and phosphoribosyl-formylglycineamide synthesis in Ehrlich ascites tumor cells (*132*) and H.Ep. #2 cells (*70*).

Henderson and Khoo (*104*) observed that diaminopurine did not inhibit PP-ribose-P synthesis in Ehrlich ascites tumor cells but did deplete PP-ribose-P concentrations, and Greene and Seegmiller (*139*) found that PP-ribose-P concentrations in human erythrocytes *in vivo* were decreased following intravenous injection of this drug.

The possibility that the ribonucleotide of diaminopurine might inhibit PP-ribose-P amidotransferase has not been explored. Although the data so far available are consistent with the view that diaminopurine inhibits purine biosynthesis through utilization of PP-ribose-P, this is by no means proved.

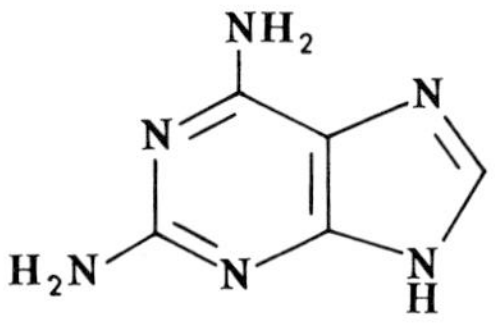

2,6 - Diaminopurine

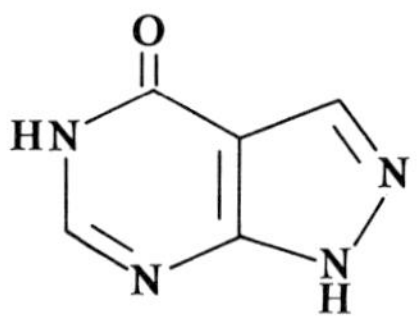

Allopurinol (4 - Hydroxypyrazolo-pyrimidine)

Effect of Allopurinol. Allopurinol (4-hydroxypyrazolopyrimidine) is a clinically useful inhibitor of xanthine oxidase and is metabolized both by oxidation and by conversion to its ribonucleotide. The first indication that allopurinol also inhibited purine biosynthesis *de novo* was the observation by Rundles *et al.* (*140*) that the total excretion of purines decreased in patients treated with this drug; Emmerson (*141*) later showed that allopurinol treatment inhibited the incorporation of glycine-^{14}C into urinary uric acid in man. Allopurinol also inhibited phosphoribosyl-formylglycineamide synthesis in H.Ep. #2 cells in culture but was not a very effective inhibitor of purine biosynthesis in Leukemia L1210 cells *in vivo* (*70*).

It has been suggested (*142*) that the inhibition of purine biosynthesis which accompanies treatment with allopurinol may be caused by feedback inhibition by elevated levels of the naturally occurring purine nucleotides following reutilization of the hypoxanthine which accumulates because of inhibition of xanthine oxidase. The conversion of hypoxanthine to inosinate would also utilize PP-ribose-P. It is difficult to evaluate this hypothesis, and indeed it may contribute to the apparent effects of allopurinol in man. However, this would seem to be less important in cells in tissue culture.

The ribonucleoside monophosphate of allopurinol has been tested as an inhibitor of a partially purified pigeon liver PP-ribose-P amidotransferase (*138*), and it produced 72% inhibition at a concentration of 1 m*M*. It was considered a weak inhibitor of this reaction.

Fox *et al.* (*143*) and Kelley and Wyngaarden (*144*) have considered the possibility that allopurinol might exert its inhibitory effect on purine biosynthesis through utilization of PP-ribose-P; they have also shown that it has no direct effect on PP-ribose-P synthetase. A 47% reduction in the PP-ribose-P concentrations of human erythrocytes was produced three to five hours after allopurinol administration, and the time course of decline in PP-ribose-P concentrations was not related to the hypoxanthine concentration of blood. Concentrations of PP-ribose-P in human skin fibroblasts in culture also declined following incubation with allopurinol. These investigators have concluded that the preponderance of evidence favors utilization of PP-ribose-P as a major factor in the inhibition of purine biosynthesis produced by allopurinol. As pointed out above, however, this is a very difficult matter to prove conclusively. Meyskens and Williams (*145*) also have shown that PP-ribose-P concentrations are lower in erythrocytes of patients treated with allopurinol than in those of normal controls.

PP-RIBOSE-P SYNTHETASE. A few purine analog inhibitors of PP-ribose-P synthetase are known, and these either have been shown experimentally to inhibit purine biosynthesis *de novo* or would be expected to do so.

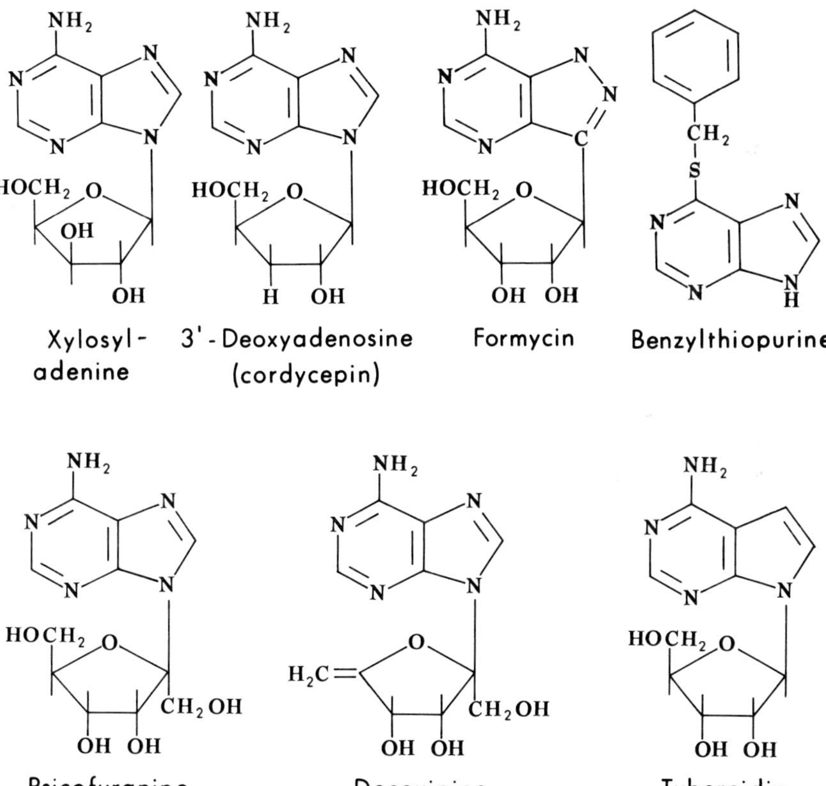

Effect of 3′-Deoxyadenosine (Cordycepin). In 1964 Rottman and Guarino (*146*) reported that an antibiotic known as cordycepin would inhibit formate-^{14}C incorporation into nucleic acid purines in *Bacillus subtilis*, as well as phosphoribosyl-formylglycineamide synthesis in the presence of diazo-oxonorleucine. Cordycepin was later identified as 3′-deoxyadenosine, and its triphosphate was shown by Klenow and Overgaard-Hansen (*147, 148*) to inhibit the synthesis of adenine nucleotides from adenine-^{14}C, ATP, and ribose 5-phosphate in extracts of Ehrlich ascites tumor cells. It had no inhibitory effect when PP-ribose-P was substituted for its precursors. It was concluded that 3′-deoxyadenosine triphosphate was an inhibitor of PP-ribose-P synthetase; whether it merely acts as a competitive inhibitor with respect to ATP or as an analog of one of the endproduct inhibitors of this enzyme is not known.

Tyrsted and Sartorelli (*149*) later measured the effect of 3′-deoxyadenosine on the accumulation of PP-ribose-P in intact Leukemia L5178Y cells incubated *in vitro* with glucose. This drug caused a 70% inhibition of PP-ribose-P accumulation under these conditions, and the related compounds 2′,3′-dideoxy-didehydro-adenosine, 2′,5′-dideoxyadenosine, and 2′,3′-dideoxyadenosine were also potent inhibitors of PP-ribose-P accumulation.

Effect of Xylosyladenine. Xylosyladenine inhibited the incorporation of both adenine-^{14}C and glycine-^{14}C into nucleic acid purines in Ehrlich ascites tumor cells and TA3 ascites carcinoma cells and also inhibited the accumulation of PP-ribose-P in cells incubated *in vitro* with glucose; phosphoribosyl-formylglycineamide accumulation in cells incubated with azaserine was also reduced (*150*). Ellis and LePage (*151*) then showed that xylosyladenine triphosphate inhibited PP-ribose-P synthetase activity in extracts of TA3 ascites carcinoma cells but did not inhibit adenine nucleotide synthesis when PP-ribose-P replaced ATP plus ribose 5-phosphate.

Effect of Decoyinine and Psicofuranine. Although decoyinine and psicofuranine were not active inhibitors of PP-ribose-P accumulation or purine biosynthesis in Ehrlich ascites tumor cells (*104*), Bloch and Nichol (*152*) showed that they inhibited PP-ribose-P synthesis in extracts of *Streptococcus faecalis*. Decoyinine was the more active drug. Inhibition of purine biosynthesis in this organism by these drugs would be expected but has not been demonstrated.

Effect of Formycin and Other Purine Analogs. Formycin, 7-amino-3-(β-D-ribofuranosyl)pyrazolo(4,3*d*)pyrimidine, inhibited the accumulation both of phosphoribosyl-formylglycineamide and of PP-ribose-P in Ehrlich ascites tumor cells *in vitro;* it did not inhibit PP-ribose-P amidotransferase in intact cells (*153*). Benzylthiopurine and tubercidin also inhibited the accumulation of PP-ribose-P (*104*) and of phosphoribosyl-formylglycineamide in the same system (*134*). It has been assumed that these compounds inhibit PP-ribose-P synthetase, but this has not been demonstrated directly.

Finally, a number of purine analogs have been identified which inhibit both phosphoribosyl-formylglycineamide synthesis and the conversion of hypoxanthine-^{14}C to ribonucleotides in intact Ehrlich ascites tumor cells *in vitro* (K. F. Lau and J. F. Henderson, unpublished). It seems likely that these drugs produce these effects through inhibition of PP-ribose-P synthesis, since most are nucleosides which would not themselves require PP-ribose-P for conversion to nucleotides. This possibility has not yet been tested directly.

PP-Ribose-P Amidotransferase. With the exception of the several compounds mentioned above as inhibitors of PP-ribose-P synthetase and those which deplete PP-ribose-P concentrations, most purine analog inhibitors of purine biosynthesis have usually been thought of as at least potential inhibitors of PP-ribose-P amidotransferase. Firm evidence for inhibition of this enzyme has been obtained for only a few drugs; these will be discussed next.

Inhibition by 6-Mercaptopurine and Related Compounds. Inhibition of purine biosynthesis by 6-mercaptopurine has been extensively investigated ever since Skipper (*154*) first observed this effect of the drug in 1954. Thus 6-mercaptopurine inhibited the incorporation of glycine-^{14}C or formate-^{14}C into acid-soluble or nucleic acid purines in Adenocarcinoma 755 (*154, 155*), Sarcoma 180 (*154, 155, 156*), mouse intestine (*154*), Ehrlich ascites carcinoma (*129, 156*), Flexner-Jobling carcinoma (*130*), rat spleen (*130*), Leukemia L1210 (*156*), *Lactobacillus casei* (*157*), *Streptococcus faecalis* (*158*), *Bacillus subtilis* (*159*), and *Escherichia coli* (*160*).

Gots and Gollub (*131*) demonstrated that 6-mercaptopurine inhibited the accumulation of aminoimidazole carboxamide in *Escherichia coli* B-96, and it inhibited the accumulation of phosphoribosyl-formylglycineamide in six ascites mouse tumors *in vivo* (*91*), in H.Ep. #2 and Adenocarcinoma 755 cells in culture (*70, 161*), and in human skin fibroblasts in culture (*162*). In addition, 6-mercaptopurine ribonucleoside inhibited this process in H.Ep. #2 cells in culture (*163*), as did bis(thioinosine)-5′,5‴-phosphate, which apparently was cleaved to 6-mercaptopurine ribonucleotide inside the cells (*164*). Purine biosynthesis was also inhibited by 6-mercaptopurine in mouse liver when it was stimulated by nicotinamide (*4*), and in man when this process was accelerated by administration of ethylamino-thiadiazole (*13*).

In some systems, however, mercaptopurine had little or no inhibitory activity. Thus Lukens and Herrington (*165*), in an early study, found that 6-mercaptopurine ribonucleotide and ribonucleoside both failed to inhibit *de novo* synthesis of inosinate in extracts of pigeon liver. Similarly, in an *in vitro* ascites tumor cell system, Henderson (*104, 132*) found that neither mercaptopurine nor its ribonucleoside had marked activity in this regard although the ribonucleoside was somewhat more active than the base.

Azathioprine, 6-(1′-methyl-4′-nitro-5′-imidazolyl)-thiopurine, is a derivative of 6-mercaptopurine which is inactive as administered but which is activated by cleavage to the free mercapto compound and subsequent conversion to 6-mercaptopurine ribonucleotide or other nucleotide derivatives. Sorensen (*166*) first observed that azathioprine reduced plasma uric acid concentrations, decreased the amount of urinary uric acid, and inhibited glycine-^{14}C

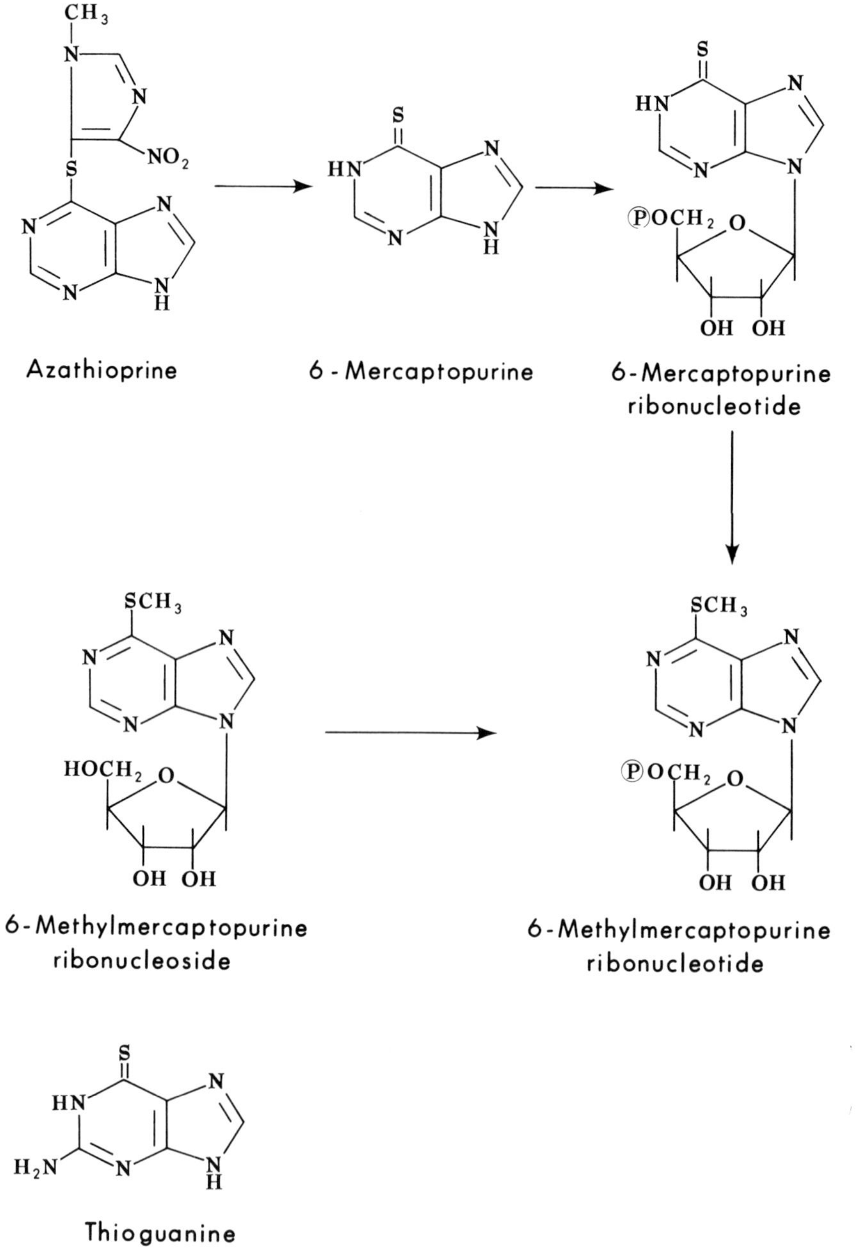

Azathioprine

6 - Mercaptopurine

6-Mercaptopurine ribonucleotide

6-Methylmercaptopurine ribonucleoside

6-Methylmercaptopurine ribonucleotide

Thioguanine

incorporation into urinary uric acid in man. Similar results have been obtained by other investigators (*167, 168*).

Inhibition by 6-Methylmercaptopurine Ribonucleoside. Henderson (*132*) demonstrated in 1965 that 6-methylmercaptopurine ribonucleoside was a very potent inhibitor of phosphoribosyl-formylglycineamide synthesis in Ehrlich ascites tumor cells *in vitro;* it was approximately 500 times more active than adenine, the most effective natural purine. This has been confirmed in other studies of the same tumor (*169, 170*) and also demonstrated in H.Ep. #2 cells in culture (*163*) and in human skin fibroblasts in culture (*171, 172, 173*). Henderson and Mercer (*174*) demonstrated that 6-methylmercaptopurine ribonucleoside inhibited glycine-^{14}C incorporation into acid-soluble adenine in mouse liver, spleen, kidney, gut, and diaphragm *in vivo.*

Inhibition by Thioguanine. Thioguanine inhibited accumulation of aminoimidazole carboxamide in *Escherichia coli* B-96 (*131*). It inhibited phosphoribosyl-formylglycineamide synthesis in TA3 Carcinoma cells (*91*) and five other mouse tumors *in vivo* (*91*) and in H.Ep. #2 cells in culture (*70*). Thioguanine ribonucleoside also inhibited purine biosynthesis in Ehrlich ascites tumor cells *in vitro* (*104, 132*); in one study of this system the free base failed to do so (*132*), but it was weakly inhibitory in another investigation (*104*).

Inhibition of PP-Ribose-P Amidotransferase. Several investigators (*105, 138, 175*) have measured the effects of thiopurine nucleotides on the PP-ribose-P amidotransferase reaction. Data for nucleotides of 6-mercaptopurine, 6-methylmercaptopurine, and thioguanine are given in Table 8-5. For the pigeon liver enzyme, 6-mercaptopurine ribonucleotide is quite an effective inhibitor, but it has only weak effects on the enzymes from Adenocarcinoma 755 and Ehrlich ascites tumor cells. The reason for this difference is not known.

Table 8-5. Inhibition of PP-Ribose-P Amidotransferase

Compound	*Source of Enzyme*	*Inhibition*
6-Mercaptopurine ribonucleotide	Pigeon liver (*138*)	$4.4–8.5 \times 10^{-5}\ M\ (K_i)$
	Adenocarcinoma 755 (*105*)	$1.1 \times 10^{-3}\ M$ (ID$_{50}$) [a]
	Ehrlich ascites tumor (*175*)	$1.6 \times 10^{-3}\ M$ (ID$_{50}$)
6-Methylmercaptopurine ribonucleotide	Adenocarcinoma 755 (*105*)	$9 \times 10^{-5}\ M$ (ID$_{50}$)
	Ehrlich ascites tumor (*175*)	$5 \times 10^{-5}\ M$ (ID$_{50}$)
6-Thioguanine ribonucleotide	Pigeon liver (*138*)	$1.7–2.0 \times 10^{-4}\ M\ (K_i)$
	Adenocarcinoma 755 (*105*)	$2.7 \times 10^{-4}\ M$ (ID$_{50}$)
	Ehrlich ascites tumor (*175*)	$4 \times 10^{-4}\ M$ (ID$_{50}$)

[a] ID$_{50}$—concentration required for 50% inhibition

Consequences of Inhibition of PP-Ribose-P Amidotransferase by Purine Analogs. Inhibition of PP-ribose-P amidotransferase by compounds such as

6-methylmercaptopurine ribonucleoside, following its phosphorylation, would be expected to have two direct consequences: accumulation or increased availability of PP-ribose-P, and lowered concentrations of purine ribonucleotides. The latter effect might have as an indirect consequence the release of endproduct inhibition of PP-ribose-P synthetase and hence increased formation of PP-ribose-P. Scholar *et al.* (*176*) have recently shown that incubation of Sarcoma 180 ascites cells *in vitro* with 6-methylmercaptopurine ribonucleoside leads to decreases in adenine and guanine nucleotide concentrations, and these changes are considerably greater when combinations of this drug with 6-mercaptopurine are employed.

Paterson and Wang (*177*) have shown that PP-ribose-P concentrations are elevated as much as 20-fold following treatment of Ehrlich ascites tumor cells *in vivo* with 6-methylmercaptopurine ribonucleoside. As a consequence, the rate of nucleotide formation from adenine, hypoxanthine, and guanine (*177*) and from 6-mercaptopurine (*176, 177*) increases dramatically. This increased anabolism of 6-mercaptopurine is believed to be the basis of the potentiation of growth inhibition observed with combinations of these two purine analogs (*177, 178, 179, 180*).

Inhibitors of Undefined Site of Action. Of the many purine analog inhibitors of purine biosynthesis *de novo* which have been identified without knowledge of exact site and mechanism of inhibition, a few have been studied sufficiently or are of sufficient interest to warrant mention at this point.

Pyrazolopyrimidines. A number of laboratories have studied 4-aminopyrazolopyrimidine, an analog of adenine. Relatively high doses inhibited formate-^{14}C incorporation into acid-soluble adenine in Adenocarcinoma 755 and mouse intestine, but it had no effect on purine synthesis in liver (*181*). Slightly lower doses inhibited purine biosynthesis in Ehrlich ascites tumor cells *in vivo* (*182*), but such an effect was not detected at therapeutic doses (*183*) or when these cells were incubated *in vitro* (*132*). Bennett and Smithers (*133*) found that this drug was a relatively weak inhibitor of purine synthesis in cultured H.Ep. #2 cells, and they also described a drug-resistant line of these cells in which this process was inhibited only at extremely high concentrations (*184*).

Purine biosynthesis was inhibited by aminopyrazolopyrimidine in wild-type *Escherichia coli* (*185*), *Escherichia coli* B-96 (*131, 185*), and *Bacillus cereus* (*185*). The related compounds 4-hydroxy-6-aminopyrazolopyrimidine and 1-methyl-4-aminopyrazolopyrimidine also inhibited purine synthesis in these systems (*185, 186*).

Other Adenine and Adenosine Analogs. Bennett and his colleagues (*133, 184, 187*) have identified a number of other adenine and adenosine analogs which are potent inhibitors of purine biosynthesis *de novo* in cultured H.Ep. #2 cells. These include 2-fluoroadenine, 2-fluoroadenosine, 8-azaadenosine, tubercidin, and the carbocyclic analog of adenosine; unfortunately, their sites and mechanisms of inhibition have not been studied in any detail.

Inhibition by 8-Azaguanine. The compound 8-azaguanine has been shown to be only a weak inhibitor of purine biosynthesis *de novo* in Flexner-Jobling carcinoma (*130*), Ehrlich ascites tumor cells *in vitro* (*129, 132*), and H.Ep. #2 cells in culture (*70*). Its ribonucleotide was a weak inhibitor of PP-ribose-P amidotransferases from pigeon liver (*138*) and Adenocarcinoma 755 (*105*). This effect is not believed to be important for the growth-inhibitory properties of this purine analog.

Relationship of Inhibition of Purine Biosynthesis to Growth Inhibition. In 1965 the author (*127*) reviewed the evidence then available regarding the relationship between the inhibition of purine biosynthesis *de novo* by purine analogs and inhibition of growth by these compounds. It was somewhat reluctantly concluded that at that time there was no firm evidence for such a relationship for any compound studied. In the last few years, however, more and more work has been done which suggests that at least one such compound, 6-methylmercaptopurine ribonucleoside, might very well inhibit tumor growth through inhibition of purine biosynthesis. Thus growth inhibition by this drug of H.Ep. #2 cells (*188*), Ehrlich ascites tumor cells (*170*), and Lymphoma L5178Y cells (A. R. P. Paterson, personal communication) in culture is reversed by adenine, hypoxanthine, and amino-imidazole carboxamide. In addition, a correlation was established between the magnitude and duration of inhibition of purine biosynthesis and the extent of tumor growth inhibition (*170*). Finally, these results are consistent with the finding that 6-methylmercaptopurine ribonucleotide is the most potent inhibitor so far identified of PP-ribose-P amidotransferase both in cell extracts (*138, 175*) and intact cells (*132*).

3-Amino-1,2,4-triazole

A commercial herbicide, 3-amino-1,2,4-triazole, is toxic not only to higher plants but also to algae, yeast, and bacteria. Its biochemical effects have been extensively studied, but its primary site of action does not appear to be the same in all organisms; the earlier literature on this compound has been reviewed by Hilton *et al.* (*189*). Thus in higher plants processes related to purine metabolism (riboflavin and nucleic acid synthesis) appear to be most sensitive (*e.g., 189, 190*) whereas in *Saccharomyces cerevisiae, Schizosac-*

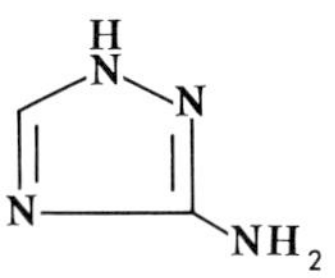

3-Amino-1,2,4-triazole

charomyces pombe, and *Torula cremoris* histidine biosynthesis is most sensitive (*e.g., 191, 192*).

Aminotriazole is a competitive inhibitor of imidazoleglycerol-phosphate dehydratase (EC 4.2.1.19) in the pathway of histidine biosynthesis (*193, 194*), and thus its effect on the availability of histidine has nothing directly to do with the involvement of ATP as a precursor of part of the histidine molecule. However, it may be expected that lowered histidine concentrations resulting from aminotriazole action would cause an increased utilization of ATP for at least the early steps of histidine biosynthesis and hence might cause a drain on the purine nucleotide pool if there were any deficiencies in the reutilization of phosphoribosyl-aminoimidazole carboxamide.

However, a second site of aminotriazole action is indicated by the observations that at higher doses of this drug adenine partially relieved inhibition in *Saccharomyces cerevisiae* and *Schizosaccharomyces pombe* (*191, 194, 195*) and was required in addition to histidine for complete reversal of the growth of *Salmonella typhimurium* (*193, 196*). Although histidine alone reversed the growth-inhibitory effects of aminotriazole in some studies with the algae *Chlorella vulgaris* and *Prototheca zopfii* (*197, 198*), adenine or combinations of adenine and histidine were more effective in other studies with *Chlorella pyroidosa* and *Prototheca zopfii* (*199, 200, 201*). In *Escherichia coli* adenine was a more potent reversing agent than histidine although both together were required for complete reversal of growth inhibition (*202, 203*).

The growth-inhibitory effect of aminotriazole on *Salmonella typhimurium* was shown by Boguslawski *et al.* (*204*) to be partially reversed by serine but potentiated by glycine. These authors suggested that aminotriazole interfered with one-carbon metabolism; although many studies with histidine and adenine are compatible with this idea, it has not been defined more precisely. More recently, Hulanicka *et al.* (*205*) have utilized mutants of *Salmonella typhimurium* blocked at various stages of purine biosynthesis in attempts to localize the site of action of aminotriazole. Using a rather indirect assay—ribose accumulation in defined mutants—they concluded that aminotriazole inhibited purine biosynthesis at a step prior to the synthesis of phosphoribosyl-aminoimidazole. Further studies are required to define the effects of aminotriazole on purine biosynthesis more precisely.

References

1. Balis, M. E., "Antagonists and Nucleic Acids," North-Holland, Amsterdam, 1968.
2. Langen, P., "Antimetabolite des Nucleinsäurestoffwechsels," Akad-Verlag, Berlin, 1968.
3. Roy-Burman, P., "Analogues of Nucleic Acid Components: Mechanisms of Action," Springer, New York, 1970.
4. Kaplan, N. O., Goldin, A., Humphreys, S. R., Ciotti, M. M., Stolzenbach, F. E., *J. Biol. Chem.* (1956) **219,** 287.

5. Ricci, C., Pallini, V., Pompucci, G., *Boll. Soc. Ital. Biol. Sper.* (1960) **36,** 1020.
6. Shuster, L., Langan, T. A., Jr., Kaplan, N. O., Goldin, A., *Nature (London)* (1958) **182,** 512.
7. Shuster, L., Goldin, A., *J. Biol. Chem.* (1958) **230,** 883.
8. Shuster, L., Goldin, A., *J. Biol. Chem.* (1958) **230,** 873.
9. Shuster, L., Goldin, A., *J. Biol. Chem.* (1959) **234,** 129.
10. Krakoff, I. H., Magill, G. M., *Proc. Soc. Exp. Biol. Med.* (1956) **91,** 470.
11. Seegmiller, J. E., Grayzel, A. I., Liddle, L., *Nature (London)* (1959) **183,** 1463.
12. Krakoff, I. H., Balis, M. E., *J. Clin. Invest.* (1959) **38,** 907.
13. Krakoff, I. H., Balis, M. E., Karnofsky, D. A., *Ann. Intern. Med.* (1961) **54,** 1045.
14. Shuster, L., Goldin, A., *Biochem. Pharmacol.* (1959) **2,** 17.
15. Seegmiller, J. E., Grayzel, A. I., Liddle, L., Wyngaarden, J. B., *Metab. Clin. Exp.* (1963) **12,** 507.
16. Duggan, D. E., Pua, K. H., Elfenbein, G., *Mol. Pharmacol.* (1963) **4,** 53.
17. Nyhan, W. L., Sweetman, L., Lesch, M., *Metab. Clin. Exp.* (1968) **17,** 846.
18. Rogers, L. L., Shive, W., *J. Biol. Chem.* (1948) **172,** 751.
19. Shive, W., *Ann. N.Y. Acad. Sci.* (1950) **52,** 1212.
20. Webb, M., *Biochem. J.* (1958) **70,** 472.
21. Biggers, J. D., Webb, M., *Biochem. J.* (1958) **70,** 487.
22. Guthrie, R., Hillman, M., Hyatt, E., *Bacteriol. Proc.* (1956) 122.
23. Hakala, M. T., Taylor, E., *J. Biol. Chem.* (1959) **234,** 126.
24. Hakala, M. T., *Science* (1957) **126,** 255.
25. Hakala, M. T., *Cancer Res.* (1971) **31,** 813.
26. Woolley, D. W., Pringle, R. B., *J. Amer. Chem. Soc.* (1954) **72,** 634.
27. Edwards, P. C., Skipper, H. E., Johnson, R. P., *Cancer (Philadelphia)* (1952) **4,** 398.
28. Braunshtein, A. E., Vinkelman, G. I., *Biokhimiya* (1958) **23,** 887.
29. McGeer, P. L., McGeer, E. G., *Biochem. Pharmacol.* (1963) **12,** 297.
30. Tomisek, A. J., Kelly, H. J., Reid, M. R., Skipper, H. E., *Arch. Biochem. Biophys.* (1958) **78,** 83.
31. Tomisek, A. J., Kelly, H. J., Reid, M. R., Skipper, H. E., *Arch. Biochem. Biophys.* (1958) **76,** 45.
32. Weaver, J. M., Shive, W., *J. Amer. Chem. Soc.* (1953) **75,** 4628.
33. Deodhar, S. P., Pittman, G., *Cleveland Clin. Quart.* (1966) **33,** 191.
34. Skipper, H. E., Mitchell, J. H., Jr., Bennett, L. L., Jr., *Cancer Res.* (1950) **10,** 510.
35. Skipper, H. E., Bennett, L. L., Jr., Law, L. W., *Cancer Res.* (1952) **12,** 677.
36. Goldthwait, D. A., Bendich, A., *J. Biol. Chem.* (1952) **196,** 841.
37. Martin, J. L., Totter, J. R., *Proc. Soc. Exp. Biol. Med.* (1954) **86,** 41.
38. Schrecker, A. W., Mead, J. A. R., Goldin, A., *Cancer Res.* (1962) **22,** 15.
39. Totter, J. R., Best, A. N., *Arch. Biochem. Biophys.* (1955) **54,** 318.
40. Wada, Y., Arakawa, T., *Tohoku J. Exp. Med.* (1968) **96,** 313.
41. Winzler, R. J., Williams, A. D., Best, W. R., *Cancer Res.* (1957) **17,** 108.
42. Wells, W., Winzler, R. J., *Cancer Res.* (1959) **19,** 1086.
43. Williams, A. D., Slater, G. G., Winzler, R. J., *Cancer Res.* (1955) **15,** 532.
44. Sartorelli, A. C., LePage, G. A., *Cancer Res.* (1958) **18,** 1336.
45. Sartorelli, A. C., Booth, B. A., *Cancer Res.* (1962) **22,** 94.
46. Sartorelli, A. C., Upchurch, H. F., Booth, B. A., *Cancer Res.* (1962) **22,** 102.
47. Schrecker, A. W., Mead, J. A. R., Lynch, M. R., Goldin, A., *Cancer Res.* (1960) **20,** 876.
48. Schrecker, A. W., Mead, J. A. R., Lynch, M. R., Venditti, J. M., Goldin, A., *Cancer Res.* (1960) **20,** 1457.
49. Skipper, H. A., Nolan, C., Newton, M. A., Simpson, L., *Cancer Res.* (1952) **12,** 369.

50. Hartman, S. C., Levenberg, B., Buchanan, J. M., *J. Amer. Chem. Soc.* (1955) **77,** 501.
51. Mandel, H. G., *Pharmacol. Rev.* (1959) **11,** 743.
52. *Cancer Chemother. Rep.* (1960) **7,** 65.
53. *Cancer Chemother. Rep.* (1960) **7,** 86.
54. Stock, J. A., "Experimental Chemotherapy," Schnitzer, R. J., Hawking, F., Eds., Vol. 4, p. 241, Academic, New York, 1966.
55. Powell, R., "Azaserine, a Current Bibliography," Calbiochem, Los Angeles, 1970.
56. Skipper, H. E., Bennett, L. L., Jr., Schabel, F. M., Jr., *Fed. Proc. Fed. Amer. Soc. Exp. Biol.* (1954) **13,** 298.
57. Bennett, L. L., Jr., Schabel, F. M., Jr., Skipper, H. E., *Arch. Biochem. Biophys.* (1956) **64,** 423.
58. LePage, G. A., Greenlees, J., Fernandes, J. F., *Ann. N.Y. Acad. Sci.* (1956) **63,** 999.
59. Fernandes, J. F., LePage, G. A., Lindner, A., *Cancer Res.* (1956) **16,** 154.
60. Greenlees, J., LePage, G. A., *Cancer Res.* (1956) **16,** 808.
61. Henderson, J. F., LePage, G. A., McIver, F. A., *Cancer Res.* (1957) **17,** 609.
62. Moore, E. C., LePage, G. A., *Cancer Res.* (1957) **17,** 804.
63. Sartorelli, A. C., LePage, G. A., *Cancer Res.* (1958) **18,** 457.
64. Smellie, R. M. S., Thomson, R. Y., Davidson, J. N., *Biochim. Biophys. Acta* (1958) **29,** 59.
65. Barclay, R. K., Garfinkel, E., Phillipps, M., *Proc. Amer. Ass. Cancer Res.* (1956) **2,** 93.
66. Sartorelli, A. C., Akers, J. R., Booth, B. A., *Biochem. Pharmacol.* (1960) **5,** 238.
67. Franklin, T. J., Cook, J. M., *Biochem. J.* (1969) **113,** 515.
68. Held, I., Wells, W., Koenig, H., *J. Neurochem.* (1969) **16,** 537.
69. McFall, E., Magasanik, B., *J. Biol. Chem.* (1960) **235,** 2103.
70. Brockman, R. W., Chumley, S., *Biochim. Biophys. Acta* (1965) **95,** 365.
71. Krakoff, I. H., Karnofsky, D. A., *Amer. J. Physiol.* (1958) **195,** 244.
72. Grayzel, A. I., Seegmiller, J. E., *J. Clin. Invest.* (1959) **38,** 1008.
73. Zuckerman, R., Drell, W., Levin, M. H., *Arthritis Rheum.* (1959) **2,** 46.
74. Krakoff, I. H., Balis, M. E., *J. Clin. Invest.* (1959) **38,** 907.
75. Wood, S., Pinsky, L., *Clin. Res.* (1969) **17,** 650.
76. Tomisek, A. J., Kelly, H. J., Skipper, H. E., *Arch. Biochem. Biophys.* (1956) **64,** 437.
77. Gots, J. S., Gollub, E. G., *J. Bacteriol.* (1956) **72,** 858.
78. Maxwell, R. E., Nickel, V. S., *Antibiot. Chemother. (Washington, D.C.)* (1957) **7,** 81.
79. Tomisek, A. J., Reid, M. R., Skipper, H. E., *Cancer Res.* (1959) **19,** 489.
80. Kaplan, L., Reilly, H. C., Stock, C. C., *J. Bacteriol.* (1959) **78,** 511.
81. Tomisek, A. J., Reid, M. R., *J. Biol. Chem.* (1962) **237,** 807.
82. Hedegaard, J., Roche, J., *C.R. Soc. Biol.* (1966) **160,** 539.
83. Clarke, D. A., Reilly, H. C., Stock, C. C., *Antibiot. Chemother. (Washington, D.C.)* (1957) **7,** 653.
84. Tarnowski, G. S., Stock, C. C., *Cancer Res.* (1957) **17,** 1033.
85. Thiersch, J. B., *Proc. Soc. Exp. Biol. Med.* (1957) **94,** 33.
86. Magill, G. B., Meyers, W. P. L., Reilly, H. C., Putnam, R. C., Magill, J. W., Sykes, M. P., Escher, G. C., Karnofsky, D. A., Burchenal, J. H., *Cancer (Philadelphia)* (1957) **10,** 1138.
87. Halvorson, H., *Antibiot. Chemother. (Washington, D.C.)* (1954) **4,** 948.
88. Reilly, H. C., *Proc. Amer. Ass. Cancer Res.* (1954) **1,** 40.
89. Aaronson, S., *J. Bacteriol.* (1959) **77,** 548.
90. Hartman, S. C., Levenberg, B., Buchanan, J. M., *J. Biol. Chem.* (1956) **221,** 1057.
91. LePage, G. A., Jones, M. A., *Cancer Res.* (1961) **21,** 642.

92. Henderson, J. F., *J. Biol. Chem.* (1962) **237,** 2631.
93. Levenberg, B., Melnick, I., Buchanan, J. M., *J. Biol. Chem.* (1957) **225,** 163.
94. Chu, S. Y., Henderson, J. F., *Biochem. Pharmacol.* (1972) **21,** 401.
95. Dawid, I. G., French, T. C., Buchanan, J. M., *J. Biol. Chem.* (1963) **238,** 2178.
96. French, T. C., Dawid, I. B., Day, R. A., Buchanan, J. M., *J. Biol. Chem.* (1963) **238,** 2171.
97. French, T. C., Dawid, I. B., Buchanan, J. M., *J. Biol. Chem.* (1963) **238,** 2186.
98. Mizobuchi, K., Buchanan, J. M., *J. Biol. Chem.* (1968) **243,** 4853.
99. Mizobuchi, K., Kenyon, G. L., Buchanan, J. M., *J. Biol. Chem.* (1968) **243,** 4863.
100. Schroeder, D. D., Allison, A. J., Buchanan, J. M., *J. Biol. Chem.* (1969) **244,** 5856.
101. Meister, A., "Biochemistry of the Amino Acids," 2nd ed., Academic, New York, 1965.
102. Hartman, S. C., *J. Biol. Chem.* (1963) **238,** 3024.
103. Hartman, S. C., *J. Biol. Chem.* (1963) **238,** 3036.
104. Henderson, J. F., Khoo, M. K. Y., *J. Biol. Chem.* (1965) **240,** 3104.
105. Hill, D. L., Bennett, L. L., Jr., *Biochemistry* (1969) **8,** 122.
106. Nierlich, D. P., Magasanik, B., *J. Biol. Chem.* (1965) **240,** 358.
107. Buchanan, J. M., Hartman, S. C., Herrmann, R. L., Day, R. A., *J. Cell. Comp. Physiol.* **54** (1959) Suppl. 1, 139.
108. Wyngaarden, J. B., Ashton, D. M., *J. Biol. Chem.* (1959) **234,** 1492.
109. Barker, S. A., Basshorn, J. A., Calvin, M., Quark, V. C., *J. Amer. Chem. Soc.* (1956) **78,** 4632.
110. Sartorelli, A. C., Booth, B. A., *Mol. Pharmacol.* (1967) **3,** 71.
111. Cramer, G. T., Sartorelli, A. C., *Biochem. Pharmacol.* (1969) **18,** 1355.
112. Hyams, D. E., Taft, E. B., Drummey, G. D., Isselbacher, K. J., *Lab. Invest.* (1967) **16,** 604.
113. Marchetti, M., Ottani, V., Paddu, P., *Proc. Soc. Exp. Biol. Med.* (1970) **133,** 30.
114. Adams, D. H., *Biochem. J.* (1963) **89,** 240.
115. Adams, D. H., *J. Neurochem.* (1965) **12,** 783.
116. Paterson, A. R. P., *Can. J. Biochem. Physiol.* (1959) **37,** 1011.
117. Paterson, A. R. P., *Acta Unio Int. Contra Cancrum* (1964) **20,** 1033.
118. Moore, E. C., LePage, G. A., *Cancer Res.* (1958) **18,** 1075.
119. Sartorelli, A. C., LePage, G. A., Moore, E. C., *Cancer Res.* (1958) **18,** 1232.
120. LePage, G. A., *Cancer Res.* (1960) **20,** 403.
121. Ellis, D. B., LePage, G. A., *Cancer Res.* (1963) **23,** 436.
122. LePage, G. A., Howard, N., *Cancer Res.* (1963) **23,** 622.
123. Sartorelli, A. C., Upchurch, H. F., Bieber, A. L., Booth, B. A., *Cancer Res.* (1964) **24,** 1202.
124. Henderson, J. F., Junga, I. G., *Biochem. Pharmacol.* (1961) **7,** 187.
125. Anderson, E. P., Brockman, R. W., *Biochem. Pharmacol.* (1963) **12,** 1335.
126. Mor, G., *Fed. Eur. Biochem. Soc. Lett.* (1971) **13,** 173.
127. Henderson, J. F., *Progr. Exp. Tumor Res.* (1965) **6,** 85.
128. Henderson, J. F., Mandel, H. G., *Advan. Pharmacol.* (1963) **2,** 297.
129. LePage, G. A., Greenlees, J. L., *Cancer Res.* (1955) **15,** Suppl. 3, 102.
130. Heidelberger, C., Keller, R. A., *Cancer Res.* (1955) **15,** Suppl. 3, 109.
131. Gots, J. S., Gollub, E. G., *Proc. Soc. Exp. Biol. Med.* (1959) **101,** 641.
132. Henderson, J. F., *Biochem. Pharmacol.* (1963) **12,** 551.
133. Bennett, L. L., Jr., Smithers, D., *Biochem. Pharmacol.* (1964) **13,** 1331.
134. Henderson, J. F., *Cancer Chemother. Rep. (Part 2)* (1968) **1,** 375.
135. Henderson, J. F., Paterson, A. R. P., Caldwell, I. C., Paul, B., Chan, M. C., Lau, K. F., *Cancer Chemother. Rep. (Part 2),* in press.

136. Caldwell, I. C., Henderson, J. F., Paterson, A. R. P., *Can. J. Biochem.* (1967) **45,** 735.
137. Sartorelli, A. C., LePage, G. A., *Cancer Res.* (1958) **18,** 1329.
138. McCollister, R. J., Gilbert, W. R., Ashton, D. M., Wyngaarden, J. B., *J. Biol. Chem.* (1964) **239,** 1560.
139. Greene, M. L., Seegmiller, J. E., *Arthritis Rheum.* (1969) **12,** 666.
140. Rundles, R. W., Wyngaarden, J. B., Hitchings, G. H., Elion, G. B., Silberman, H. R., *Trans. Ass. Amer. Physicians* (1963) **76**, 126.
141. Emmerson, B. T., *Ann. Rheum. Dis.* (1966) **25,** 621.
142. Pomales, R., Bieber, S., Friedman, R., Hitchings, G. H., *Biochim. Biophys. Acta* (1963) **72,** 119.
143. Fox, I. H., Wyngaarden, J. B., Kelley, W. N., *N. Eng. J. Med.* (1970) **283,** 1177.
144. Kelley, W. N., Wyngaarden, J. B., *J. Clin. Invest.* (1970) **49**, 602.
145. Meyskens, F. L., Williams, H. E., *Metab. Clin. Exp.* (1971) **20,** 737.
146. Rottman, F., Guarino, A. J., *Biochim. Biophys. Acta* (1964) **80,** 640.
147. Klenow, H., Overgaard-Hansen, K., *Biochim. Biophys. Acta* (1964) **80,** 500.
148. Overgaard-Hansen, K., *Biochim. Biophys. Acta* (1964) **80,** 504.
149. Tyrsted, G., Sartorelli, A. C., *Biochim. Biophys. Acta* (1968) **155,** 619.
150. Ellis, D. B., LePage, G. A., *Mol. Pharmacol.* (1965) **1,** 231.
151. Ellis, D. B., LePage, G. A., *Can. J. Biochem.* (1965) **43,** 617.
152. Bloch, A., Nichol, C. A., *Biochem. Biophys. Res. Commun.* (1964) **16,** 400.
153. Henderson, J. F., Paterson, A. R. P., Caldwell, I. C., Hori, M., *Cancer Res.* (1967) **27,** 715.
154. Skipper, H. E., *Ann. N.Y. Acad. Sci.* (1954) **60,** 315.
155. Dixon, G. J., Dulmadge, E. A., Brockman, R. W., Shaddix, S. C., *J. Nat. Cancer Inst.* (1970) **45,** 681.
156. Bennett, L. L., Jr., Simpson, L., Golden, J., Barker, T. L., *Cancer Res.* (1963) **23,** 1574.
157. Balis, M. E., Levin, D. H., Brown, G. B., Elion, G. B., Nathan, H. C., Hitchings, G. H., *Arch. Biochem. Biophys.* (1957) **71,** 358.
158. Balis, M. E., Hylin, V., Coultas, M. K., Hutchison, D. J., *Cancer Res.* (1958) **18**, 440.
159. Bolton, E. T., Mandel, H. G., *J. Biol. Chem.* (1957) **227,** 833.
160. Tomisek, A., Reid, M., *Proc. Amer. Ass. Cancer Res.* (1962) **3,** 368.
161. Brockman, R. W., *Cancer Res.* (1963) **23,** 1191.
162. Seegmiller, J. E., Rosenbloom, F. M., Kelley, W. N., *Science* (1967) **155,** 1682.
163. Bennett, L. L., Jr., Brockman, R. W., Schnebli, H. P., Chumley, S., Dixon, G. J., Schabel, F. M., Jr., Dulmage, E. A., Skipper, H. E., Montgomery, J. A., Thomas, J., *Nature (London)* (1965) **205,** 1276.
164. Montgomery, J. A., Dixon, G. J., Dulmage, E. A., Thomas, H. J., Brockman, R. W., Skipper, H. E., *Nature (London)* (1963) **199,** 769.
165. Lukens, L. N., Herrington, K. A., *Biochim. Biophys. Acta* (1957) **24,** 432.
166. Sorensen, L. B., *Proc. Nat. Acad. Sci.* (1966) **55,** 571.
167. Kelley, W. N., Rosenbloom, F. M., Seegmiller, J. E., *J. Clin. Invest.* (1967) **46,** 1518.
168. Nyhan, W. L., Sweetman, L., Carpenter, D. G., Carter, C. H., Hoefnagel, D., *J. Pediat.* (1968) **72,** 111.
169. Henderson, J. F., Caldwell, I. C., Paterson, A. R. P., *Cancer Res.* (1967) **27,** 1773.
170. Shantz, G. D., Fontenelle, L. J., Henderson, J. F., *Biochem. Pharmacol.* (1972) **21,** 1203.
171. Rosenbloom, F. M., Henderson, J. F., Kelley, W. N., Seegmiller, J. E., *Biochim. Biophys. Acta* (1968) **166,** 258.
172. Henderson, J. F., Rosenbloom, F. M., Kelley, W. N., Seegmiller, J. E., *J. Clin. Invest.* (1968) **47,** 1511.

173. Rosenbloom, F. M., Henderson, J. F., Caldwell, I. C., Kelley, W. N., Seegmiller, J. E., *J. Biol. Chem.* (1968) **243**, 1166.
174. Henderson, J. F., Mercer, N. J. H., *Nature (London)* (1966) **212**, 507.
175. Tay, B. S., Lilley, R. M., Murray, A. W., Atkinson, M. R., *Biochem. Pharmacol.* (1969) **18**, 936.
176. Scholar, E. M., Brown, P. R., Parks, R. E., Jr., *Cancer Res.* (1972) **32**, 259.
177. Paterson, A. R. P., Wang, M. C., *Cancer Res.* (1970) **30**, 2379.
178. Schabel, F. M., Jr., Laster, W. R., Jr., Skipper, H. E., *Cancer Chemother. Rep.* (1967) **51**, 111.
179. Paterson, A. R. P., Moriwaki, A., *Cancer Res.* (1969) **29**, 681.
180. Paterson, A. R. P., Wang, M. C., *Can. J. Biochem.* (1970) **48**, 79.
181. Bennett, L. L., Jr., Smithers, D., Teague, C., Baker, H. T., Stutts, P., *Biochem. Pharmacol.* (1962) **11**, 81.
182. Booth, B. A., Sartorelli, A. C., *J. Biol. Chem.* (1961) **236**, 203.
183. Henderson, J. F., Junga, I. G., *Cancer Res.* (1961) **21**, 173.
184. Bennett, L. L., Jr., Allan, P. W., Smithers, D., Vail, D. H., *Biochem. Pharmacol.* (1969) **18**, 725.
185. Zimmerman, E. F., Mandel, H. G., *Exp. Cell Res.* (1964) **33**, 138.
186. Zimmerman, E. F., Mandel, H. G., *Exp. Cell Res.* (1964) **33**, 130.
187. Bennett, L. L., Jr., Allan, P. W., Hill, D. L., *Mol. Pharmacol.* (1968) **4**, 208.
188. Bennett, L. L., Jr., Adamson, D. J., *Biochem. Pharmacol.* (1970) **19**, 2172.
189. Hilton, J. L., Jansen, L. L., Hull, H. M., *Annu. Rev. Plant Physiol.* (1963) **14**, 353.
190. Sund, K. A., Putala, E. C., Little, H. N., *J. Agr. Food Chem.* (1960) **8**, 210.
191. Hilton, J. L., *Weeds* (1960) **8**, 392.
192. Klopotowski, T., Hulanicka, D., *Acta Biochim. Polon.* (1963) **10**, 209.
193. Hilton, J. L., Kearney, P. C., Ames, B. N., *Arch. Biochem. Biophys.* (1965) **112**, 544.
194. Klopotowski, T., Wiater, A., *Arch. Biochem. Biophys.* (1965) **112**, 562.
195. Klopotowski, T., Bagdasarian, G., *Acta Biochim. Polon.* (1966) **13**, 153.
196. Hilton, J. L., Kaufman, D. D., *Weed Sci.* (1968) **16**, 152.
197. Casselton, P. J., *Physiol. Plant.* (1966) **19**, 411.
198. Siegel, J. N., Gentile, A. C., *Plant Physiol.* (1966) **41**, 670.
199. Wolf, F. T., *Nature (London)* (1962) **193**, 901.
200. Casselton, P. J., *Nature (London)* (1964) **204**, 93.
201. Casselton, P. J., *Can. J. Microbiol.* (1967) **13**, 1564.
202. Weyter, F. W., Broquist, H. P., *Biochim. Biophys. Acta* (1960) **40**, 567.
203. Bond, T. J., Akers, J., *J. Bacteriol.* (1961) **81**, 327.
204. Boguslawski, J., Walczak, W., Klopotowski, T., *Acta Biochim. Polon.* (1967)
205. Hulanicka, D., Klopotowski, T., Bagdasarian, G., *Acta Biochim. Polon.* (1969) **16**, 127.

Chapter

9

Pathological Abnormalities of Purine Biosynthesis *de novo*

A NUMBER OF human diseases are either caused by or associated with accelerated rates of purine biosynthesis. In addition, abnormal rates of this process are also suspected in several other conditions, but this has not yet been demonstrated directly. To date patients with unusually low rates of purine synthesis have not been detected; whether such conditions would be lethal or merely asymptomatic is not certain.

Only the biochemical bases of these abnormalities of purine biosynthesis in man will be discussed here; no attempt will be made to cover the clinical or other aspects of these diseases.

Lesch-Nyhan Syndrome

The Lesch-Nyhan syndrome, hypoxanthine-guanine phosphoribosyltransferase deficiency, was first described in detail and recognized as a distinct disease state in 1964 (*1*); a few cases had been described previously. Patients with the Lesch-Nyhan syndrome are characterized by spastic cerebral palsy, choreoathetosis, developmental retardation, aggressive behavior, and bizarre self-mutilation. It occurs only in boys and is inherited as an X-linked recessive trait. Several reviews are available (*2, 3*).

Hypoxanthine-Guanine Phosphoribosyltransferase Activities. In 1968 Seegmiller *et al.* (*4*) showed that there was no detectable activity of the enzyme hypoxanthine-guanine phosphoribosyltransferase (EC 2.4.2.8) in the erythrocytes of patients with the Lesch-Nyhan syndrome; this has subsequently been confirmed by numerous other investigators. The assay of this enzyme activity is now used for diagnostic purposes.

McDonald and Kelley (*5*) have recently reported studies of a patient who had the typical clinical signs of the Lesch-Nyhan syndrome but who still had

$$\begin{matrix}\text{Hypoxanthine} \\ \text{or} \\ \text{Guanine}\end{matrix} + \text{PP-Ribose-P} \xrightarrow[\text{Phosphoribosyl-transferase}]{} \text{PP}_i + \begin{matrix}\text{Inosinate} \\ \text{or} \\ \text{Guanylate}\end{matrix}$$

detectable phosphoribosyltransferase activity when assays were done on erythrocyte extracts. Detailed study of this enzyme revealed that its maximum activities with hypoxanthine and guanine were 12% and 94% of normal, respectively. The Michaelis constant of this mutant enzyme for PP-ribose-P was 13 times that for the normal enzyme, and it would appear that intracellular concentrations of this substrate are too low to permit significant activity of the enzyme *in vivo.*

Fujimoto and Seegmiller (*6*) have observed small but significant amounts of hypoxanthine-guanine phosphoribosyltransferase activity in fibroblasts derived from Lesch-Nyhan patients, and the physical properties of these enzymes are abnormal. The levels of hypoxanthine-guanine phosphoribosyltransferase activity that might actually function in the cells of Lesch-Nyhan patients *in vivo* are of course unknown.

Bases of Accelerated Purine Biosynthesis. Biochemically, a prominent feature of the Lesch-Nyhan syndrome is pronounced hyperuricemia and urinary excretion of large amounts of uric acid. On a body-weight basis such patients excrete up to six times more uric acid per day than normal, and the rate of purine biosynthesis *de novo* in these patients is accelerated as much as 20-fold. Urinary excretion of aminoimidazole carboxamide is increased 10-fold (*7*).

Among the possible causes of accelerated purine biosynthesis *de novo* in the Lesch-Nyhan syndrome that have been considered experimentally are the following: decreased sensitivity of PP-ribose-P amidotransferase to endproduct inhibition, decreased concentrations of inhibitory endproducts, increased availability of PP-ribose-P, and an increased amount of PP-ribose-P amidotransferase.

ENDPRODUCT INHIBITION. The possibility was first considered that the PP-ribose-P amidotransferase in Lesch-Nyhan cells might be less sensitive than normal to endproduct inhibition. The studies on endproduct inhibition were conducted using skin fibroblasts grown in tissue culture; those of Lesch-Nyhan patients showed a six-fold acceleration of purine biosynthesis and so were considered a valid experimental system (*8*). Addition of various concentrations of adenine (which would be converted to adenine nucleotides) and of 6-methylmercaptopurine ribonucleoside (which would be phosphorylated to form its ribonucleotide) produced the same, or perhaps even greater, inhibition of purine biosynthesis in fibroblasts deficient in hypoxanthine-guanine phosphoribosyltransferase as in normal cells. Addition of hypoxanthine or guanine to incubation media of course produced no inhibition of purine biosynthesis, because these cannot be converted to nucleotides in Lesch-Nyhan fibroblasts; curiously, they appeared instead to stimulate purine synthesis somewhat. It was concluded from these studies that the PP-ribose-P amidotransferase of Lesch-Nyhan fibroblasts is normally sensitive to the action of at least exogenously supplied endproduct inhibitors.

Attempts were also made to treat a Lesch-Nyhan patient with 6-methylmercaptopurine ribonucleoside, a drug that inhibits purine biosynthesis *de novo* in cultured fibroblasts from such patients. Treatment was limited by upper gastrointestinal tract toxicity, and the highest doses used had no effect either on urinary excretion of uric acid or incorporation of radioactive glycine into urinary uric acid (W. N. Kelley, F. M. Rosenbloom, J. F. Henderson, and J. E. Seegmiller, unpublished work).

Early in the study of the Lesch-Nyhan syndrome attempts were made to treat such patients by inhibiting purine biosynthesis with azathioprine (4′-nitro-5′-imidazolyl-6-mercaptopurine). This drug must be converted in the body to 6-mercaptopurine ribonucleotide, which is probably the active inhibitory form and which apparently inhibits the first enzyme of the purine biosynthetic pathway as an analog of natural endproduct inhibitors (Chapter 8).

Azathioprine → 6-Mercaptopurine —PP-Ribose-P→ 6-Mercaptopurine ribonucleotide + PP_i

Such attempts were unsuccessful (*9, 10, 11*); this lack of inhibition results from the deficiency of hypoxanthine-guanine phosphoribosyltransferase, which is the enzyme that also converts 6-mercaptopurine to its nucleotide.

PURINE NUCLEOTIDE CONCENTRATIONS. Because Lesch-Nyhan cells lack an alternative pathway of purine ribonucleotide synthesis, it was suspected that the concentrations of potential endproduct inhibitory nucleotides, such as guanylate and GTP, might be present in lower concentrations than normal in these cells and hence might exert a reduced degree of inhibition. Extracts were made of nearly confluent monolayers of normal and Lesch-Nyhan fibroblasts, and concentrations of acid-soluble purine nucleotides were estimated after chromatographic separation. Guanylate was not detected either in normal or Lesch-Nyhan fibroblasts, and the concentrations of other nucleotides were considered normal (*8*). Such experiments have recently been repeated with much more sensitive methods, and again it was found that purine ribonucleotide concentrations were not lower in Lesch-Nyhan cells than in normal fibroblasts (J. E. Seegmiller, personal communication). Whether concentrations of purine nucleotide endproduct inhibitors are also normal in all tissues of Lesch-Nyhan patients *in vivo,* however, is quite another question and as yet remains unanswered.

AMOUNT OF PP-RIBOSE-P AMIDOTRANSFERASE. It remained possible that increased rates of purine biosynthesis *de novo* in Lesch-Nyhan patients were caused in whole or in part by increases in the total amount of PP-ribose-P amidotransferase present in their cells. Because of the difficulty with which this enzyme is assayed in crude extracts of tissues, this question was not studied in early investigations of this disease. Some recent studies, however, have showed that the total activity of PP-ribose-P amidotransferase is the same in extracts of fibroblasts from normal persons and in those from patients with the Lesch-Nyhan syndrome (*12*).

PP-RIBOSE-P CONCENTRATIONS. Finally, the possibility was considered that PP-ribose-P concentrations might be elevated in cells of Lesch-Nyhan patients and that this might account for the observed accumulation of purine biosynthesis. Rosenbloom *et al.* (*8*) measured concentrations of PP-ribose-P in normal and Lesch-Nyhan fibroblasts incubated with glucose but without added glutamine and found a 4.5-fold 'elevation in Lesch-Nyhan cells. Increased PP-ribose-P concentrations in fibroblasts deficient in hypoxanthine-guanine phosphoribosyltransferase have also been reported by Kelley *et al.* (*13*). The PP-ribose-P concentrations of erythrocytes *in vivo* can also be measured, and several investigators (*14, 15*) have demonstrated that these values are much higher in blood samples taken from patients with the Lesch-Nyhan syndrome than in normal erythrocytes. Indirect assessments of the rate of PP-ribose-P synthesis suggested that this was normal in Lesch-Nyhan cells.

It has been concluded from these studies that because of the loss of an alternative route of PP-ribose-P metabolism (hypoxanthine-guanine phosphoribosyltransferase) a greater amount of this substrate becomes available for purine biosynthesis *de novo*. Increased PP-ribose-P concentrations could stimulate the rate of purine synthesis both by increasing the rate of PP-ribose-P amidotransferase as substrate and because inhibition of this enzyme by purine ribonucleotides is competitive with respect to PP-ribose-P (*see* Chapter 5). At the present time, an increased concentration of PP-ribose-P arising from loss of an alternative pathway for its utilization appears to be the most likely cause of accelerated purine biosynthesis *de novo* in patients with the Lesch-Nyhan syndrome.

It should be pointed out, however, that the rate of purine biosynthesis in Lesch-Nyhan patients is still far lower than the total capacity of this pathway. As pointed out in Chapter 8, administration of ethylamino-thiadiazole stimulated purine synthesis markedly even in these patients (*16*).

Glucose 6-Phosphatase Deficiency

Patients who have inherited less than normal amounts of liver and kidney glucose 6-phosphatase (EC 3.1.3.9) (*e.g.*, about 10% of normal activity) have what is called glycogen storage disease type I. They show a pronounced hyperuricemia which may rise to three times the normal serum uric acid concentrations. This is caused in part by increased retention of uric acid by the kidneys, which in turn arises at least partly from increased blood lactate concentrations.

Studies using labeled glycine have also shown, however, that purine biosynthesis *de novo* is increased in these patients twofold to sixfold (*17–21*). It has been suggested that the increased purine biosynthesis may be secondary to increased availability of PP-ribose-P arising from elevated concentrations of glucose 6-phosphate. Concentrations of glucose 6-phosphate and other phosphorylated sugars have been reported in erythrocytes (*22*) or blood (*23*) of patients with glucose 6-phosphatase deficiency, but Greene and Seegmiller (*14*) have found that PP-ribose-P concentrations were completely normal in such erythrocytes. The latter result is what one might expect, because glucose 6-phosphatase is normally present only in liver and kidney; the basis of any abnormalities in erythrocyte sugar phosphates is therefore unclear.

Although the hypothesis that PP-ribose-P concentrations are elevated in glucose 6-phosphatase deficiency, and that this leads to accelerated purine biosynthesis *de novo*, is most attractive, it has not yet been evaluated in sufficient detail.

Gout

Gout is really a whole group of diseases which have in common the precipitation of uric acid from supersaturated serum and other body fluids. The uric acid may precipitate in joints, in which case arthritis may result, or it may precipitate in the kidneys and other tissues, with greater or lesser ill effect. Gout is usually accompanied by painful intermittent acute attacks. As already implied, blood levels of uric acid are elevated in gout patients, and this hyperuricemia may have accurred for many years prior to the onset of symptoms. Excretion of uric acid in the urine may or may not be increased. Among many excellent reviews of gout and its biochemistry, the most recent are those of Seegmiller (*24*) and Kelley and Wyngaarden (*25*); these may be consulted for discussions of the causes of uric acid precipitation and the various clinical manifestations of gout.

Classification of Causes of Hyperuricemia. The fact that gout has many causes has been recognized only gradually. In early isotope studies of gout, patients were found who had normal rates of glycine incorporation into urinary uric acid while in other patients this process was clearly faster than normal. At first the basis of this apparent discrepancy was unclear, but eventually it was accepted as demonstrating a fundamental distinction between so-called normoproducing and overproducing patients.

Over the last 20 years the list of clinically significant causes of hyperuricemia in patients with normal rates of purine biosynthesis has been extended so often that diversity within this group of patients is generally accepted (*26*). This is particularly true of hyperuricemia associated with accelerated rates of cell turnover or death, and hyperuricemia caused by decreased rates of urate excretion. However, the genetic and biochemical heterogeneity of hyperuricemia produced by accelerated purine biosynthesis or increased rates of nucleotide or nucleic acid turnover has become apparent only relatively recently and in practice is not fully accepted. One consequence of such diversity is that it will not necessarily be possible to average the results of studies on different patients and in different laboratories, unless one is sure that all of the patients studied really are of the same type. At the present time a certain amount of controversy has arisen about the reproducibility of certain findings; this may stem from experimental difficulties, but it may also result from the study of unique patients. It is probably inevitable that this situation will lead to considerable frustration until one type of patient can be distinguished more easily from another.

Bases of Accelerated Purine Biosynthesis. Only hyperuricemia arising from accelerated purine biosynthesis *de novo* will be discussed here. Some such cases have already been described; in glucose 6-phosphatase deficiency, for example, it is proposed that the rate of PP-ribose-P synthesis is increased because of the increased concentration of glucose 6-phosphate.

In patients with the Lesch-Nyhan syndrome there seems to be greater availability of PP-ribose-P because of its decreased use by an alternative pathway, hypoxanthine-guanine phosphoribosyltransferase.

Accelerated rates of purine biosynthesis are obviously more difficult to detect when such obvious clues as the Lesch-Nyhan syndrome or glycogen storage disease are absent. Four methods have so far been used to measure rates of purine biosynthesis in human patients. The most common, and the most accurate, measures the rate of incorporation of glycine-^{15}N or glycine-^{14}C into urinary uric acid, with corrections made for the size of the body pools of uric acid, and when possible, for the extent of uricolysis.

The first studies of this type were performed in 1952 by Benedict *et al.* (*27, 28*). Glycine-^{15}N was fed first to normal subjects, and the ^{15}N concentration in urinary uric acid rose slowly to a maximum in three to four days and declined slowly thereafter. Gouty patients, in contrast, showed rapid increases in ^{15}N concentration in uric acid to maximum values about three times normal. Although overproduction in some gouty patients was also reported by other investigators (*e.g., 29, 30, 31*) using glycine-^{14}C and formate-^{14}C to measure this process, cases were soon observed in which the rate of purine biosynthesis was normal (*e.g., 30, 32*). Stetten (*33*) and later, Wyngaarden (*34*) concluded that gouty patients could be divided into two populations on the basis of measurements of the rate of purine biosynthesis *de novo* and that the biochemical bases of gout were fundamentally different in the two cases.

Two newer methods have been introduced but so far have been used in only a few cases. Henderson *et al.* (*35*) showed that skin fibroblasts from two patients known to have increased rates of purine synthesis *in vivo* also synthesized purines faster than did those from controls when these cells were grown in tissue culture. Differences from threefold to fivefold were noted. Diamond *et al.* (*36*) compared the rates of incorporation of glycine-^{14}C into nucleic acid purines in leucocytes obtained from normal and gouty subjects and observed an average increase of about 80% in the cells from the patients. Not all of the gouty patients showed accelerated purine synthesis, however, and a few of the controls also had high rates of this process.

The simplest method for determining rates of purine biosynthesis *de novo* is merely to measure the daily total urinary excretion of uric acid after the patient has been on a low-purine diet for three to four days. If the total excretion of uric acid is elevated under these conditions, one must presume that there is either accelerated purine biosynthesis or accelerated nucleotide or nucleic acid catabolism. It is usually—but probably not always—possible to detect the occurrence of the latter process independently, and this method therefore produces presumptive but not positive evidence of high rates of purine biosynthesis. Table 9-1 presents data obtained by this method (*24*).

Table 9-1. Uric Acid Excreted in Clinical Disorders[c]

Subject	*Number Studied*	*Ratio,*[a] *Mean mg Uric Acid / Kg Body Weight*
Control	20	6.1
Gout		
Normal uric acid production	3	5.7
Excessive uric acid production		
Normal PRT[b]	9	9.0
Incomplete PRT deficiency	11	22.1
Virtually complete PRT deficiency (Lesch-Nyhan syndrome)	4	51.7

[a] From 24-hour urine samples, with patient on a purine-free diet
[b] PRT represents hypoxanthine-guanine phosphoribosyltransferase
[c] From Seegmiller (*24*)

Although no really systematic survey has been done, it is a general impression among workers in this field that between 25 and 40% of gouty patients synthesize purines *de novo* at accelerated rates.

The real biochemical bases of accelerated purine biosynthesis leading to gout have been identified in only a few patients although suggestive evidence has been presented for a few other cases. This work will be discussed at this point.

ELEVATED PP-RIBOSE-P CONCENTRATIONS. The possibility that increased synthesis or availability of PP-ribose-P might contribute to accelerated purine biosynthesis and gout has been considered for some time. In 1962 Jones *et al.* (*37*) detected increased turnover of PP-ribose-P in certain gouty patients, but this could just as well have been a consequence of accelerated purine synthesis as its cause. More conclusive evidence came from the studies of Hershko *et al.* (*38*), who found that erythrocytes of at least seven out of 19 patients synthesized PP-ribose-P at accelerated rates when incubated *in vitro* with glucose. Because there was no change in total PP-ribose-P synthetase activity, it was concluded that ribose 5-phosphate concentrations might be unusually high in these cells.

Greene and Seegmiller (*14*), however, did not find any cases of elevated PP-ribose-P concentrations in erythrocytes of 14 patients studied, and Fox and Kelley (*15*) also found no relationship between erythrocyte PP-ribose-P concentration and either serum uric acid concentration or daily urinary uric acid excretion in a series of 34 patients. Normal PP-ribose-P synthetase activity and normal sensitivity of this enzyme to inhibition by ADP, GDP, and 2,3-diphosphoglycerate have recently been reported by Meyskens and

Williams (*39*) in comparative studies of erythrocytes from normal and hyperuricemic individuals.

Partial Deficiency of Hypoxanthine-Guanine Phosphoribosyltransferase. Some cases of gout are associated with only partial deficiencies of hypoxanthine-guanine phosphoribosyltransferase (*40, 41*), in contrast to the virtually complete loss of this enzyme activity observed in the Lesch-Nyhan syndrome. These patients clincally present severe gouty arthritis with onset in adolescence or early adult life; in some cases a relatively mild neurological disease may accompany the gout. As little as 1% of normal enzyme activity seems to protect against severe neurological disfunction, and uric acid production varies between two and three times normal (Table 9-1).

As in the case of the Lesch-Nyhan syndrome accelerated purine biosynthesis *de novo* in patients with partial deficiencies of hypoxanthine-guanine phosphoribosyltransferase is believed to be caused by increased availability of PP-ribose-P consequent to the decreased activity of an alternate route of its utilization. Increased concentrations of PP-ribose-P have been demonstrated in cultured skin fibroblasts from such patients (*42*), and elevated PP-ribose-P concentrations in erythrocytes of three such patients were detected by Greene and Seegmiller (*14*).

Decreased Endproduct Inhibition of Purine Biosynthesis. Henderson *et al.* (*35*) have reported studies of fibroblasts cultured from two patients who had gout with excessive purine synthesis, frequent uric acid crystalluria, and renal calculus formation. Purine biosynthesis in the fibroblasts was accelerated about fivefold, but in contrast to results with fibroblasts deficient in hypoxanthine-guanine phosphoribosyltransferase, addition of adenine or 6-methylmercaptopurine ribonucleoside produced much less inhibition of purine synthesis than was found in control cells. Nucleotide formation from adenine and hypoxanthine was normal (that from 6-methylmercaptopurine ribonucleoside was not measured), and the interconversion of purine ribonucleotides was also normal in these cells. It was suggested that the fibroblasts from these two gouty patients might contain altered PP-ribose-P amidotransferases with reduced sensitivity to endproduct inhibition. It should be noted, however, that both patients responded in apparently normal fashion to the inhibitory effects of azathioprine on purine synthesis when this was measured *in vivo* (*9*). In addition, fibroblasts of these patients contained twofold to threefold elevated concentrations of PP-ribose-P. These patients deserve more detailed study.

Abnormal Glutamine Metabolism. It has been suggested that abnormalities in the metabolism of glutamine might lead to elevated intracellular concentrations of this amino acid and consequent acceleration of purine biosynthesis. Evidence on this point unfortunately remains inconclusive or controversial, and the situation has probably been complicated considerably by failure to recognize the biochemical individuality of gouty patients.

In 1950 Örström and Örström (*43*) reported low plasma glutamine concentrations in gouty patients, but Segal and Wyngaarden (*44*) recorded normal values, as did Yü *et al.* (*45*). More recently, Pagliara and Goodman (*46*) have raised the possibility that plasma glutamate concentrations may be elevated in some gouty patients; the implication is that this either causes or is a result of elevated intracellular concentrations of this amino acid. This remains to be investigated further.

Gutman and Yü (*47, 48*) reported in 1965 abnormalities of gouty patients in the urinary excretion of ammonia and in the pattern of incorporation of ^{15}N from glycine-^{15}N within the various nitrogen atoms of urinary uric acid. A defect in the activity of renal glutaminase has been proposed to account for these observations; it was also postulated that this leads to an increased availability of glutamine for purine biosynthesis. Studies with other gouty patients failed to confirm these observations, however (*49*).

It would be surprising if abnormalities in glutamine metabolism did not account for some individual cases of gout. Unfortunately, such patients have not yet been unequivocably identified.

OTHERS. Despite the progress that has recently been made in the elucidation of the biochemical bases of accelerated purine biosynthesis *de novo* in certain cases of gout, it remains true that these remain unknown in the vast majority of overproducing gouty patients. Recent advances in the use of cultured fibroblasts, leucocytes, and erythrocytes for the study of purine metabolism provide hope, however, that faster progress will be made in the future.

Other Diseases

Two patients with different types of neurological abnormalities have been described who also have marked increases in rates of purine biosynthesis *de novo.* So far, the biochemical bases of the pathologies and abnormal rates of purine biosynthesis have not been ascertained.

In 1968 Hooft *et al.* (*50*) reported the case of a girl who in many respects resembled Lesch-Nyhan patients, with self-biting, motor problems, irritability, and mental retardation. The rate of incorporation of glycine-^{14}C into urinary uric acid was about 200 times normal. Hypoxanthine-guanine phosphoribosyltransferase deficiency occurs only in boys, however, and detailed studies of other aspects of purine metabolism in this patient have not yet been reported.

A three-year-old boy with mental retardation, failure to cry with tears, lack of speech, and unusual but not self-destructive behavior was studied by Nyhan *et al.* (*51*). Purine biosynthesis was accelerated about sevenfold, and while hypoxanthine-guanine phosphoribosyltransferase activity was normal, that of adenine phosphoribosyltransferase was elevated by about 80%. The latter abnormality has also been observed in other conditions associated with elevated PP-ribose-P concentrations (PP-ribose-P stabilizes adenine phosphoribosyltransferase), but studies of PP-ribose-P metabolism have not been reported. These cases remain interesting problems for further investigation.

References

1. Lesch, M., Nyhan, W. L., *Amer. J. Med.* (1964) **36,** 561.
2. "Proceedings of the Seminars on the Lesch-Nyhan Syndrome," *Fed. Proc. Fed. Amer. Soc. Exp. Biol.* (1968) **27,** 1017.
3. Henderson, J. F., *Clin. Biochem.* (1969) **2,** 241.
4. Seegmiller, J. E., Rosenbloom, F. M., Kelley, W. N., *Science* (1967) **155,** 1682.
5. McDonald, J. A., Kelley, W. N., *Science* (1971) **171,** 689.
6. Fujimoto, W. Y., Seegmiller, J. E., *Proc. Nat. Acad. Sci.* (1970) **65**, 577.
7. Newcombe, D., Lopes, M., Thomson, C., Wright, E. Y., *Clin. Res.* (1967) **15,** 45.
8. Rosenbloom, F. M., Henderson, J. F., Caldwell, I. C., Kelley, W. N., Seegmiller, J. E., *J. Biol. Chem.* (1968) **243,** 1166.
9. Kelley, W. N., Rosenbloom, F. M., Seegmiller, J. E., *J. Clin. Invest.* (1967) **46,** 1518.
10. Sorensen, L. B., Benke, P. J., *Nature (London)* (1967) **213**, 1122.
11. Nyhan, W. L., Sweetman, L., Carpenter, D. G., Carter, C. H., Hoefnagel, D., *J. Pediat.* (1968) **72,** 111.
12. Wood, A. W., Seegmiller, J. E., *Fed. Proc. Fed. Amer. Soc. Exp. Biol.* (1971) **30,** 1113.
13. Kelley, W. N., Fox, I. H., Wyngaarden, J. B., *Clin. Res.* (1970) **18,** 457.
14. Greene, M. L., Seegmiller, J. E., *Arthritis Rheum.* (1969) **12,** 666.
15. Fox, I. H., Kelley, W. N., *Ann. Intern. Med.* (1971) **74,** 424.
16. Nyhan, W. L., Sweetman, L., Lesch, M., *Metab. Clin. Exp.* (1968) **17,** 846.
17. Howell, R. R., Ashton, D. M., Wyngaarden, J. B., *Pediatrics* (1962) **29,** 553.
18. Howell, R. R., *Arthritis Rheum.* (1965) **8,** 780.
19. Jackovcic, S., Sorensen, L. B., *Arthritis Rheum.* (1967) **10,** 129.
20. Alepa, F. P., Howell, R. R., Klineberg, J. R., Seegmiller, J. E., *Amer. J. Med.* (1967) **42**, 58.
21. Kelley, W.N., Rosenbloom, F. M., Seegmiller, J. E., Howell, R. R., *J. Pediat.* (1968) **72,** 488.
22. Hsia, D. Y. Y., Kot, E. G., *Nature (London)* (1959) **183,** 1331.
23. Wagner, R., Meyerriecks, N., Sparaco, R., *J. Pediat.* (1958) **53,** 683.
24. Seegmiller, J. E., "Duncan's Diseases of Metabolism," Bondy, P. K., Rosenberg, L. E., Eds., 6th ed., Vol. 1, p. 516, Saunders, Philadelphia, 1969.
25. Kelley, W. N., Wyngaarden, J. B., "The Metabolic Basis of Inherited Disease," Stanbury, J. B., Wyngaarden, J. B., Fredrickson, D. S., Eds., 3rd ed., p. 889, McGraw, New York, 1972.
26. Kelley, W. N., *Med. Times (Port Wash. N.Y.)* (1969) **97**, 230.
27. Benedict, J. D., Roche, M., Yü, T. F., Bien, E. J., Gutman, A. B., Stetten, D., Jr., *Metab. Clin. Exp.* (1952) **1,** 3.
28. Benedict, J. D., Yü, T. F., Bien, E. J., Gutman, A. B., Stetten, D., Jr., *J. Clin. Invest.* (1953) **32,** 775.
29. Spilman, E. L., *Fed. Proc. Fed. Amer. Soc. Exp. Biol.* (1954) **13,** 302.
30. Seegmiller, J. E., Laster, L., Liddle, L. V., *Metab. Clin. Exp.* (1958) **7,** 376.
31. Wyngaarden, J. B., *Arthritis Rheum.* (1960) **3,** 414.
32. Wyngaarden, J. B., *Metab. Clin. Exp.* (1958) **7,** 374.
33. Stetten, D., Jr., *Geriatrics* (1954) **9,** 163.

34. Wyngaarden, J. B., *J. Clin. Invest.* (1957) **36,** 1508.
35. Henderson, J. F., Rosenbloom, F. M., Kelley, W. N., Seegmiller, J. E., *J. Clin. Invest.* (1968) **47,** 1511.
36. Diamond, H. S., Friedland, M., Halberstom, D., Kaplan, D., *Ann. Rheum. Dis.* (1969) **28,** 275.
37. Jones, O. W., Jr., Ashton, D. M., Wyngaarden, J. B., *J. Clin. Invest.* (1962) **41,** 1805.
38. Hershko, A., Hershko, C., Mager, J., *Isr. J. Med. Sci.* (1968) **4,** 939.
39. Meyskens, F. L., Williams, H. E., *Metab. Clin. Exp.* (1971) **20,** 737.
40. Kelley, W. N., Greene, M. L., Rosenbloom, F. M., Henderson, J. F., Seegmiller, J. E., *Ann. Intern. Med.* (1969) **70,** 155.
41. Kogut, M. D., Donnell, G. N., Nyhan, W. L., Sweetman, L., *Amer. J. Med.* (1970) **48,** 148.
42. Rosenbloom, F. M., Henderson, J. F., Kelley, W. N., Seegmiller, J. E., *Biochim. Biophys. Acta* (1968) **166,** 258.
43. Örström, A., Örström, M., *Acta Med. Scand.* (1950) **138,** 108.
44. Segal, S., Wyngaarden, J. B., *Proc. Soc. Exp. Biol. Med.* (1955) **88,** 342.
45. Yü, T., Adler, M., Bobrow, E., Gutman, A. B., *J. Clin. Invest.* (1969) **48,** 885.
46. Pagliara, A. S., Goodman, A. D., *N. Engl. J. Med.* (1969) **281,** 767.
47. Gutman, A. B., Yü, T.-F., *N. Engl. J. Med.* (1965) **273,** 313.
48. Gutman, A. B., Yü, T.-F., *Amer. J. Med.* (1963) **35,** 820.
49. Pollak, V. E., Mattenheimer, H., *J. Lab. Clin. Med.* (1965) **66,** 564.
50. Hooft, C., Van Nevel, C., De Schaepdryver, A. F., *Arch. Dis. Childhood* (1968) **43,** 734.
51. Nyhan, W. L., James, J. A., Teberg, A. J., Sweetman, L., Nelson, L. G., *J. Pediat.* (1969) **74,** 20.

Chapter

10

Conclusions

THE PRECEDING CHAPTERS have for the most part addressed themselves to the following two questions.

(1) *Is the pathway of purine biosynthesis* de novo *regulated or at least regulatable?* In other words, is its rate normally less than its maximum potential rate, or can it be made to be less? The answer to this qustion is an unqualified "yes," based on the fact that purine synthesis can be stimulated beyond the rates normally observed in cells. Thus purine biosynthesis can be accelerated in animals by drugs such as nicotinamide and ethylaminothiadiazole (Chapter 8), in human patients with the Lesch-Nyhan syndrome and with some kinds of gout (Chapter 9), in most cells by increasing concentrations of one or another substrate of this pathway (Chapter 4), or as a consequence of mutations affecting the properties of enzymes or control mechanisms (Chapters 5 and 6). In addition, numerous drugs can depress the rate of purine biosynthesis or inhibit it completely (Chapter 8).

(2) *How is the pathway of purine biosynthesis regulated?* It is clear that purine biosynthesis is regulated by many different mechanisms. In one organism or another the following regulatory factors have been identified: the amount or kinetic properties of one or more of the 10 enzymes of the purine biosynthetic pathway, the concentration of one or more of its eight substrates, the concentration of one or another of its purine ribonucleotide products, or the concentration of histidine or thiamine.

To conclude this discussion several additional questions may be posed regarding more general aspects of the problem of regulation of purine biosynthesis.

Exactly what is meant by the phrase "regulation of purine biosynthesis"? The meaning of the title of this volume has deliberately not been defined precisely up to this point. This term is commonly used to include the following three phenomena:

(a) regulation of the net synthesis of all compounds containing the purine ring and of compounds derived from them; this is the most literal use of the phrase and that which has been used most frequently here.

(b) regulation of the synthesis of purine ribonucleotides; this would include not only the pathway of synthesis *de novo* but also the purine phosphoribosyltransferases and the purine nucleoside kinases. It represents not only the net synthesis of purine compounds but also the reutilization of previously formed purine bases and ribonucleosides.

(c) regulation of purine ribonucleotide concentrations; this is a common, though not literal, use of the phrase. It would include all routes of synthesis of purine ribonucleotides as well as of their anabolic and catabolic utilization.

The shade of meaning given to the phrase "regulation of purine biosynthesis" is usually clear from the context, and there is rarely much confusion on this point. From a conceptual point of view, however, it would be well to keep these distinctions clear, because the mechanisms and sites of regulation involved are somewhat different for each of the three meanings.

Although inosinate is the first purine ribonucleotide formed as endproduct of the pathway of purine synthesis *de novo*, it is in most cells a quantitatively minor component of the purine nucleotide pool. It is rapidly and efficiently converted to the adenine and guanine nucleotides which form the bulk of this pool, but it can also be dephosphorylated to form inosine. The relative rates of the reactions that convert inosinate to other ribonucleotides (adenylosuccinate synthetase and inosinate dehydrogenase) and of the dephosphorylation of inosinate define the distinction between net inosinate synthesis *de novo* and net adenine and guanine ribonucleotide synthesis.

In many microorganisms there is little dephosphorylation of inosinate, and this distinction is not particularly important. In uricotelic animals, however, the vast preponderance of the inosinate formed is dephosphorylated. Ureotelic animals form an intermediate group, and human fibroblasts in culture (*1, 2, 3*), Ehrlich ascites tumor cells *in vitro* (A. A. Letter and J. F. Henderson, unpublished observations), and man (*e.g., 4, 5*) convert a small proportion (up to perhaps 10%) of the inosinate formed *de novo* to inosine. If, however, the rate of purine biosynthesis *de novo* is accelerated for whatever cause, the bulk of the extra inosinate synthesized is dephosphorylated rather than converted to adenine and guanine ribonucleotides (*1–5*). In the older literature on gout this is called the "shunt" pathway of uric acid synthesis; the term itself is a misnomer, but the importance of the dephosphorylation of inosinate in some cases of gout is not in any question.

These considerations lead to the conclusion that, although net purine synthesis is regulated prior to the formation of inosinate, the dephosphorylation of inosinate is also an important site of regulation of purine ribonucleotide concentrations. This fact is often lost sight of in discussions of the regulation of purine ribonucleotide concentrations.

How well is purine biosynthesis de novo *regulated?* In microorganisms and ureotelic animals a criterion for good regulation might be that inosinate is produced at a rate which leads to minimal dephosphorylation of this endproduct. It would appear that on these grounds microorganisms regulate purine biosynthesis effectively. Ureotelic animals would rank lower, but under normal circumstances they seem to dephosphorylate a relatively small proportion of the inosinate formed. In fact, cells of ureotelic animals seem to be so responsive to altered substrate concentrations (Chapter 4) that it is quite uncertain exactly how the normal rates of purine synthesis are maintained *in vivo.*

In uricotelic animals, a criterion for good regulation might be that which maintains ammonia concentrations at nontoxic levels. Whether this regulation consists of anything more than a passive response to glutamine, glycine, and aspartate concentrations is, in fact, not known.

What is the relative importance of the different regulatory mechanisms, and how are their actions integrated? Practically nothing is known about these extremely important questions. One presumes that enzyme amount plays a greater role in micororganisms than in animals and also that substrate concentrations may not fluctuate as much in microorganisms as in animal cells. The status of regulation by purine ribonucleotides is quite uncertain, and in this regard it must be remembered that other enzymes besides PP-ribose-P amidotransferase are also inhibited by nucleotides (*e.g., 6, 7*).

The statement is often made that PP-ribose-P amidotransferase is the rate-limiting step in purine biosynthesis *de novo.* In fact there is no evidence for this, and the observations that addition of any of the substrates of this pathway may cause its acceleration and that aminoimidazole carboxamide is a normal urinary constituent suggest that this is not necessarily true. At the moment it seems unwise to speak of a single rate-limiting step but instead to conclude that almost any of the reactions might become rate limiting, depending on the conditions.

What still needs to be learned about the regulation of purine biosynthesis? We have a great deal of information regarding the individual factors that actually or potentially contribute to the regulation of purine synthesis *de novo,* but we have almost no idea of how these factors actually operate in intact cells and organisms.

References

1. Rosenbloom, F. M., Henderson, J. F., Caldwell, I. C., Kelley, W. N., Seegmiller, J. E., *J. Biol. Chem.* (1968) **243,** 1166.
2. Henderson, J. F., Rosenbloom, F. M., Kelley, W. N., Seegmiller, J. E., *J. Clin. Invest.* (1968) **47,** 1511.
3. Rosenbloom, F. M., Henderson, J. F., Kelley, W. N., Seegmiller, J. E., *Biochim. Biophys. Acta* (1968) **166,** 258.
4. Benedict, J. D., Roche, M., Yü, T.-F., Bien, E. J., Gutman, A. B., Stetten, D., Jr., *Metab. Clin. Exp.* (1952) **1,** 3.
5. Benedict, J. D., Yü, T.-F., Bien, E. J., Gutman, A. B., Stetten, D., Jr., *J. Clin. Invest.* (1953) **32,** 775.
6. Howard, A. H., Appel, S. J., *Clin. Res.* (1968) **16,** 344.
7. Chu, S. Y., Ph.D. Thesis, University of Alberta, 1971.

AUTHOR INDEX

Numbers in parentheses are reference numbers and indicate that an author's work is referred to although his name is not cited in the text. Numbers in italics show the page on which the complete reference is listed.

B

C

D

E

H

I

J

M

N

O

S

Y

Z

SUBJECT INDEX

D

E

U